PHILOSOPHY OF SCIENCE:
A Formal Approach

PHILOSOPHY OF SCIENCE: A Formal Approach

HENRY E. KYBURG, JR.
The University of Rochester

The Macmillan Company
NEW YORK

Collier-Macmillan Limited
LONDON

501
K99

For Sarah, who helped in more ways than I can list

PREFACE

This book has been written to fulfill a particular need, and it has been written from a particular point of view. But the need is a pervasive one and, it is hoped, the point of view is neither biased nor local. Each science has its own language and techniques, and it is impossible to study a science seriously—or even to appreciate it in any depth—without mastering the language and the technique. One cannot understand physics without knowing calculus. The same is true of the philosophy of science. The philosophy of science can be understood without knowing physics (though perhaps not without really understanding some science), but it cannot be understood without knowing some logic, an essential ingredient of every science. That much technical facility is necessary; there is no way of making the path smoother. I have therefore presupposed either some familiarity with symbolic logic, or some degree of talent for learning it. All of the logical machinery that is required is developed here—the book is self-contained—but it is developed in brief compass; and I have supposed that most students will have had at least one semester of logic.

To say that this book has been written from a particular point of view is not to say that it is incompatible with a wide variety of philosophical viewpoints—it is

[vii]

not a philosophical treatise—but that its approach presupposes a tolerance for close reasoning, and even for formal logic. Most of those contemporary philosophers—there are exceptions—who work in the philosophy of science agree that formalization is an important technique for analyzing and understanding the sciences in detail, and even that the student of the philosophy of science may profit by a somewhat formal orientation. They disagree only on the degree to which formalization should be introduced into a first course, and not on whether it should be introduced into the philosophy of science at all. My own point of view is that formalization should be the first step in any discussion belonging to the philosophy of science—but this point of view need not dictate the character of a course based on this text because the systematic parts of the book can be treated in half the available time, and the remainder given over to the less formal parts and to the supplementary readings listed in the bibliographies that conclude each chapter.

There are two quite different groups of students for whom this book is intended: the philosophy major (I believe that all philosophy majors should have some familiarity with the philosophy of science, just as they should be familiar with formal symbolic logic) and the science major (many people feel that science majors, too, should have some contact with the philosophy of science).

There are many students of the sciences who have philosophical interests—that is, who are interested in the foundations of their subject or in its general structure as a branch of human knowledge. These students can withstand the rigors of close reasoning, but often have difficulty taking the concerns of professional philosophers of science seriously. The essential structure of *space* or *time*, the character of *causality*, the problem of *counter-factual conditionals*, the difficulties that beset formal reconstructions of the concept of confirmation—these problems arise naturally enough in pursuing the philosophy of science, but they do not arise immediately. It is not these questions that cause a chemistry major to take an interest in the philosophy of science. It thus seems inappropriate to offer such a student a textbook in the philosophy of science which is oriented toward these problems—though not at all inappropriate to suggest such a book as collateral reading.

The philosophy student generally takes easily to a problem-oriented course; abstract problems are what he is familiar with and what he enjoys most. But it is easy for such a student to find himself doing the same kind of philosophy, and even examining the same problems in the philosophy of science course as in a course in epistemology or metaphysics. In the long run, that is appropriate enough, but not in a first course. Just as the first course in the philosophy of science for the science major should help him look at his field from a point of view both more *fundamental* and more *abstract*, so the first course in the philosophy of science for the philosophy student should help him look at science in a more concrete and down to earth way—i.e., in a *less* abstract way.

[viii]

This book is intended to serve the needs of both philosophy majors and science majors by steering a middle course between the peaks of abstraction and the depths of scientific detail. It presents a central core of widely accepted doctrine. This central core must be supplemented, but the character of the supplement will and should vary widely with the background of the student, his familiarity with one science or another, his level of philosophical sophistication, etc.

The bibliographies at the end of each chapter are intended to be full enough so that a student interested in writing a term paper on a particular topic covered in that chapter will have a reasonable introduction to the literature. The annotations are intended to provide the student with some orientation toward the history and literature of the various topics—at least every name mentioned in a chapter will receive some reference in the bibliography for that chapter. The bibliographies thus also serve the function of footnotes, without interrupting the flow of the text.

My indebtednesses are too numerous to mention and no doubt easily enough identifiable, but special mention should be made of some of them. My teacher, Professor Ernest Nagel, taught me as well as he could the most important single lesson in the philosophy of science and the hardest to learn: sweeping and dramatic answers in the philosophy of science are usually wrong or misleading. I hope that some of his carefulness and accuracy are reflected in the work that follows. To Professor Rudolf Carnap I owe much of my sense of the importance of formalization, and particularly of the semantical aspects of formalization. My debt to Professor W. V. O. Quine is less easy to characterize, but it is no less profound. Professor Carl Hempel, who made helpful comments on some of the chapters of the manuscript, has helped to form my ideas in the philosophy of science, though it should be mentioned here that he would prefer to see less emphasis on formalization than I have provided.

Professor Wesley Salmon has been over the manuscript in word-by-word detail, and has provided a lengthy budget of suggestions, most of which I have been pleased to follow, and the rest of which I would have liked to follow had I the space, the time, and the ability. I am grateful for his care and honesty and for his friendship.

To my student and friend, John Cairns, I am grateful for painstakingly reading the entire manuscript, symbol by symbol, and for calling my attention to a variety of infelicities, ranging from spelling and diction to philosophical obscurity and downright inconsistency. He has also performed the essential and arduous task of compiling a useful index.

I am also grateful to Anonymous, who has made a number of helpful comments on earlier versions of the manuscript.

Rochester, New York   H. E. K.

[ix]

CONTENTS

[xi]

CONTENTS

PHILOSOPHY OF SCIENCE:
A Formal Approach

Chapter 1

THE CONCEPT OF A FORMAL

SYSTEM

I

A number of notions may be taken as key concepts in the philosophy of science: entropy, for example, or information, or explanation, or problem-solving. I have chosen to organize this book around the concept of a *formal system*. To some extent, this is a matter of taste—all of these concepts are related, of course, and each finds its proper role to play in the framework supplied by whichever concept is taken as fundamental. But I think it is also more than a matter of taste, although to show that it is more than that will require (at least) the contents of this book.

The study of the philosophy of science from the point of view of a formalist has one disadvantage: if one is not formalistically inclined, one may tire of the formalities and abstractions, one may get fed up with axioms and rules of inference and want to return to the exciting realities of moon rockets and psychedelic drugs. This disadvantage I shall try to compensate for in two ways. First, in this chapter, I shall try to exhibit the way in which the formal view of science can be used as an effective tool in the investigation of some of the serious philosophical questions often raised by or about the scientific enterprise. Looking at science as a formal system, or as a collection of formal systems, does yield results. Second, in this chapter and throughout the book, I shall attempt to keep the explicit treatment of the formalities of particular systems of knowledge to a minimum. This is certainly appropriate; the philosophy of science is not science; our aim is not to become familiar with the details of bodies of scientific knowledge. Neither is our aim the popularization of science. Our purpose is rather to become familiar with those details that are relevant to philosophical problems. For example, we might be concerned with the details of a *test* of a scientific hypothesis, in order to explore the philosophical problem of the way in which empirical support is given to theoretical assertions. We might be concerned with the analysis of some small group of terms from a scientific theory, in order to attempt to clarify how theoretical terms get their meanings, and how those meanings are related to the meanings of words of ordinary language.

What are these philosophical problems of science, and how does this systematic approach hope to shed light on them? One group of problems centers around the motivation for doing science: what can science achieve for us? Can we properly expect to succeed? What are the limits, if any, that circumscribe the answers that science can give to our questions? Another group of problems centers around the justification and discovery of scientific theories: what are the roles played by observation, experiment, pure cogitation, in the creation of scientific theory? What is the nature of justification in science—i.e., what standards are called upon when the justification of a theory is at issue? What are the relations between discovery, test, and validation? What, if anything, is presupposed by the standards of validation? A final group of problems concerns the general philosophical implications of the scientific enterprise. These are problems that might be termed metaphysical: What does the fact that science exists at all tell us about the world? Or about the human mind? What is the import of psychology, or of biology, in its present state, for such classical issues as vitalism (the doctrine that there is a vital force differentiating living from nonliving matter) and teleology (the doctrine that goals are casually efficacious —e.g., that people grow eyes in order to see)? What has quantum mechanics to say that bears on such questions as causality, determinism, indeterminism, free will?

Since my object in this book is not to answer such questions as these, but rather to provide the logical and technical framework that is indispensable to the discussion of them, I shall not devote much space to addressing them. Some remarks will appear in the final chapter. But, since these questions are the ones that bring people to the philosophy of science, I had better show how the formal systems that I am going to talk about are relevant to them.

What do we do science for? Among the answers are *control* of our environment, *explanation* of individual happenings, *prediction* of future events, *understanding* of a general kind of phenomenon. Each of these answers raises new questions: to what extent can we expect to succeed in controlling our environment? What are the limits of our control? In physics, for example, one learns that a perpetual motion machine is impossible. Does this represent a limit to our control of our environment, for example, to our ability to transform heat into useful work? Or might it be regarded as a defect of our system of physics, to be removed by the next Newton, or another Einstein? To answer such a question as this, we must be able to examine the logical relationships that hold among various statements of physics. What laws, or sets of laws, would have to be rejected in order to construct a system of physics in which the existence of a perpetual motion machine was no longer impossible? Or would we find it *logically impossible* to construct such a system of physics? In addition to these laws, we would have to reject, perhaps, various consequences of these laws. What are they? In order to understand why it is that no reasonable man spends his time looking for a perpetual motion machine, we must be able to examine the role that the statement "A perpetual motion machine is impossible" plays in the edifice of physics; or rather, the role that its formal counterpart, the second law of thermodynamics (the entropy of a closed system tends to increase), plays. In order to do this, we will find it advantageous to look at physics in a formal and systematic way, as a coherent and highly organized network of well-supported statements.

According to one well-known and generally accepted point of view (Hempel's), explanation and prediction are essentially the same: we *explain* an event that has already occurred, we *predict* an event that has yet to occur. The difference lies in whether the event is in the future or in the past. (We can sometimes convert a prediction into an explanation by waiting.) In either case, what we do is this: we are given a set of laws; we are given a set of boundary conditions—i.e., the set of circumstances to which we are going to apply these laws; and from these two things we infer deductively (or statistically) a statement asserting the occurrence of the event which is to be explained or predicted. Considered within the framework of a formal system, this view of explanation and prediction becomes even simpler. We begin with a formal system consisting of a set of statements (constituting the scientific subject matter of our explanation or prediction); we conjoin to this a new set of statements describing the circumstances of the predicted or explained event; we infer another statement from this complex system of statements, which inferred statement is a description of the event to be explained or predicted.

As an example, suppose we want an explanation of the fact that the tide was

[3]

so high it nearly covered the dock yesterday. Newtonian theory implies that when the earth, the sun, and the moon are in a straight line, the tides will be extreme. Astronomical observation informs us that the sun, moon, and earth were in line yesterday. Common observation has shown us that in the ordinary course of events the dock is a foot higher than the high water level; an extreme tide is a tide a foot higher than normal. We abbreviate this whole explanation by saying simply that the dock was awash because the sun, moon, and earth were in a straight line.

To put the matter in terms of formal relationships (and to avoid some obscurities that can all too easily arise in connection with "facts"), we can say: Let N be a complex statement embodying the relevant parts of Newtonian theory; let A be a complex statement representing the astronomical state of affairs (including statements about the relative masses of the earth, sun, and moon, as well as their relative positions); let C be a statement of the physical characteristics of the dock; and let W be the statement that the dock was awash at high tide today. The explanation of W lies, on this reconstruction, simply in the purely logical fact that the sentence W follows deductively from the conjunction of the sentences N, A, and C, together with the fact that we have reason to accept N and A and C. The case of prediction, it is often argued, is just the same: we could use the same example, but take the date to be the day before the monthly springs of the tide, and regard the calculation to be the grounds of a *prediction* for the next day.

There is, of course, much more to be said about both prediction and explanation than this. One thing in particular seems to be open to question, and that is the symmetry of prediction and explanation. To use a well-known example, due to Michael Scriven, we would not predict of an individual who had syphilis that he would develop paresis, because most syphilitics do not develop paresis; but as an explanation of the fact that a certain individual had paresis a physician would cite the fact that he had had syphilis. It might be that there is a way of reestablishing the symmetry, even in this case. But what counts here is simply the fact that again the formal and systematic framework seems to be an ideal one within which to examine these questions. What we are after, ultimately, is not an understanding of prediction and explanation as they apply to this particular application of scientific theory or that one, but a general understanding of scientific prediction and explanation.

There are those (Bar-Hillel, for example) who regard such expressions as "scientific prediction" (only prophets make predictions) and "scientific explanation" (it is superstitious to seek an *explanation* for an event) as inherently inconsistent. But even this extreme thesis is defended within a formal framework; indeed it boils down to the claim that the science *is* the formal system, the set of axioms and theorems the scientist works with, and not any use that the scientist makes of it.

[4]

Consider the question of our scientific understanding of the world. Does a body of scientific knowledge increase the depth of our understanding of the world? Does it make the world seem more familiar, or ourselves more at home in it? In what sense, if any, is this true? How does it come about? Understanding is perhaps analogous to explanation, but concerned with classes of phenomena rather than with single events. We explain the fact that a particular crow stole a shiny button on a particular occasion by saying that all crows like shiny things and will often take them back to their nests; but we understand the button-stealing behavior of crows in general when we see how that type of behavior fits in with the rest of our knowledge of the behavior of crows. It is then that it becomes a familiar, homey, fact. We can claim to *understand* it only when we have a general system of knowledge, into which that bit of knowledge fits coherently. At least, that is one meaning of the word "understand". Again, though there remains a great amount to learn about what *fitting in coherently* is, it is clear that the framework provided by a relatively formal point of view is a natural one for discussing these questions.

The problems of the justification and of the discovery of scientific theories are generally regarded as quite distinct; the question of justification arises when we are given a theory or hypothesis or law, and a body of empirical evidence that is or might be alleged to support the theory. Under what conditions, we ask in general, does empirical evidence support a scientific theory or law? Discovery is another and knottier problem. Discovery is at issue when we are given a body of empirical data, and asked to discover the law or theory (or to explain the historical discovery of the law or theory, if any exists) which will render that body of data comprehensible, understandable. How should we go about discovering the appropriate law?

The answer to the first question requires the development of an inductive logic, or a theory of evidential support. In this logic, as in deductive logic, we will be concerned with forms of argument, rather than with the particulars of individual cases. In order to expose the formal structure of these arguments, we shall, as in the case of deductive logic, want to work within formalized language systems, in which the syntax of the arguments can be spelled out explicitly and in detail. There also are those, like K. R. Popper, who take the logic of evidential support to be simply the logic of tests of hypotheses; but this is essentially just classical deductive logic—we *deduce* a consequence of the hypothesis which we can then put to experimental test. Deductive logic, as we know, is best clarified within a formal and systematic framework.

The existence of a logic of discovery is more problematic. Most writers today discount the existence of such a logic, although there are exceptions, like N. R. Hanson. If there is such a thing—that is, if, in addition to a *psychology* of theory-creating or law-finding (we can, of course, look for the *empirical* facts of the scientist's mental activities), there is a *logic* that can provide clues as to the

[5]

kinds of hypotheses that are worth testing—then it, too, will be the sort of thing that can be explored most effectively in a relatively general and abstract way. It is true that in exploring any of these problems we must keep in constant touch with concrete scientific realities; we must avoid cutting ourselves loose from the machines and test tubes and living beasts which are our subject matter; but we are doing philosophy, not science, and we are looking for broad logical generalities. Even if these generalities did not exist, even if every case of scientific discovery or scientific justification or scientific test had to be dealt with completely in its own terms, and in isolation from every other case, still we could perhaps only uncover that generalization by approaching these problems in an abstract and formal way.

The metaphysical presuppositions and implications of the body of scientific knowledge that we have can also be explored best when we have given that knowledge its clearest and most meticulously articulated form—that is, when we have given it the structure of a formal system. To answer the question, "What are the premises that current biological theory takes for granted, or are there none?" we need to be precisely aware of what the content of current biological theory is, and that content must be expressed in a formal enough manner so that questions about logical entailment, logical contradiction, and logical independence, can be given clear and definite answers. The same is true, on some views, of the probability relationships that hold between statements of the formal system. And it would be true also of probability relationships holding between those statements and others that might be regarded as in some sense metaphysical. Thus it might be maintained that although in modern scientific biology no concept of a *vital force* is required, and although no such concept is presupposed by the biological system as it stands, yet there are probability considerations that render the existence of such a force more probable than not. I shall not maintain this—I don't think it is true—but the point here is that either to establish or to refute such a view requires the biological system in question to be laid out in enough detail (and that the relevant sense of probability be closely enough defined) so that a fair degree of uniformity of opinion can be expected concerning whether or not, in point of fact, the biological facts cited do lend probabilistic force to the claim that a vital force exists.

It is sometimes claimed that philosophy makes no progress, and is still fretting, in the same way, about the very problems that bothered Greek philosophers. There may be a sense in which this is true, though I doubt that it is a very important sense; surely the arguments get better, even if the conclusions are often the same. But I think this is very definitely not the case in the philosophy of science; no one, I think, who has examined the development of the philosophy of science over the past hundred years, and in particular over the past fifty years, can fail to see the enormous strides that have been made in the analysis of evidential support, in the analysis of causality and determinism, and

[6]

in the examination of the nature of the scientific enterprise. It is also clear that this progress is due in large part to the increasing tendency of philosophers of science to forego juicy generalizations in favor of the meticulous, point-by-point examination of philosophical and scientific claims. In the past thirty-five years, this has involved more and more the formalization of existing scientific languages, or the creation of artificial languages of science, or (at the very least) the supposition that such languages are available. It has become clearer and clearer to many that the necessary condition of progress in the philosophy of science is the willingness to deal in abstractions, and in many cases to operate with carefully delineated formal systems. There are still those who think otherwise. But the plan of this book hinges on the belief that the most important concept for the philosophy of science is that of a formal system, and that the concept of a formal system, and the related concept of a body of rational beliefs, together provide the framework in which the solution of many of the traditional problems of the philosophy of science have often been sought successfully.

II

What is a formal system? Before we can define, or even describe, a formal system, we must make some distinctions. The most important of these is the distinction between object language and metalanguage. We look upon a formal system as a kind of language, with a vocabulary, a grammar, etc. At the same time, we want to talk about the formal system, and we require a language for this. For talking about a formal system (for talking about any of the several formal systems we will be talking about), we shall use English, supplemented with a few technical terms which will be carefully defined as they are introduced. This we shall call the *metalanguage*. The formal system, regarded as a language, will be called the *object language*. In the metalanguage, when we talk about expressions of the object language, we must use names for those expressions; in general we shall form names for expressions, just as we do in ordinary English, by enclosing the expression in quotation marks. Thus, just as Chicago is a large windy city, so "Chicago" is a certain word in English which is used as the name of a city. Another way of referring to a certain expression will be by displaying it on a separate line:

Chicago is a city.

This is one way of referring to a certain sentence that we might also refer to with the help of quotation marks, namely, "Chicago is a city."

We wish, in the metalanguage, not only to describe expressions of the object language, but also to make assertions concerning these expressions—e.g., that such and such an expression is a theorem, that this expression and that are contradictories, that one expression entails another. We also want to refer to meanings. Thus we want to be able to say in our metalanguage that the

[7]

expression "red" in the object language means *red*. And sometimes, we are concerned with the complicated emotive or affective components in the use of the object language—e.g., with what is communicated when one person says to another of a third, "He is a red."

Within this broad range of metalinguistic activity, we can make a three-fold distinction between syntax, semantics, and pragmatics. *Syntax* is the part of the study of languages concerned with the bare arrangement of expressions of certain types—grammar (as opposed to diction) in English is primarily a matter of syntax. To know that "John between is" is not a sentence of English, we do now have to know what the words mean. Neither do we have to know who John and Mary are, nor even what loving is, to know that "John loves Mary," and "John doesn't love Mary," are contradictory. In the study of formal systems or formal languages, we generally give syntactical descriptions of the expressions that are regarded as forming the language; of the statements of the language that are to be regarded as axioms; and of the rules of inference of the language. (E.g., a rule of inference might be: From an expression of the form "If... then ___" and an expression of the form "...", the expression of the form "___" may be inferred, where the blanks of the two sorts are occupied by any sentential expressions of the object language.) Thus such metalinguistic terms as "... is a well-formed expression of such and such a language," "... is a theorem of such and such a language," etc, are syntactical. The part of a formal or linguistic system which is concerned simply with the manipulation of the expressions of that formal system according to the syntactical classes ("predicate", "variable", "parenthesis") that they fall into, is called a *calculus*. (A detailed definition will be given shortly.) The calculus of a formal system has, with some justice, been likened to a game played with the expressions of the object language. The justice of this metaphor lies in the fact that what we do in the calculus of a formal system depends on syntax alone, and the justification of any move we make, any inference we make, hinges solely on syntactical criteria. Meaning does not enter into our concerns at all, or need not, so long as we are merely playing the syntactical calculus game.

Of course, the game, as such, is not generally of much interest. We are interested in the manipulation of the expressions of the object language, according to the syntactical rules of manipulation, because these expressions do have meaning; if they had no meaning, we wouldn't be interested in the system. *Semantics* is the study of the meanings of the expressions of the object language. In our study of formal systems of various branches of science, we shall be concerned not only with the calculus of a formal system, but with the interpretation of that calculus. We are concerned not only with the expressions of the calculus of the formal system, but with the things that those expressions denote or designate or stand for. Semantics will be as much a matter for our study as syntax.

[8]

Although pragmatic considerations will guide us in our choice of formal systems for study, and in our formulation of the parts of those formal systems, *pragmatics* as such will not be of much concern to us. We are going to be concerned with the formal features of scientific languages and with the relationships between those languages and the world they purport to describe, but not specifically with the relations between the languages and the users of the languages, which is the relation with which pragmatics is primarily concerned.

One concept, however, which will be important in much of what follows is pragmatic. That is the concept of *relative interpersonal uniformity*. We shall say that one term has a higher degree of interpersonal uniformity than another (in a certain kind of situation) when users of the language are more uniform (potentially, as well as in historical fact) in their use of the first term than in their use of the second term. For example, in judging ambient temperature, a thermometer reading has a higher degree of interpersonal uniformity than intuitive judgments represented by terms like "hot", "cool", "cold", and "just right". This notion of interpersonal uniformity does involve essential reference to the users of the language, and thus is pragmatic. If we were to consider seriously the question of measuring interpersonal uniformity, we should have to do so by conducting empirical tests—it would be a scientific, empirical question. When we make use of this concept, it will be clear enough which terms have greater uniformity, without making empirical tests. But if tests were required, they would be part of the sociology of science or the linguistics of science; this is not to say that the philosophy of science is properly another science—not philosophy—but merely to point out that here as elsewhere the lines between analytical philosophy and empirical science are not clear and sharp.

One other matter should be mentioned now. I shall distinguish between a strict formal system, and a not-so-strict formal system. I shall regard bodies of scientific knowledge as they stand to be not-so-strict formal systems; that is, I shall take them to have roughly the same structure and components, implicitly, as a strict formal system, as I define it below. A not-so-strict formal system can be turned into a formal system by making explicit what is only implicit. This is a slight oversimplification, because there is more than one way, generally, of formalizing a bit of science—i.e., of turning it from a not-so-strict formal system into a strict formal system. Nevertheless, formalization is a useful procedure, as I shall attempt to bring out later.

In order to explain what a formal system is, in general, let me begin with the standard characterization of a strict formal system, and then proceed to show where the definition can be loosened along the seams while still keeping the garment the same.

A strict formal system consists of two parts:

I. A calculus
II. An interpretation.

[9]

Although there are some semantic systems (Carnap has presented some) in which the interpretation is provided formally, it is generally the case, even in a strict formal system, that the interpretation is treated more or less casually and informally. It is the interpretation, however, that provides the connection between the syntactical game of the calculus and the real world, and thus the interpretation is of the greatest importance to us in attempting to understand the connection between scientific theories and the world of toadstools and toolsheds.

The calculus of a formal system consists of the part of the formal system that can be dealt with by syntax alone. This part of a formal system is sometimes called a syntactical system. Though the calculus is quite literally meaningless without an accompanying interpretation, it is generally much easier to describe the syntax (the calculus) than the semantics (the interpretation), and (therefore?) the calculi of formal systems have received more attention than their interpretations.

To fix our ideas, let us consider the calculus of ordinary sentential or propositional logic. It is generally convenient to distinguish four parts of a calculus:

A. Vocabulary
B. Formation Rules
C. Axioms
D. Rules of Inference.

The *vocabulary* of a formal system consists of a list of all those signs that are used in writing the statements of the system, except those signs which are introduced explicitly by definition. The elements of the vocabulary are the *primitive signs* of the system. In our sentential calculus, they will consist of sentential variables X, Y, Z, X', Y', Z', ..., logical constants, and punctuation. These variables (under the usual interpretation of this calculus) take as their values, declarative statements. ("Socrates is wise," "The moon is between the sun and the earth," "The head of a horse is the head of an animal," and so on.) Note that in our vocabulary for sentential logic we allow for an infinity of sentential variables—this is the sense of the three dots "..."—but that we do so on the basis of precisely four signs: "X", "Y", "Z", and "$'$". The logical constants will be just these four: "$\sim$", "$\vee$", "$\&$", and "$\supset$". The first, "$\sim$", will be interpreted as logical negation; it corresponds to the judicious insertion of "not" in a declarative sentence: "Socrates is not wise," "The moon is not between the sun and the earth," etc. The wedge, "$\vee$", will be interpreted as logical disjunction, corresponding to the inclusive sense of the English "or". Logical conjunction is represented by "$\&$" in our formal system for sentential logic; under the usual interpretation it corresponds to the English "and", and sometimes to "but", "as well as", "also", etc. The sense of "$\&$" is also

[10]

represented in English by simple juxtaposition: "John is foolish; Socrates is wise." The horseshoe, " $\supset$ ", is sometimes represented in English by "If . . . then ___"; but unfortunately matters are complicated for our interpretation by the fact that the English locution "If . . . then ___" is often used, not to express a *conditional*, but to express an *implication*—i.e., a certain logical relation between " . . . " and " ___ ". The conditional, in logic, is simply a truth functional connective like "and" "or" and "not"—that is, it is an operation which you perform on two simple sentences to get a single more complicated sentence; it is *truth functional*, because the truth value of the more complicated sentence is taken to be determined once the truth values of the simpler sentences are given. The truth-functional character of these logical signs allows us to take the following table as giving their interpretation. (But more will be said about their interpretation below.)

X	Y	$\sim X$	$(X \lor Y)$	$(X \,\&\, Y)$	$(X \supset Y)$
T	T	F	T	T	T
T	F	F	T	F	F
F	T	T	T	F	T
F	F	T	F	F	T

Punctuation consists of the left and right parentheses: "(" and ")".

The *formation rules* tell us how to construct the meaningful or well-formed expressions of the object language whose syntax we are describing. First we specify the sentential variables: a sentential variable is " X " or " Y " or " Z ", or else it consists of a sentential variable followed by an accent. A sentential variable alone is a well-formed formula; and if " . . . " and " ___ " are well-formed formulas, so are " $(\ldots \lor \text{___})$ ", " $(\ldots \,\&\, \text{___})$ ", " $\sim(\ldots)$ " and " $(\ldots \supset \text{___})$ ". Furthermore, we shall stipulate that only the expressions that are classified as well-formed by these rules are to be well-formed formulas of our calculus.

Notice that these rules are expressed in such a way that, given any expression whatsoever made up from pieces of the primitive vocabulary, we can follow a definite procedure which will determine, after a finite number of steps, whether or not that expression is well formed. A well-formed expression can have only one of five forms: it must either be a sentential variable, a disjunction, a conjunction, a negation, or a conditional. If it is a sentential variable, it must be " X " or " Y " or " Z ", or else it must consist of a sentential variable followed by an accent. If it is a negation, it must consist of " $\sim$ ", followed by a well-formed expression enclosed in parentheses. If it is a disjunction, conjunction, or conditional, it must consist of two well-formed expressions, separated by the

[11]

ampersand, the wedge, or the horseshoe, and enclosed in parentheses. The new well-formed expressions referred to in this analysis—the components of the conjunction, disjunction, or whatever—will be subject to the same analysis as the first one; they will be sentential variables, or disjunctions, or conjunctions, or . . ., but they will be at least one symbol shorter than the original expression. The process of analyzing a given expression to see if it is well formed will thus come to an end.

The *axioms* of any system consist of a set of statements in the object language of that system. Syntactically, they are an arbitrary set of statements; semantically, they are generally a set of statements *assumed* to be true, from which (pragmatically) interesting statements of the system can be deduced. Sometimes this set of statements is finite, and then the axioms can simply be exhibited; sometimes the set of axioms is infinite, and then they must be described by means of axiom *schemata* (e.g., "Every well-formed expression of the form "((. . . ∨ . . .) ⊃ . . .)" is an axiom"), or by some other technique of description in the metalanguage (e.g., "Every statement consisting of a well-formed formula followed by a horseshoe, followed by the same well-formed formula, is an axiom.")

To express the *rules of inference*, we again need to use general descriptions in the metalanguage. I have used dots and dashes (. . ., ___) so far, for simplicity; but now it will help to introduce the concept of a metalinguistic variable. I shall use "*A*", "*B*", etc, as metalinguistic variables. They stand for expressions of the object language; they are variables taking as their values expressions of the object language. To refer to a particular statement or expression of the object language, we follow the perfectly standard (English language) technique of enclosing that statement or expression in quotation marks. To refer to an expression of a certain *form*—e.g., to a well-formed expression which is a conditional whose antecedent is a conjunction—we use metalinguistic variables: we speak of a statement of the form $((A \mathbin{\&} B) \supset C)$.

Let us now take the syntactical system I have been describing discursively, and express it as a calculus.

Calculus I

A. Vocabulary:
    1. Nonlogical signs:
        primitive sentential variables: X, Y, Z;
        operator for generating new sentential variables: '.
    2. Logical signs: ∼, ∨, ⊃, &.
    3. Punctuation: (,).
B. Formation Rules:
    1. "*X*", "*Y*", and "*Z*" are sentential variables.
    2. If *A* is a sentential variable, *A* followed by "'" is a sentential variable.

3. The only sentential variables are those expressions satisfying 1 or 2.
4. A sentential variable is a well-formed formula.
5. If A and B are well-formed formulas, so are $\sim A$, $(A \lor B)$, $(A \,\&\, B)$, and $(A \supset B)$.
6. An expression is a well-formed formula only if it satisfies 4 or 5.

C. Axioms:
1. $((X \lor X) \supset X)$
2. $((X \lor Y) \supset (Y \lor X))$
3. $((X \supset Y) \supset ((Z \lor X) \supset (Z \lor Y)))$
4. $(X \supset (X \lor Y))$
5. $((\sim X \lor Y) \supset (X \supset Y))$
6. $((X \supset Y) \supset (\sim X \lor Y))$
7. $((X \lor Y) \supset \sim(\sim X \,\&\, \sim Y))$
8. $(\sim(\sim X \,\&\, \sim Y) \supset (X \lor Y))$

D. Rules of Inference:
1. From well-formed formulas of the form A and $(A \supset B)$, B may be inferred.
2. If A is like B, except for containing some well-formed formula C wherever B contains a certain sentential variable, then A may be inferred from B.

This calculus for sentential logic is now completely specified. We have not said what a proof is, or a theorem; but these concepts are the same for any formal system. We define both notions perfectly generally:

Proof:

A proof of a well-formed formula A in a given formal system, from a sequence of well-formed formulas $B_1, B_2, \ldots, B_n$ as premises, consists of a sequence of well-formed formulas, each of which is one of the formulas B_i, or an axiom of the system, or may be inferred by the rules of inference of the system from earlier formulas in the sequence, the last formula of which is A. (Provided no substitution is made—except in axioms—for variables of the premises.)

THEOREM:

A is a theorem of a given formal system if and only if there is a proof of A in that system from a set of premises which has no members.

Just to illustrate these two definitions, I shall give the formal proof of a theorem here, before continuing on to consider the interpretation of this calculus in more detail.

THEOREM: $(\sim X \vee X)$.

Proof:

1. $((X \supset Y) \supset ((Z \vee X) \supset (Z \vee Y)))$	axiom 3
2. $(((X \vee X) \supset X) \supset ((\sim X \vee (X \vee X)) \supset$ $(\sim X \vee X)))$	1, rule 2
3. $((X \vee X) \supset X)$	axiom 1
4. $((\sim X \vee (X \vee X)) \supset (\sim X \vee X))$	2, 3, Rule 1
5. $(X \supset (X \vee Y))$	axiom 4
6. $(X \supset (X \vee X))$	5, rule 2
7. $((X \supset Y) \supset (\sim X \vee Y))$	axiom 6
8. $((X \supset (X \vee X)) \supset (\sim X \vee (X \vee X)))$	7, rule 2
9. $(\sim X \vee (X \vee X))$	6, 8, rule 1
10. $(\sim X \vee X)$	4, 9, rule 1

Q.E.D.

Here is a proof of a formula from premises: the proof of the formula Z, from the premises Y, $(Z \vee X)$, and $(X \supset \sim Y)$.

1. $((X \supset Y) \supset ((Z \vee X) \supset (Z \vee Y)))$	axiom 3
2. $((X \supset \sim Y) \supset ((Z \vee X) \supset (Z \vee \sim Y)))$	1, rule 2
3. $(X \supset \sim Y)$	premise
4. $((Z \vee X) \supset (Z \vee \sim Y))$	2, 3, rule 1
5. $(Z \vee X)$	premise
6. $(Z \vee \sim Y)$	4, 5, rule 1
7. $((X \vee Y) \supset (Y \vee X))$	axiom 2
8. $((Z \vee \sim Y) \supset (\sim Y \vee Z))$	7, rule 2
9. $(\sim Y \vee Z))$	6, 8, rule 1
10. $((\sim X \vee Y) \supset (X \supset Y))$	axiom 5
11. $((\sim Y \vee Z) \supset (Y \supset Z))$	10, rule 2
12. $(Y \supset Z)$	9, 11, rule 1
13. Y	premise
14. Z	12, 13, rule 1

Q.E.D.

It should be observed that the axioms are also theorems, according to the definition of theoremhood on page 13. The proof for Axiom 1, in virtue of which it is a theorem, for example, is just Axiom 1 itself. The sequence of formulas in question happens to be very short: one formula.

The usual interpretation of the calculus that I have just presented, the interpretation that justifies calling it a *sentential* calculus, is the interpretation mentioned earlier: The sentential variables, "X", "Y", etc., are taken to range over (to take as their values) declarative sentences of English. The logical signs are taken to represent the truth-functional aspects of their English counterparts.

[14]

Under this interpretation, the calculus represents the totality of all those expressions in English that are true by virtue of their truth-functional form alone (i.e., all the expressions like "It is raining or it is not raining"). If we let the variable "X" take the value "It is raining," then the conclusion of the first theorem proved is "It is not raining or it is raining." The calculus also embodies all of those valid arguments in English whose validity hinges only on their truth-functional structure. An argument in English is truth-functionally valid—valid, that is, because of its truth functional occurrences of "and", "or", "not", "if... then...", etc.—if and only if there is a corresponding derivation in the sentential calculus. Of course, there are many logical truths of English that are not true by virtue of their truth functional structure: "Everything is either red or not red," for example. And there are arguments that are valid, but not valid merely in virtue of their truth functional structure: "All men are mortal, and Socrates is a man; therefore Socrates is mortal," for example. Nevertheless, important parts of any kind of argument can be represented in this calculus.

An example of an argument that can be completely represented in our sentential calculus is the following:

> If the diamonds were really stolen, it was not an amateur job.
> Either the client is trying to defraud the insurance company,
> or the diamonds were really stolen. It was an amateur job.
>
> Therefore the client is trying to defraud the insurance company.

Suppose we let the variable "X" have the value "The diamonds were really stolen," and the variable "Y" have the value "It was not an amateur job," and the variable "Z" have the value "The client is trying to defraud the insurance company." Then the premises of this argument in English have the same form as the premises of the sample proof on page 14; and the conclusion of the argument in English is precisely the conclusion of the proof on page 14. The argument in English is truth-functionally valid, and there exists a corresponding proof in the sentential calculus.

That this is always the case—i.e., that if there is a proof in the calculus corresponding to an argument in English, then the English argument is truth-functionally valid—hinges on the fact that the rules of inference are truth preserving (we can never get from a true sentence to a false one using the two rules of inference of the calculus) and the fact that the axioms of the calculus are always true, regardless of the truth values of their components. (Regardless of the truth values of the sentences that the variables are taken to stand for, the axioms remain true, under the truth table interpretation of the connectives given on page 11). The detailed proof of the fact that there is a proof in the calculus if and only if the corresponding English argument is valid is beyond the scope of our discussion here, though it may be made plausible by reflection on the two facts mentioned.

[15]

The purpose of the formal system whose calculus has been presented above is to establish a standard mechanism to facilitate the assessment of validity in sentential argument. What happens is this: we find some arguments in our native tongue to be universally regarded as satisfactory. Some of the satisfactory arguments, arguments that we and all ordinary people regard as valid, involve nothing more than the English connectives "but", "and", "or", "not", etc., in their truth functional roles. That is to say, the validity of the argument rests solely on the relation between the truth-functional connections among sentences of the premises, and the truth-functional connections among sentences of the conclusion. What comes first is the recognition of a particular class (whose boundaries may be quite vague) of satisfactory arguments, of arguments that anyone *in his right mind* would regard as valid. This bare recognition is not science; it is not logic; it becomes logic when we begin to systematize and organize these types of arguments; and it becomes logic in the modern sense when we begin to construct a formal system, with a calculus such as Calculus I as its syntactical part, in which we can represent all possible arguments of truth-functional type.

A formal system of sentential logic is more than a calculus. It is a calculus together with an interpretation which provides some connection between the calculus and the things that are really of concern to us. As logicians, as mathematicians, or simply as playful people, we may be concerned with the calculus *qua* calculus. As scientists, or philosophers of science, or (applied) logicians, we are concerned with interpreted systems and not with pure calculi. Calculus I is intended to be a sentential calculus, and its interpretation is therefore relatively straightforward. But there are still alternatives even among standard interpretations. One alternative is the one given above. Another is this: we could take the variables "X", "Y", "Z", etc., to stand for any propositions (i.e., we could interpret the variables as taking particular propositions as their values), and we could take the logical connectives "$\sim$", "$\vee$", etc., to stand for the negation, disjunction, etc., of propositions. Propositions themselves, we must take to be the meanings of sentences. Now the negation, disjunction, etc., of propositions we may simply take to be truth-functional, so that the truth tables, rather than constituting an interpretation of the corresponding symbols, elucidate their given character. The calculus, thus interpreted, is called a propositional logic. The interpretation is perfectly coherent and sound, though it is a different one from the interpretation I offered first. It should be noticed, however, that this interpretation leaves vague the relation between sentences and propositions (and it is only sentences that can be exhibited), between propositional negation, and particular negating expressions of a given language, between propositional disjunction and the disjunctive locutions of a given language. In short, it leaves vague the relation between propositional logic and common discourse.

Although there is nothing very objectionable in this interpretation, I think it is

[16]

more profitable, and throws far more light on the function of formal systems as embodiments of scientific knowledge, to locate the vagueness and imprecision in the interpretation itself, rather than in the relation between the entities referred to in the interpretation and the entities (sentences, in this case) that we encounter in the world. The interpretation of Calculus I given first brings this out. The variables " X ", " Y ", " Z ", etc., stand for sentences of (say) English; the logical constants correspond to the logical particles of English, insofar as the use of those particles in English is truth-functional. That is to say that " $\sim$ " corresponds to ordinary English negation, insofar as ordinary English negation is simply truth functional, which is pretty far. Similarly, although conjunction in English sometimes contains elements of meaning that involve time only the aspects of English conjunctions such as "and", "but", ";", etc., that are truth functional are represented in the formal system of sentential logic by " $\&$ ". Another way of expressing precisely the same thing, although it sounds different, is to say that the logical constants are to be *defined* by truth tables. Thus we can give an interpretation of the logical constants by means of truth tables, together with the concept of truth. The concept of truth focuses attention on the truth-functional aspects of the particles: to say that conjunction is to be such that the conjunction of A and B is true when A is true and when B is true, but not otherwise, is merely a roundabout but precise way of saying that logical conjunction is to function like conjunction in English insofar as conjunction in English is truth-functional.

In the interpretation we are now considering, we must also decide, more or less explicitly, what sentences of English the variables " X ", " Y ", etc., are to take as their values. Generally we say: simple declarative sentences. This characterization is all right; we understand what is meant. But here, too, there is an element of vagueness; it is not hard to imagine sentences whose form is declarative, but whose function is quite otherwise ("You haven't finished your assignment yet!"), and sentences whose form seems not to be declarative, but whose function is: ("Ouch!"). And there are any number of kinds of sentences whose truth-value is dependent on the circumstances of their utterance: "Today is Tuesday," "I am hot," "You are a liar," "That car is moving too fast." It is obviously necessary to take account of these systematic ambiguities in any application of the formal system to ordinary discourse.

It was stated earlier that one function of the formal system of sentential logic was to provide a simple mechanism by means of which to assess the validity of relatively complicated arguments. The concept of validity, applied to complicated arguments in ordinary language, was asserted to be equivalent to the concept of provability within the calculus. Whether or not a certain sequence of object language statements in the calculus is (say) a proof of A from premises $B_1 \ldots B_n$, is a question that admits of a simple, straightforward answer, that can be determined by inspection of the sequence of statements. It is characteristic of

[17]

all formal systems that there is always a mechanical procedure for deciding whether or not an alleged proof of a particular statement is indeed a proof: we need simply inspect the sequence of statements that is alleged to be the proof, and see that each statement of the sequence is (*a*) an axiom, (*b*) a premise, if we are concerned with a proof from certain premises, or (*c*) derivable by one of the official rules of inference from earlier statements in the sequence.

This characteristic of formal systems has given rise to the (somewhat justified) assertion that they are designed to eliminate the necessity of intelligence. It takes a much higher order of intelligence to assess the validity of an argument directly than it does to check the steps in the proof (in a formal system) of the theorem that corresponds to that argument. In general this is the case: formal systems in the sciences are calculational devices as well as codifications of the facts.

III

Calculus I is not the only way of representing the syntax of sentential logic. Calculus II, borrowed from Hilbert and Ackermann, is easier to present than Calculus I, and easier to prove things *about*. It has the same interpretation as Calculus I, ordinarily; but, like the calculus of any formal system, it admits of other interpretations than that for which it was designed.

Calculus II

A. Vocabulary:
  1. Nonlogical signs:
     sentential variables: $X, Y, Z, X', Y', \ldots$
  2. Logical constants: $\sim$, $\vee$.
  3. Punctuation: (,).

B. Formation Rules:
  1. A sentential variable is a well-formed formula.
  2. If A and B are well-formed formulas, so are $\sim A$ and $(A \vee B)$.
  3. An expression is a well-formed formula only if it satisfies 1 or 2.

C. Axioms
  1. $(\sim(X \vee X) \vee X)$.
  2. $(\sim X \vee (X \vee Y))$.
  3. $(\sim(X \vee Y) \vee (Y \vee X))$.
  4. $(\sim(\sim X \vee Y) \vee (\sim(Z \vee X) \vee (Z \vee Y)))$.

D. Rules of Inference:
  1. From well-formed formulas of the form A and $(\sim A \vee B)$, B may be inferred.
  2. If A is like B, except for containing some well-formed formula C, wherever B contains a particular sentential variable, then A may be inferred from B.

[18]

There are a number of differences between Calculus I and Calculus II. The most striking of these differences is that the logical constants "&" and "⊃" do not appear in Calculus II. Nevertheless, if we introduce "∼" and "∨" by means of a truth table interpretation, as we did before, then we can *define* "⊃" and "&" contextually:

> D1. "$A ⊃ B$" is defined to be "$(∼A ∨ B)$."
> D2. "$A \& B$" is defined to be "$∼(∼A ∨ ∼B)$."

A check of the truth tables of "$(∼A ∨ B)$" and "$∼(∼A ∨ ∼B)$" will show that they are precisely the same, in every possible case, as the truth tables we took in Calculus I to define "⊃" and "&". If we introduce these two definitions it turns out that every theorem of Calculus I is also a theorem of Calculus II, and every theorem of Calculus II is a theorem of Calculus I. The two calculi are thus equivalent. They contain the same body of theorems.

Another striking difference is that there are only half as many axioms, and half as many formation rules; and the formation rules of Calculus II are simpler. The difference in the number of axioms and the difference in simplicity of the formation rules are direct consequences of the fact that there are fewer logical constants in Calculus II than in Calculus I. The reduction in the number of formation rules (through the deletion of the formation rules concerning the construction of sentential variables) is due to the fact that the vocabulary is intended to contain an infinite number of sentential variables; that is the intent of the three dots that follow "Y'". Since the *primitive* vocabulary contains an infinite number of primitive variables, we do not need formation rules to enable us to construct an infinite number of sentential variables from a finite number of primitive variables and a variable operator.

A third difference would quickly become apparent if we were to begin to construct proofs of theorems in Calculus II; we would find it far more tedious and awkward than it is in Calculus I.

Calculus I and Calculus II, together with their normal interpretations, are simply two different ways of formalizing the same subject matter, truth functional logic. For some purposes one is advantageous, for some purposes the other. Given the usual interpretation of the sentential variables and of the logical constants, every theorem of one calculus will also be a theorem of the other.

Given a certain set of statements, it is possible to construct more than one calculus that will yield that set of statements as theorems. (Both Calculus I and Calculus II yield all the truth-functional truths as theorems.) It is also possible, given a calculus, to provide it with more than one interpretation. Calculus II, for example, can be taken as an arithmetic of the two numbers 0 and 1, if we take "∨" to represent ordinary multiplication, and "∼" to be interpreted thus: "$∼1$" is to be interpreted as 0; "$∼0$" is to be interpreted as 1. The variables, "X", "Y", "Z", etc., take as values, on this interpretation, the

[19]

numbers 0, and 1; the well-formed formulas also represent numbers (0 and 1); the axioms, and the theorems, represent the number 0 however the numbers 0 and 1 are assigned to the sentential variables.

Yet another interpretation of this calculus (one that is useful to engineers!) takes the variables " X ", " Y ", " Z ", etc., to represent the *states* of switches (open—no current can flow; closed—current can flow). The operator " $\sim$ " changes the open state into the closed state, and the closed state into the open state. " $\sim X$ " represents the state of a switch that is open when the switch corresponding to X is closed and closed when the switch corresponding to X is open. If " X " and " Y " stand for the states of two switches, " $(X \vee Y)$ " stands for the state of the compound switch, consisting of those two switches in parallel (Fig. 1): If either of them is closed, current can flow. " $(X \& Y)$ " (defined by D2)

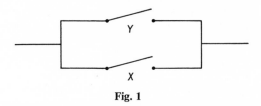

Fig. 1

stands for the state of the compound switch consisting of the two switches in series (Fig. 2): if either of them is open, no current can flow. The axioms of the

Fig. 2

calculus represent switching systems through which current can flow, regardless of the positions of the switches. The theorems of the calculus represent the set of all possible switching circuits with this characteristic.

IV

In most of the formal systems that will be discussed here, the subject matter is not logic, but physics or chemistry or biology. The formal systems of logic play a special role in each of these other formal systems; instead of restricting the rules of inference to two or three (sometimes to one!), as we do in setting up formal systems of pure logic, we will generally allow any valid principle of inference to serve as a rule. The logical formal system lurks in the background, providing both a standard of validity and a means of assessing validity; but we are interested neither in the economy nor in the elegance of the logical formal system, so much as we are interested in the economy or elegance of the overall formal system. We will therefore choose to embed in most of our formal systems a system of

[20]

logic which is messy in the sense that it incorporates a great many rules, but which is simple in that it is easy to construct proofs in that system of logic, and also in the sense that the allowable inferences are just (about) those inferences that one would intuitively expect to be allowable.

The vocabulary and the formation rules cannot be specified in general, because they depend on the terminology required for the science whose formalization is being considered. Thus "Patient A is schizophrenic," and "Patient B's I.Q. is over 110," represent the sort of sentences we might find in a body of psychological knowledge, whereas "$\sum M_i = 0$", "$E = mc^2$", and the like are the kinds of sentences we might expect to find in a body of physics. Axioms are required in order to be able to prove logical truths as theorems; but since the point of these applied formal systems is not to codify logical truths, but psychological, or physical, or chemical, or sociological truths, these axioms are of less importance than the rules of inference. I begin therefore by listing a number of rules of inference that will be taken for granted (unless otherwise stipulated) in each of the formal systems that follow. The first group concerns inferences that are truth-functionally valid; they can therefore each be justified by reference to Calculus I or to Calculus II: it is possible to show that any inference that is validated by the following truth functional rules of inference could also be validated by the axioms and rules of inference of either Calculus I or Calculus II.

Rules of Inference

Modus Ponens: From premises A and $(A \supset B)$, B may be inferred.
Modus Tollens: From premises $\sim B$ and $(A \supset B)$, $\sim A$ may be inferred.

> If the temperature falls below 20°F, the pond freezes.
> The pond did not freeze last night. Therefore the temperature did not fall below 20°F last night.

Hypothetical Syllogism: From premises $(A \supset B)$ and $(B \supset C)$, $(A \supset C)$ may be inferred.

> If the temperature falls below 20°F the horsetrough freezes.
> If the horsetrough freezes, the horse can't drink. Therefore, if the temperature falls below 20°F, the horse can't drink.

Disjunctive Syllogism: From premises $(A \lor B)$ and $\sim A$, B may be inferred.

> Tom will come to the party or Mary will come to the party.
> Tom won't be able to come to the party. Therefore Mary will come to the party.

Simplification: From premise $(A \ \& \ B)$, A may be inferred.

> There are two black cards and three red cards in my hand.
> Therefore there are two black cards in my hand.

[21]

Conjunction: From premises A and B, $(A \mathbin{\&} B)$ may be inferred.

> There are two black cards in my hand. There are three red cards in my hand. Therefore there are two black cards in my hand and three red cards in my hand.

Addition: From the premise A, $(A \lor B)$ may be inferred.

> The die landed with a five-spot up. Therefore the die landed with either a five or a three up.

Replacement: If A and B are logically equivalent, and C is like D, except for containing one or more occurrences of A where D contains occurrences of B, C may be inferred from D.

In order to apply this rule, we must know what logical equivalence is. In general we say that if $(A \supset B)$ and $(B \supset A)$ are theorems, in a pure logical calculus, such as Calculus I or Calculus II, then A and B are truth-functionally, and thus logically equivalent. A useful list of truth-functional equivalences (which may be considered part of the rule of replacement) follows.

DeMorgan's Laws

$\sim(A \lor B)$	is equivalent to	$(\sim A \mathbin{\&} \sim B)$
$\sim(A \mathbin{\&} B)$	is equivalent to	$(\sim A \lor \sim B)$

Distributive Laws

$(A \mathbin{\&} (B \lor C))$	is equivalent to	$((A \mathbin{\&} B) \lor (A \mathbin{\&} C))$
$(A \lor (B \mathbin{\&} C))$	is equivalent to	$((A \lor B) \mathbin{\&} (A \lor C))$

Associative Laws

$(A \lor (B \lor C))$	is equivalent to	$((A \lor B) \lor C)$
$(A \mathbin{\&} (B \mathbin{\&} C))$	is equivalent to	$((A \mathbin{\&} B) \mathbin{\&} C)$

Commutative Laws

$(A \lor B)$	is equivalent to	$(B \lor A)$
$(A \mathbin{\&} B)$	is equivalent to	$(B \mathbin{\&} A)$

Double Negation

$\sim \sim A$	is equivalent to	A

Transposition

$(A \supset B)$	is equivalent to	$(\sim B \supset \sim A)$

Exportation

$((A \mathbin{\&} B) \supset C)$	is equivalent to	$(A \supset (B \supset C))$

Conditional Law

$(A \supset B)$	is equivalent to	$(\sim A \lor B)$

Conditionalization: B may be inferred from premises $A_1, A_2, \ldots, A_n$ if and only if $(A_n \supset B)$ may be inferred from premises $A_1, A_2, \ldots, A_{n-1}$.

[22]

This is an exceedingly valuable rule of inference; in proving a conclusion of the form $(B \supset D)$, it allows us to take as a *conditional premise* the antecedent B, of the conditional; we then construct a proof of D, from premises that include B; we then argue by conditionalization that $(B \supset D)$ follows from the remainder of the premises. We can argue, for example, that a conclusion of the form $(A \supset (A \& B))$ follows from a premise of the form $(A \supset B)$. The schematic outline of the proof would be

1. $(A \supset B)$ premise
2. A conditional premise
3. B 1,2, Modus Ponens
4. $(A \& B)$ 2,3, conjunction
5. $(A \supset (A \& B))$ 2–4, conditionalization

Another use of conditional proof is in the reconstruction of *reductio ad absurdum* arguments. Assume as a conditional premise, the denial of the conclusion: $\sim C$. Derive a contradiction, $(P \& \sim P)$. Conditionalize: $(\sim C \supset (P \& \sim P))$ is yielded by the remainder of the premises. But $\sim (P \& \sim P)$ is a theorem (is obtainable from purely logical axioms), and so by Modus Tollens, we have $\sim \sim C$, or C.

The definitions of "proof from premises" and of "theorem" are unchanged from page 13. Here are two examples of arguments in ordinary English, and the corresponding proofs.

> If we urge Smith to come, he will come to visit us now. If Smith doesn't come to visit us now, then he'll visit us some other time. But either we urge Smith to come, or he'll not visit us another time. Therefore Smith will come to visit us now.

Let us write "S" as an abbreviation of "Smith does come to visit us now," "U" as an abbreviation of "We urge Smith to come," and "O" as an abbreviation of "Smith will visit us some other time." The premises of the argument become

1. $(U \supset S)$
2. $(\sim S \supset O)$
3. $(U \lor \sim O)$

And the proof of the conclusion becomes

1. $(U \supset S)$ premise
2. $(\sim S \supset O)$ premise
3. $(\sim O \supset \sim \sim S)$ 2, replacement
4. $(U \lor \sim O)$ premise
5. $(\sim \sim U \lor O)$ 4, replacement
6. $(\sim U \supset O)$ 5, replacement

7. $(\sim U \supset \sim \sim S)$	3, 6, hypothetical syllogism
8. $(\sim U \supset S)$	7, replacement
9. $((U \supset S) \& (\sim U \supset S))$	1, 8, Conjunction
10. $((\sim U \vee S) \& (\sim U \vee S))$	9, replacement
11. $((\sim U \& \sim \sim U) \vee S)$	10, distributive law
12. $((\sim U \& U) \vee S)$	11, replacement.
13. $\sim(\sim U \& U)$	An instance of the axioms of this system
14. S	12, 13, disjunctive syllogism

When it rains, the crows are excitable. When it doesn't rain plants don't thrive. Either farming is a poor proposition, or plants thrive. The crows aren't excitable. Therefore farming is a poor proposition.

Let "R" abbreviate "It rains," "C" abbreviate "The crows are excitable," "P" abbreviate "The plants thrive," and "F" abbreviate "Farming is a poor proposition." The proof of the validity of the argument becomes:

1. $(R \supset C)$	premise
2. $(\sim R \supset \sim P)$	premise
3. $(F \vee P)$	premise
4. $\sim C$	premise
5. $\sim R$	1,4, modus tollens
6. $\sim P$	2,5, modus ponens
7. $(P \vee F)$	3, replacement
8. F	6,7, disjunctive syllogism

The logical framework of most of the systems we shall deal with must be taken to contain more than sentential logic. We must suppose that it contains a standard quantification theory as well. Quantification theory is the part of logic that corresponds to the implicit logic of the English terms "all", "some", "every", "there is...", etc. The key idea behind the treatment of the logic of these terms is the analysis of sentences into subject and predicate form. ("Subject" and "predicate" are not to be understood in their grammatical sense.) The statement "Socrates is mortal", for example, would be analyzed into a subject, "Socrates", and a predicate, "is mortal". If we symbolize the predicate "is mortal" by "M", and the subject "Socrates" by "s", we can symbolize the whole statement by "$M(s)$". If we abbreviate "John" by the symbol "j", we can represent the statement, "John is mortal" by "$M(j)$". If we let "H" stand for the predicate "is human", we can symbolize "John is human" and "Socrates is human" by "$H(j)$" and "$H(s)$", respectively. We can, of course, combine these sentences by means of the truth-functional connectives "$\sim$", "$\vee$", "$\supset$", etc. Thus "Socrates is human and John is human" becomes "$(H(s) \& H(j))$"; "Socrates is human or mortal", becomes "$(H(s) \vee M(s))$"; "If

[24]

John is human, then John is mortal" becomes "$(H(j) \supset M(j))$"; and "If Socrates is human, then he is mortal", becomes "$(H(s) \supset M(s))$".

These last two sentences are true (it happens), and indeed they remain true no matter whose name you put in place of Socrates' name, because all humans are mortal. One way of paraphrasing this last clause is this: "Whatever you may name (or refer to), if it is human, then it is mortal." Since naming is not relevant to the mortality of all humans (and does not enter into our first statement), we can also paraphrase: "Whatever it is, if it is human, it is mortal." Replacing "it" by "x", we have "Whatever x is, $(H(x) \supset M(x))$". One standard way of symbolizing the phrase "Whatever x is" is simply to enclose the "x" in parentheses: we can thus represent "All men are mortal", as "$(x)(H(x) \supset M(x))$". "Everything is either human or not human", becomes "Whatever x may be, x is human or x is not human", or "$(x)(H(x) \vee \sim H(x))$". The sentence, "Everything is human," becomes "$(x)(H(x))$".

The expression "(x)" is called a quantifier; it is called a *universal* quantifier, for its function is to embody the universality expressed in English by such words as "all", "every", as well as "no", and "none". Thus "None of the players is a star," becomes "Whatever x may be, if it is one of the players, it is not a star." Symbolizing "is one of the players" by "P", and "is a star" by "S", we have, "$(x)(P(x) \supset \sim S(x))$". "No humans are mortal", becomes "$(x)(H(x) \supset \sim M(x))$".

Corresponding to the English locutions, "some", "there is a", "there are", 'is the existential quantifier,' "$(\exists x)$"; "Some humans are stars," can be paraphrased, "Something is such that it is a human, and it is a star," which in turn can be phrased, "For some x, $H(x)$ and $S(x)$," or, finally, "$(\exists x)(H(x) \& S(x))$".

The formulas we construct with quantifiers and sentential connectives may themselves be combined by means of sentential connectives. Thus "Either some human is immortal, or all men are mortal," becomes "$((\exists x)(H(x) \& \sim M(x)) \vee (x)(H(x) \supset M(x)))$".

There is nothing special about the letter "x"; we shall use a whole alphabet of variables, "x", "y", "z", "x'", "y'" in the same way. (Thus the last sentence symbolized could alternatively be symbolized: "$((\exists y)(H(y) \& \sim M(y)) \vee (z)(H(z) \supset M(z)))$".) These variables are called individual variables; they take individuals as their values. Before starting a discussion on the four basic modes of inference involving these quantifiers, we must define the *scope* of a quantifier. The scope of a quantifier consists of all the material between the first left parenthesis (not part of another quantifier) following that quantifier, and the right parenthesis that is the mate of the left parenthesis. For example:

$$(z)\ (\ (x)\ (\exists y)\ (\ H(x)\supset P\ (y)\ )\ )\supset M(z)\ )$$
$$①②③④⑤⑥⑦⑧\ ⑨⑩\quad ⑪⑫⑬\quad ⑭\ ⑮⑯$$

The scope of the first quantifier "(z)" is the material between parenthesis ③,

[25]

the first left parenthesis not part of another quantifier, and parenthesis ⑯ , its mate. The scope of the quantifier "(x)" is all the material between parenthesis ⑧ and parenthesis ⑬. Parenthesis ⑥ is the first left parenthesis after the quantifier "(x)", but it is part of the quantifier "$(\exists y)$", and thus doesn't count. The scope of the quantifier "$(\exists y)$" is just the same: the material between parenthesis ⑧ and parenthesis ⑬.

An occurrence of an individual variable is *bound* if it occurs within the scope of a quantifier of that variable, and is said to be bound to that quantifier. The occurrence of the variable within the quantifier is also bound. Thus in the preceding formula every occurrence of every variable is bound to the corresponding quantifier. An occurrence of an individual variable that is not a bound occurrence of that variable, is a *free* occurrence of that variable. For example:

$$(x)((x)(H(x)) \supset ((M(x) \lor (\exists y)(H(y))) \lor M(y)))$$

① ②   ③   ④   ⑤   ⑥   ⑦

The occurrence of "x" in "$H(x)$" is bound to quantifier ②; the scope of that quantifier is "$H(x)$". The occurrence of "x" in "$M(x)$" is bound to quantifier ①, whose scope extends from the second left parenthesis to the last right parenthesis. Occurrence ⑤ of "y", like occurrences ① and ② of "x", is bound because it occurs in a quantifier. The occurrence of "y" in "$H(y)$" is bound to quantifier ⑤; since ⑤ is the only quantifier of the variable "y", and its scope is only "$H(y)$", the "y" in "$M(y)$" does not fall within the scope of any quantifier of "y", and is thus not bound, but is a free occurrence of "y".

I shall use lower case "v_1", "v_2", ... as metalinguistic variables taking as their values individual variables (e.g., "x", "y") of the object language. I shall use Greek letters "ϕ", "ψ", "χ", etc., as metalinguistic variables taking as their values well formed expressions of the object language that may (or may not) contain free individual variables. I shall use "n_1", "n_2", etc., as metalinguistic variables taking as their values proper names ("John", "Socrates", "5", "$\sqrt{2}$") of the object language, or definite descriptions ("the father of John", "the largest prime number less than 100", "the melting point of lead", etc.). Definite descriptions may also contain free variables: "the father of x", "the smallest prime number greater than y", etc. I shall say that an occurrence of (a name or definite description) n_1 in an expression $\phi(n_1)$ is a *free occurrence of* n_1 provided n_1 is a proper name, or a definite description that does not contain any free variable that becomes bound in $\phi(n_1)$ by a quantifier occurring in $\phi(n_1)$. "$\phi(v_1)$" is a variable-expression of the metalanguage, taking as its values well-informed expressions of the object language which contain at least one free occurrence of the individual variable v_1. "$\phi(v_2)$" and "$\phi(n_2)$" then denote the result of replacing all free occurrences of v_1 in $\phi(v_1)$ by v_2 or n_2, respectively, subject to the condition that v_2 (or n_2) must be free in $\phi(v_2)$ (or $\phi(n_2)$) at all those places at which v_1 occurs free in $\phi(v_1)$.

[26]

The quantification rules that follow are adapted from Copi.

Universal Instantiation: From $(v_1)\phi(v_1)$, $\phi(v_2)$ and $\phi(n_2)$ may be inferred.

Existential Generalization: From $\phi(v_2)$ or $\phi(n_2)$, $(\exists v_1)\phi(v_1)$ may be inferred.

Existential Instantiation: From $(\exists v_1)\phi(v_1)$, $\phi(v_2)$ may be inferred, provided v_2 occurs free in no earlier step.

Universal Generalization: From $\phi(v_1)$, $(v_2)\phi(v_2)$ may be inferred, provided v_1 occurs free in $\phi(v_1)$ at all and only those places in which v_2 occurs free in $\phi(v_2)$, and provided no variable introduced by existential instantiation is free in any unconditionalized assumption of the argument.

Principle of Identity:

From $\phi(v_1)$ and $v_2 = v_1$, we may infer $\phi(v_2)$.

From $\phi(v_1)$ and $n_2 = v_1$, we may infer $\phi(n_2)$.

Four useful equivalences involving quantifiers, that may be considered to be added to the replacement rule, are listed below:

$(\exists v)\phi(v)$	is equivalent to	$\sim(v) \sim \phi(v)$
$(\exists v) \sim \phi(v)$	is equivalent to	$\sim(v)\phi(v)$
$\sim(\exists v)\phi(v)$	is equivalent to	$(v) \sim \phi(v)$
$\sim(\exists v) \sim \phi(v)$	is equivalent to	$(v)\phi(v)$

These principles of inference suffice for a logic involving sentential connectives, quantifiers, and identity. It is the logic we shall suppose to be built into each of the formal systems to follow.

Let us look at a couple of proofs by way of illustration. It should be borne in mind that we are here trying to elucidate the structure of formal systems, and not trying to learn logic for its own sake; nevertheless, we shall in the future call on some of the logical principles laid down in this chapter.

Consider the argument:

> All vegetables either taste good, or are nutritious. No legumes
> that are vegetables taste good. Therefore if all legumes are
> vegetables, then all legumes are nutritious.

Let us write "$L(x)$" for "x is a legume," "$V(x)$" for "x is a vegetable," "$N(x)$" for "x is nutritious," and "$G(x)$" for "x tastes good." The premises become

(1) $(x)(V(x) \supset (G(x) \lor N(x)))$

(2) $(x)((L(x) \,\&\, V(x)) \supset \sim G(x))$

and the conclusion becomes

(3) $((x)(L(x) \supset V(x)) \supset (y)(L(y) \supset N(y)))$.

[27]

The proof goes like this:

1. $(x)(L(x) \supset V(x))$	conditional premise
2. $L(x) \supset V(x)$	1, universal instantiation
3. $L(x)$	conditional premise
4. $V(x)$	2,3, modus ponens
5. $(x)(V(x) \supset (G(x) \lor N(x)))$	premise (1)
6. $V(x) \supset (G(x) \lor N(x))$	5, universal instantiation
7. $(G(x) \lor N(x))$	6,4, modus ponens
8. $(L(x) \& V(x))$	3,4, conjunction
9. $(x)(L(x) \& V(x)) \supset \sim G(x))$	premise (2)
10. $((L(x) \& V(x)) \supset \sim G(x))$	9, universal instantiation
11. $\sim G(x)$	8,10, modus ponens
12. $N(x)$	7,11, disjunctive syllogism
13. $(L(x) \supset N(x))$	conditionalization, 3–12
14. $(y)(L(y) \supset N(y))$	3, universal generalization

(Observe that in lines 3–12, "x" is a variable that is free in a premise of each of these lines. In line 13 this no longer is the case: line 3 is *not* a premise of line 13. We are therefore free to generalize on the variable "x" in line 13.)

15. $((x)(L(x) \supset V(x)) \supset (y)(L(y) \supset N(y)))$	conditionalization, lines, 1–14

The following argument involves relational predicates, as well as simple predicates.

> There is a movie star who is liked by everyone who likes at least one movie star. Everybody likes some movie star. Therefore there is a movie star who is liked by everybody.

Let us write "$M(x)$" for "x is a movie star" and "$L(x,y)$" for "x likes y". The premises are

> (1) $(\exists x)(M(x) \& (y)((\exists z)(M(z) \& L(y,z)) \supset L(y,x)))$,
> (2) $(y)(\exists z)(M(z) \& (y,z))$,

and the conclusion is

> (3) $(\exists x)(M(x) \& (y)(L(y,x)))$.

The formalization of the argument is as follows:

1. $(\exists x)(M(x) \& (y)((\exists z)(M(z) \& L(y,z)) \supset L(y,x)))$	premise
2. $(y)(\exists z)(M(z) \& L(y,z))$	premise
3. $\sim(\exists x)(M(x) \& (y)(L(y,x)))$	conditional premise
4. $(x)(\sim (M(x) \& (y)(L(y,x))))$	3, replacement
5. $(M(x) \& (y)((\exists z)(M(z) \& L(y,z)) \supset L(y,x)))$	1, EI
6. $\sim(M(x) \& (y)(L(y,x)))$	4, UI

[28]

7. $\sim M(x) \vee \sim(y)(L(y,x))$	6, De Morgan, replacement
8. $M(x)$	5, simplification
9. $\sim\sim M(x)$	8, double negation
10. $\sim(y)(L(y,x))$	7,9, disjunctive syllogism
11. $(\exists y)(\sim L(y,x))$	10, replacement
12. $\sim L(y,x)$	11, EI

(Observe that "y" has occurred free in no earlier line.)

13. $(y)((\exists z)(M(z) \& L(y,z)) \supset L(y,x)))$	5, replacement and simplification
14. $((\exists z)(M(z) \& L(y,z)) \supset L(y,x)))$	13, UI
15. $\sim(\exists z)(M(z) \& L(y,z))$	12, modus tollens
16. $(\exists z)(M(z) \& L(y,z))$	2, UI
17. $(P \& \sim P)$	15,16, conjunction
18. $(\sim(\exists x)(M(x) \& (y)(L(y,x))) \supset (P \& \sim P))$	conditionalization

(Observe that the particular form of the contradiction we arrive at is irrelevant; it is thus abbreviated by $(P \& \sim P)$.)

19. $\sim(P \& \sim P)$	derivable from logical axioms
20. $(\exists x)(M(x) \& (y)(L(y,x)))$	18,19, modus tollens, replacement

(Observe that at no point did we have to quantify over variables.)

We are now in a position to give a general description of the kind of formal system we shall be concerned with from here on. It is a formal system which includes, as a framework, the quantificational logic just outlined. In addition to the rules of inference adumbrated above, it will include a primitive vocabulary, formation rules, axioms, and an interpretation.

V

In the general case, the vocabulary will include, beside the logical signs, "$\sim$", "$\vee$", etc., a vocabulary of variables "x", "y", "z", etc., and punctuation "(" and ")", and a number of nonlogical signs. These may be divided into two groups: individual constants, generally single lower-case letters, standing for individuals, like Socrates, John, a certain eclipse of the sun, a particular crow, etc. In addition to individual constants, there will be predicate constants, generally represented by capital letters, standing for properties ("$R(x)$" abbreviates "x is red", "$P(x)$" abbreviates "x is prime", "$D(x)$" represents "x is a dream"), standing for two-place relations ("$G(x,y)$" abbreviates "x is greater than y," "$M(x,y)$" represents "x is the mother of y")

[29]

standing for three place relations ("$B(x,y,z)$" abbreviates "y lies between x and z", "$G(x,y,z)$" abbreviates "x gives y to z"), and so on.

The formation rules will help to sort out the predicates; thus if we are going to interpret "$G(x,y)$" as meaning that x is greater than y, our formation rules will generally rule out such expressions as "$G(x)$", "$G(x,y,z)$", as not being well-formed formulas at all. In general, the formation rules will have this form:

A. A one-place predicate constant, followed by an individual variable enclosed in parentheses is a well-formed formula.
B. A two-place predicate constant, followed by two individual variables separated by a comma and enclosed in parentheses, is a well-formed formula.
C. A three-place predicate constant, followed by . . ., and so on.
D. If S is a well-formed formula according to (a), (b), (c), and S^* is like S, except for containing individual constants at one or more places where S contains individual variables, then S^* is a well-formed formula.
E. If S and T are well-formed formulas, then $\sim S$ and $(S \vee T)$ are well-formed formulas.
F. If S is a well-formed formula, and v an individual variable, then $(v)S$ and $(\exists v)S$ are well-formed formulas.
G. These are all the well-formed formulas there are.

The axioms will in general include appropriate axioms for deriving logical truths (such as $\sim(P \& \sim P)$, used above). They will also generally include certain laws concerning the subject matter being formalized. In formalizing a bit of physics, for example, we might take as axioms, Newton's laws; or in formalizing a bit of chemistry, we might take as axioms certain basic chemical principles like the law of constant proportions.

The interpretation of the logical constants will follow the lines already indicated; the interpretation of the individual variables has been indicated roughly, that is, "$(x)(\ldots)$" is interpreted as meaning that whatever it, x, may be, . . . ; and "$(\exists x)(\ldots)$" is interpreted as, meaning that there exists, somewhere, something, x, such that it . . . . The problematic part of the interpretation of a formal system generally concerns the interpretation of the nonlogical constants; and we shall find that this part of the interpretation really is problematic more often than not. There are certain special cases in which we do not encounter much difficulty: We can interpret a predicate like " . . . is red" as applying to just those things that are red; to say "x is red" is simply to say that x is red, and it will be true to say "x is red" if and only if x is red; and we can find out whether or not x is in fact red, most of the time, the moment an individual constant replaces the individual variable "x". But most scientific predicates are not so straightforward as "is red".

Even in a simple language with simple color words, like "red", "blue", "green", etc., we must recognize and deal with the problem that color

[30]

words are essentially vague: their range of application is not completely determined. There is a class of things that I would unhesitatingly call "blue"; there is a class of things that I would unhesitatingly call "not blue"; but there is also a class of things that would cause me to hesitate. Should I say that this is blue or shouldn't I? I could come to a decision, in each case, simply by tossing a coin: but I might very well be inconsistent in the sense that I classified something (thus arbitrarily) as blue on one occasion, which I might classify as not-blue on another. More important in a social institution like science than the fact that I find some things that are hard to classify as blue or not blue, is the fact that you, too, will find an area of vagueness in your application of the word "blue". Furthermore, the area of vagueness that you find will not correspond precisely to the area of vagueness that I have found.

All of this could be made quite precise, if it seemed worthwhile; we could construct a three-dimensional continuum (hue, brightness, saturation) of color samples; we could find a distribution function for a given person that would characterize his use of the word "blue" (it would be expressed as the probability that he would classify the objects in a certain region of the three-dimensional color space as blue); and we could then measure the ways in which two people differed in their use of color terms. This would be interesting for certain parts of linguistics or psychology, but not for the philosophy of science; for one of the ways in which science progresses and changes is by the refinement of the vocabularies in its formal systems; and one of the ways in which vocabularies are refined is by replacing terms that cannot be applied very uniformly by all people who are in a position to use them (color terms, for example), by terms which can be applied with a higher degree of uniformity by the people who know what they mean (expressions for wavelengths, for example). We seek terms with a high degree of interpersonal uniformity. We shall have occasion to look more closely at this phenomenon later on, and in fact, to trace some of the changes that have occurred historically along these lines.

A complication in the interpretation of nonlogical formal systems that is of another order of magnitude, is that involved in the use of so-called theoretical terms. While there is a fairly obvious sense in which a person can point to something that is blue, and say, "There, see that? That's blue!" there is no corresponding sense in which he can point and say, "There, see that? That's a gravitational field with such and such characteristics," or "That's an ego," or "That's a gene." We shall see later that this distinction can by no means be drawn as sharply as this argument suggests, and that the difference between *theoretical terms* and *observational terms* had best be regarded as a difference of degree. But the difference in degree between terms like "cat" and "dog", on the one hand, and terms like "force" and "field" on the other, is a difference that should be kept in mind when it comes to discussing the interpretation of scientific calculi.

[31]

Yet another complication introduced in the theoretical formal systems of science is the fact that theoretical terms—the primitive, nonlogical theoretical terms, like "mass" and "charge"—are introduced in such a way that they are only partly (if at all) interpreted independently of the formal system in which they function. Thus such terms as "mass" and "force" do not have independent interpretations outside of the axioms of physics that relate them to each other. But on the other hand, the axioms of physics are not the only things that determine their meaning; there are also stipulations about their meanings embodied in the system in the form of meaning postulates which relate them ultimately and indirectly to things we can touch and see and feel.

VI

I have been writing as if scientific theories were presented as formal systems; this is not the case, of course. But it is generally possible to take a scientific theory, or a body of scientific knowledge, and to transform it, to formalize it, in such a way that it then has the characteristics of a strict formal system. There are generally a number of alternative formalizations possible, for a given body of knowledge, and these alternatives may not differ merely in the choice of axioms or in the choice of primitive terms. In a given science, for example, a given statement may be taken as partially determining the meaning of one of its component terms, or it may be taken as making an assertion about the things denoted by those terms. Its role will depend, in a given formalization, on our arbitrary choice. But I shall take as a principle that nothing that depends on the particular form of formalization can be terribly significant philosophically.

The formal systems with which we have to deal here are not all strict formal systems in the sense in which I have defined them. There is a large element of idealization in what I have proposed that we consider. Nor do I suggest that the proper form for a scientific system is that of a strict formal system. It may well be that to the extent that formalization and systematization are feasible, they are all to the good; but it is surely not feasible to start to develop a specific formal system to correspond to the theory of psychoanalysis. Nevertheless, it is feasible, and it is helpful to our understanding of the character of psychoanalytic theory, to look at psychoanalytic theory as a system having somewhat the same structure as a strict formal system. It is worthwhile to look at its vocabulary, and at the possibility of defining some terms with the help of others; it is worthwhile to attempt to isolate those fundamental principles or laws from which psychoanalytic conclusions are intended to follow; it is worthwhile considering what statements are intended to follow; it is worthwhile considering what statements might be construed as specifying (or helping to specify) the meanings of technical theoretical terms, rather than as embodying factual assertions about mental or behavioral events.

Thus the concept of a strict formal system is not being presented here as one to which all sciences do conform, nor even as one to which all sciences ought to conform; but rather it is being offered only as an ideal to which all sciences approximate, more or less, according to the degree of their development, and which serves to make clear the role that is played by some of the procedures, concepts, terms, and so on, in those sciences as they are. The concept of a formal system, then, offers two immediate advantages as a fundamental concept for the philosophy of science: first, it plays a fundamental role in every branch of science, and even in the explanation and systematization of other concepts that might be taken as fundamental (e.g., entropy, or information, or problem-solving, or decision-making); and second, it is a flexible concept. If we understand it broadly, much scientific talk and theorizing and assessment of experimental evidence, just as it stands, can be understood as falling within the framework of a formal system that is not presented strictly, but could be so presented. And if we want to talk about the formal system as such, we can understand the term more strictly, so that what we are talking about is a well-known thing that has been investigated, in the abstract, in great detail.

BIBLIOGRAPHICAL NOTES TO CHAPTER 1

Two authors who take the concepts of information and of entropy as their key concepts, are David Hawkins, *The Language of Nature*, (San Francisco: Freeman and Co., 1964), and Leon Brillouin *Science and Information Theory* (New York: Academic Press, 1962). John Dewey takes problem-solving to be the key concept of science in *Logic: The Theory of Inquiry* (New York: Holt, Rinehart and Winston, 1938). Ernest Nagel, *The Structure of Science: Problems in the Logic of Scientific Explanation* (New York: Harcourt, Brace and World, 1961), Carl Hempel, *Aspects of Scientific Explanation* (New York: The Free Press, 1965), and R. B. Braithwaite, *Scientific Explanation* (Cambridge, England: Cambridge University Press, 1953), all take explanation as a focal concept. Among other authors who take the concept of a formal system as central, Rudolf Carnap is the most distinguished, *Introduction to Symbolic Logic and its Applications* (New York: Dover Publications, 1958).

Most textbooks in the philosophy of science are organized around problems of a philosophical nature that are encountered in one form or another in most bodies of scientific knowledge: the problem of confirmation of hypotheses, the problem of the role of theoretical terms and the status of theoretical entities, the problem of reducibility of one science to another (e.g. the reduction of psychology to physics), etc. Four fine texts organized along these lines are: Ernest Nagel, *The Structure of Science* (New York: Harcourt, Brace and World, 1961), Arthur Pap, *An Introduction to the Philosophy of Science* (New York: The Free Press, 1962), and Israel Scheffler, *The Anatomy of Inquiry* (New York: Alfred Knopf, 1963). These three books are standard textbooks; C. G. Hempel, *Philosophy of*

Natural Science (Englewood Cliffs, N.J.: Prentice-Hall, 1966) is a small, eminently readable paperback.

The extreme view attributed to Yehoshua Bar-Hillel may be found in two articles (and in items of the bibliography appended thereto): "Comments on 'Degree of Confirmation'" by Professor Karl Popper, *British Journal for the Philosophy of Science*, 6, 1955–56; "Further Comments on Probability and Confirmation", *Ibid.* 7, 1956–57.

Michael Scriven's most detailed treatment of the problems of explanation and prediction is: "Explanations, Predictions, and Laws," in *Minnesota Studies in the Philosophy of Science* (Feigl and Maxwell, eds.), Vol. III (Minneapolis: University of Minnesota Press, 1962).

N. R. Hanson's defense of his claim that there is a logic of discovery, is to be found in its most complete form in: N. R. Hanson, *Patterns of Discovery* (Cambridge, England: Cambridge University Press, 1958).

For an introduction to the general nature and content of formal systems and of the relationship between formal systems and scientific knowledge, the following three monographs of the *Foundations of the Unity of Science* (Chicago: University of Chicago Press), are good: Vol. I., No. 1 (1938): *Encyclopedia of Unified Science*; Vol. I., No. 2 (1938): C. W. Morris, *Foundations of the Theory of Signs*; Vol. I., No. 3 (1939): R. Carnap, *Foundations of Logic and Mathematics*.

There are a large number of perfectly good textbooks in logic that will provide a more detailed introduction to the logical concepts very briefly introduced in this chapter. Among them are

> Quine, W. V. O. *Methods of Logic* (New York: Holt, Rinehart, and Winston, 1959).
>
> Rescher, N. *Introduction to Logic* (New York: St. Martin's Press, 1964).
>
> Kalish and Montague, *Logic* (New York: Harcourt, Brace and World, 1964).
>
> Suppes, P. *Introduction to Logic* (Princeton, N.J.: Princeton Univ. Press, 1957).
>
> Copi, I. *Symbolic Logic*, Third Edition (New York: Macmillan, 1967).

Finally, there are a number of collections of essays concerning the philosophy of science; a few of them are

> *Philosophy of Science* (Danto and Morgenbesser, eds.) (New York: Meridian Books, 1960).
>
> *Current Issues in the Philosophy of Science* (Feigl and Maxwell, Eds.) (New York: Holt, Rinehart, and Winston, 1961).
>
> *Minnesota Studies in the Philosophy of Science*, Vol. I. (Feigl and Scriven, eds.), Minneapolis, 1956.
>
> ———, Vol. II (Feigl, Scriven, Maxwell, eds.), Minneapolis, 1958.
>
> ———, Vol. III (Feigl and Maxwell, eds.), Minneapolis, 1962.

Chapter 2

A SIMPLE FORMAL SYSTEM

I

The formal system I propose to discuss in this chapter is a small one, but it embodies in a form easy to grasp all the elements of more complex systems. Let us suppose that there is a certain community in which social exclusiveness is the supreme value. Since the best index of social exclusiveness is membership in a club, everyone in the community belongs to at least one club. Since club membership isn't much of an index of exclusiveness if everybody belongs to all the clubs, there is a rule to the effect that two individuals can both belong to no more than one club. On the other hand, since everyone in this society is very friendly, every pair of people belong to at least one club together. Furthermore, unless there were some clubs whose memberships did not overlap, we could hardly consider them exclusive; so it is also established that if a person does not belong to a given club, there is exactly one club to which he does belong which has no members in common with the given club. Of course, not everyone belongs to the same club.

There are a number of ways of describing this society. There is the one that has just been offered, for example. We could make it briefer and more elegant by presenting it as a set of axioms:

A1. Every person belongs to at least one club.
A2. There are at least two persons.
A3. Given any two people, there is one and only one club to which they both belong.
A4. No club contains as members all people.
A5. Given a club, if a person doesn't belong to that club, there is exactly one club to which he does belong which is completely exclusive of the given club.

The vocabulary of the not-so-strict formal system embodied in these five axioms, includes besides the usual logical terminology of English, three nonlogical terms: "person", "club", and "member of". In the not-so-strict formal system, these terms have their ordinary English interpretation. This may be an odd society we are talking about, but we take the notions of "person", "club", and "membership", to be perfectly ordinary. When we construct a strict formal system, parallel to the not-so-strict one, we must pay more attention to questions of interpreting the terms of the system. It suffices here simply to note that these terms differ in character: "person" is an ordinary physical object term, like "stone" or "dog". "Club" is quite a different sort of term; there is no way in which one can point to a club, as one points to a person or a dog or a stone. Similarly, just as "club" is a somewhat abstract term, so the relational term "is a member of" must be taken to be somewhat abstract, relating, as it does, a relatively concrete entity (a person) to a relatively abstract entity (a club).

From these five axioms, we can draw a number of conclusions concerning the society. Thus:

Statement 1: Every person belongs to at least two clubs.
Consider any person, Peter, say. By A2, there is another person, say John. By A3, John and Peter belong to one club (Elks, say). By A4, not everybody belongs to the Elks, so there is somebody, Albert, who does not belong to the Elks. But by A3, again, there is a club to which both Peter and Albert belong; and thus there are (at least) two clubs to which Peter belongs.

Statement 2: Every club has at least two members.
By A2, there is one person, say Tom. By Statement 1, there are two clubs (Elks and Lions) to which Tom belongs. If there were a club *K* with no members, then (contrary to A5) there would be two clubs to which Tom, not a member of *K*, belongs, and which are completely exclusive from *K*. Therefore, every club has at least one member. (Note that there is nothing *absurd* about considering a club with no mem-

[36]

bers—e.g., a club all of whose members have resigned. Such a club might perfectly well be a legal entity, and perhaps even have a bank account.)

Now suppose there is a club, say the Anchorite Club, that has only one member. Its member, the anchorite, must belong to some other club as well, by Statement 1. Let us call this the Hermit Club. By A4, there is somebody who does not belong to the Hermit club; let us call him Sam. By A5, there is a club to which Sam belongs (the Odd Fellows) which has no members in common with the Hermit Club; i.e., the Anchorite does not belong to the Odd Fellows. This also means that the Anchorite club has no members in common with the Odd Fellows. But this contradicts A5, according to which there can be only one club to which the Anchorite belongs that has no members in common with the Odd Fellows. We therefore must reject our initial supposition, that there is a club, like the Anchorite Club, which has only one member.

Statement 3: There are at least four people.

By A2, there are two people. Call them John and Peter. By A3, there is a club to which they belong (say Elks). By A4, there is somebody who doesn't belong to the Elks Club; let him be called Albert. And by A5 there is a club to which Albert belongs (Lions, say), which is wholly exclusive from the Elks. But by Statement 2, Lions must contain at least two members—i.e., at least one member (say, Tom) in addition to Albert.

Statement 4: There are at least six clubs.

The argument is left for the student to construct.

What we have here is a miniature formal system of the sort that we find in fairly well-developed sciences, such as physics. (Although the subject matter is sociological, one would not find formal systems of this degree of rigor in most sociological work.) It may not look much like the kind of thing that has been defined earlier as a strict formal system; yet it may quickly be put in that form. In the ordinary course of events, there is no reason at all, of course, for putting it in the strict form, except for the purpose of conducting special inquiries. For instance, we may be interested in clarifying the role that a particular statement plays in the system. Is it a definition of a term? An axiom helping to define a term? A material generalization about the subject matter? What are the consequences for the system in each of these cases?

II

Since this is just a practice system, let us go through the process of rendering this *ordinary* formal system, into a *strict* formal system. Let us also, in the process, keep an eye open for the kinds of facts about the system that the formalizing process may (sometimes) reveal.

Let us begin with the Calculus. First we need a vocabulary list. I shall introduce abbreviations as I go along.

A. Vocabulary:
    1. Constants:
        M (for the club-membership relation)
        P (for person)
        C (for club).
    2. Variables: x, y, ... (individual variables).
    3. Logical signs: the usual logical signs, and identity.
    4. Punctuation: parentheses.

B. Formation Rules:
    1. Atomic statements:
        a. "P", followed by a variable is a well-formed formula, or wff, for short;
        b. "C" followed by a variable is a wff;
        c. "M" followed by two variables is a wff;
        d. A variable followed by "$=$" followed by another variable is a wff.
    2. If A and B are wff's, then $(A \supset B)$, $(A \,\&\, B)$, $(A \lor B)$, $(A \equiv B)$, and $\sim A$ are wff. And furthermore, if v is a variable, $(v)A$ and $(\exists v)A$ are wff.

Note that it is unnecessary, pointless, even wrong-headed, to attempt to minimize the number of logical signs in our system by defining some in terms of others. And note also, what is already apparent in this small example, that the greater the need for formalization, the harder it is likely to be. In this case we started with a system which was almost perfectly clear as it stood. Therefore it is easy to formalize. But therefore also it doesn't add much to make the formalization more strict.

C. Axioms:
    1. $(x)(Px) \supset (\exists y)(Cy \,\&\, Mxy)$.
    2. $(\exists x)(\exists y)(Px \,\&\, Py \,\&\, \sim x = y)$.
    3. $(x)(y)((Py \,\&\, \sim x = y \,\&\, Px) \supset (\exists z)(Cz \,\&\, Mxz \,\&\, Myz \,\&\, (w)((Cw \,\&\, Mxw \,\&\, Myw) \supset w = z)))$.
    4. $(x)(Cx \supset (\exists y)(Py \,\&\, \sim Myx))$.
    5. $(x)(y)((Cx \,\&\, Py \,\&\, \sim Myx) \supset (\exists z)(Cz \,\&\, Myz \,\&\, (w)((Pw \,\&\, Mwz) \supset \sim Mwx) \,\&\, (z')((Cz' \,\&\, Myz' \,\&\, (w)((Pw \,\&\, Mwz') \supset \sim Mwx)) \supset z = z')))$.

D. Rules of Inference:
    1. If the conditional "$(A_1 \,\&\, A_2 \,\&\, \ldots \,\&\, A_n) \supset C$" is a theorem of first-order logic (with identity), then "C" may be inferred from "A_1", "A_2", ..., "A_n".

Although one might think of clubs as being of a different *logical type* than the members of clubs (as sets and their members are often taken to differ in logical type), there is no need to have that distinction reflected in our formal system. Again, there is no point at all in trying to minimize the power of the rules of

[38]

inference we introduce in our formal system. If we have some *reason* to want to be explicit about the details of the underlying logic, then instead of specifying that any first-order rule of inference is all right, we will include axioms for a first-order logic as part of the system, and then include as rules of inference a few rules appropriate to the first-order logic.

Before passing on to the interpretation of the calculus, let us state and prove some theorems corresponding to the numbered statements above. Note that in a strict formal system, the theorems can be stated and proved quite independently of the interpretation given to the calculus. Indeed, this is one of the prime functions of the approach to strict formalization: to be sure that the facts on which the truth of the theorems depend are all stated in the axioms, and that nothing that is an unrecognized presupposition is depended on in getting from the axioms to the theorems.

In stating proofs, since we have allowed that any valid first-order inference is a permissible step, we need, strictly speaking, write no more than the axioms and the theorems. We don't need detailed proofs. But due to the weakness of the human intellect, and the fact that we are not immediately aware of all valid first-order inferences, we may need a few steps to help us see that indeed the inference from the axioms to the theorem *is* a valid first-order inference. The steps simply serve to break the inference down into steps whose validity we can recognize easily. Thus we have no strict notion of what is permissible and what is not permissible, as we had in the case of sentential logic. But there is a good reason for that: we are not doing proof theory here, and we have no cause to lay bare the bones of argument as we did there.

LEMMA: $(x)(Px \supset (\exists y)(Py \ \& \ {\sim}y = x))$

Proof:

1. Pz	hypothesis
2. $(Px \ \& \ Py \ \& \ {\sim}x = y)$	A2, EI
3. $({\sim}x = y \supset ({\sim}x = z \lor {\sim}y = z))$	identity principle
4. $({\sim}z = x \lor {\sim}z = y)$	2,3, modus ponens
5. $(Px \ \& \ {\sim}z = x) \ \& \ (Py \ \& \ {\sim}z = y)$	2,4, simplification, conjunction, distribution
6. $(\exists y)(Py \ \& \ {\sim}y = z) \ \& \ (\exists y)(Py \ \& \ {\sim}y = z)$	3, EG
7. $Pz \supset (\exists y)(Py \ \& \ {\sim}y = z)$	1,6, conditionalization
8. $(x)(Px \supset (\exists y)(Py \ \& \ {\sim}y = x))$	7, UG

THEOREM 1: $(x)(Px \supset (\exists y)(\exists z)(Cz \ \& \ Cy \ \& \ Mxz \ \& \ Mxy \ \& \ {\sim}y = z))$

Proof:

1. Px	hypothesis
2. $(\exists y)(Py \ \& \ {\sim}y = x)$	Lemma, UI, modus ponens
3. $Px_1 \ \& \ {\sim}x_1 = x$	2, EI

[39]

4. $(Px_1 \& Px) \supset (\exists z)(Cz \& Mxz \& Mx_1z \&$
   $(w)((Cw \& Mxw \& Mx_1w) \supset w = z))$ A3, UI
5. $Cz \& Mxz \& Mx_1z$ 1,3,4, modus ponens, EI, simplification

6. $Cz \supset (\exists y)(Py \& \sim Myz)$ A4, UI
7. $Px_2 \& \sim Mx_2z$ 4,5, modus ponens, EI
8. $(Px \& Px_2) \supset (\exists z)(Cz \& Mxz \& Mx_2z \&$
   $(w)((Cw \& Mxw \& Mx_2w) \supset w = z))$ A3, UI
9. $Cy \& Mxy \& Mx_2y$ 1,7,8, modus ponens, EI, simplification

10. $Mx_2y \& \sim Mx_2z$ 6,8, simplification, conjunction

11. $\sim y = z$ 10, identity principle
12. $Cz \& Cy \& Mxy \& Mxz \& \sim y = z$ 4,8,10, conjunction
13. $(\exists y)(\exists z)(Cz \& Cy \& Mxy \& Mxz \& \sim y = z)$ 12, EG
14. $Px \supset (\exists y)(\exists z)(Cz \& Cy \& Mxy \& Mxz \&$
   $\sim y = z)$ 1,13, conditionalization
15. $(x)(Px \supset (\exists y)(\exists z)(Cz \& Cy \& Mxy \&$
   $Mxz \& \sim y = z))$ 14, UG

THEOREM 2: $(x)(Cx \supset (\exists y)(\exists z)(Py \& Pz \& Myx \& Mzx \& \sim y = z))$.

The proof of this theorem follows the pattern of the informal argument above. It is quite long (every proof making extensive use of A5 will turn out to be quite long), but whereas a fair amount of insight is needed to see the validity of the informal proof, the formal version of the proof can be made just as detailed as necessary in order to insure agreement concerning whether or not Theorem 2 is in fact a theorem.

No proof will be given here (in the formal system) for either this theorem or subsequent ones. Those who find the reading of proofs congenial will find the construction of such a proof even more enlightening; and those who do not find the reading of proofs congenial will no doubt take my word for it when I say, "The proofs exist."

THEOREM 3: $(\exists x_1)(\exists x_2)(\exists x_3)(\exists x_4)(Px_1 \& Px_2 \& Px_3 \& Px_4 \& \sim x_1 = x_2 \& \sim x_1 = x_3 \& \sim x_1 = x_4 \& \sim x_2 = x_3 \& \sim x_2 = x_4 \& \sim x_3 = x_4)$.

THEOREM 4: $(\exists x_1)(\exists x_2)(\exists x_3)(\exists x_4)(\exists x_5)(\exists x_6)(Cx_1 \& Cx_2 \& Cx_3 \& Cx_4 \& Cx_5 \& Cx_6 \& \sim x_1 = x_2 \& \sim x_1 = x_3 \& \sim x_1 = x_4 \& \sim x_1 = x_5 \& \sim x_1 = x_6 \& \sim x_2 = x_3 \& \sim x_2 = x_4 \& \sim x_2 = x_5 \& \sim x_2 = x_6 \& \sim x_3 = x_4 \& \sim x_3 = x_5 \& \sim x_3 = x_6 \& \sim x_4 = x_5 \& \sim x_4 = x_6 \& \sim x_5 = x_6)$.

A possibility which might come to mind is that there should be two different clubs having the same group of people as members. Do the axioms A1–A5 allow this possibility? Here is a question which one might find hard to answer in the not-so-strictly formalized system, but which admits of a definitive answer in the formalized version of the system. (This is not to say it is impossible to answer this question in the first form of the system, but only that the question is both easier to state and easier to answer in the second form of the system.) I call this theorem the *Principle of Extensionality* for clubs:

THEOREM 5: $(x)(y)((Cx \cdot Cy \cdot (z)(Mzx \equiv Mzy)) \supset x = y)$.

It will be noticed by anyone who attempts to construct them, that the proofs in our strictly formal system are considerably longer and more difficult than the proofs in the original not-so-formal system. In a sense this is paradoxical, for the calculus has as axioms just the formalized statements of those principles accepted in the original system; and the theorems of the calculus (except for Theorem 5) correspond precisely to the statements of the original system. Furthermore, since the statements in the calculus are constructed along the pattern of statements in the simple first-order logic of Chapter One, and since the rules of inference are precisely those rules that can be formulated in first-order logic, one would think that the relations of entailment among such statements would be much clearer than relationships of entailment among the unformalized statements. In fact they are not. The reason is that the arguments in the original system made use of principles that are themselves rather complex, and in our reconstruction of those proofs in the calculus, we use only very general (and not very complex) principles; furthermore, many facts can be taken for granted in an informal argument that must be justified explicitly in its formal analog. One consequence of this fact is that the business of science cannot be carried on conveniently in strictly formal systems. They are just too unwieldy for everyday argument and the drawing of consequences in the system. Furthermore, they are unnecessary. Surely we do not need to have the calculus I have just outlined in order to draw the conclusions that I have labeled as Theorems 1–4.

All of this is true in general; and yet there are functions served by strict formalization. First of all, in the calculus, it is very easy to determine precisely which axioms are required for the deduction of a given theorem. Furthermore, we know, in the case of the calculus of a strict formal system, that we have indeed written down, as axioms, every single thing that is needed for the deduction of the theorems, while in a formal system that is not strict, it is easy, without realizing it, to use properties of the empirical concepts that the system deals with in arguing from one statement to another. It is also possible that the calculus itself may suggest theorems, as the principle of extensionality for clubs was suggested above. The possibility of strict formalization leading to a calculus is important for one more reason: in the calculus, the concept of theoremhood is defined explicitly—it can be characterized in a simple way, so that anyone who is capable of following a proof in first-order logic will be equally capable of following a proof in our formal calculus. Now there is generally no reason for

[41]

actually doing this; but the fact that it could be done insures that theoremhood in our less formal system is also clear and definable in a simple way. So long as our informal system *can* be translated into a strict formal system in the sense I have outlined, just so long will there be no excuse for disagreement concerning whether or not a given sequence of statements, say, constitutes a proof of a given theorem–statement.

But the most important consequence of strict formalization is not a consequence that follows (as the preceding do) from the existence of a calculus reflecting the manipulations and operations of the original system. It follows, rather, from the existence of an interpretation. This is an aspect of formal systems that has been somewhat neglected—not without reason, for it is a difficult topic, and also a rather muddy one. In general, a number of interpretations can be offered for a given calculus; and not only that, there are generally a number of interpretations for a given strictly formal calculus which are such that they lead to precisely the same observational results. This we shall see later.

III

First, let us return to our sociological theory, strictly formalized, and provide an interpretation for it. The variables require semantical rules only in a special sense; they do not designate particular individuals, but stand ambiguously for individuals of a certain kind or kinds. What we must specify, then, is the *range* of entities, among which the variables may take their values. The range of the variables in the sociological system consists of the individuals of the special society in question, together with the clubs formed in that society. Observe that the range of the variables is *not* homogeneous: it embraces both individuals and clubs. It is also possible to give semantic rules (strictly, this is part of the interpretation of the underlying logic) which determine the meaning of a variable in a quantificational context. Thus we may say a complex expression of the form "$(\exists x)\phi$" is true in case there is some individual in the domain of the variables such that if a name of that individual is put for all the free occurrences of "x" in "ϕ", then the resulting unquantified expression is true. And correspondingly, "$(x)\phi$" may be explained as a statement which is true just when, whatever name of an individual of the domain is put for the free occurrences of "x" in "ϕ", the resulting sentence is true.

What is of more interest than the role of quantifiers (which, anyway, is the same in all theories, and the same in scientific theories as in purely logical systems), is the interpretation of the nonlogical constants. Rules for the interpretation of the nonlogical constants are, however, far harder to come by. In mathematics and in logic, an interpretation can quite generally be defined as a domain of objects (generally the same one that the variables range over), together with a function or rule, which assigns to each individual constant an individual of the domain, which assigns to each predicate of the calculus a set of objects in the

[42]

domain, and which assigns to each relation–term (two-place predicate) of the calculus a set of pairs of objects, and so on. If we take the *rule* to be a rule of designation, we have the concept of interpretation which is often used in formal semantics. In this sense we can provide the following interpretation for our formal sociological system:

The domain of the variables of the system is to be the set of individuals and the set of clubs belonging to a certain society. For something to be admissible as a value of a variable in the formal system, is for it to be a person of that society, or a club in that society.

The nonlogical term "P" is a one-place predicate designating just those elements of the domain that happen to be people; put another way, the propositional function "Px" is satisfied by people who belong to the special society, and only by such people.

The nonlogical term "C" is a one-place predicate designating just those elements of the domain that happen to be clubs; put another way, the propositional function "Cx" is satisfied only by clubs in the special society.

The nonlogical term "M" is a two-place predicate, or a relation-term, designating ordered pairs of objects, just in case (1) the first of the ordered pair is a person belonging to the society; (2) the second member of the ordered pair is a club in that society; and (3) that particular person happens to belong to that particular club.

This interpretation is a perfectly good one for our formal system, since in point of fact the English language is rich enough so that we can, by means of the rules of designation, come to understand what "P", "M", and "C" mean. In general, it will not be so easy to give interpretations for scientific formal systems. We need a means of specifying an interpretation of a formal system that does not presume that we have at our disposal a language that we already understand and that contains the names of all the entities referred to in the formal system. If we were considering a formal system for chemistry, for example, it is not plausible to suppose that we can provide a useful interpretation for the system by specifying that "ion" is to designate just the elements of the domain that are ions, that "hydrogen" is to designate just those elements of the domain that are samples of hydrogen gas, and so on. The rules are correct, but they are only helpful if we already *know*, in a perfectly good sense, what hydrogen is, what an ion is, etc.

In the general case, we should like to be able to present an interpretation for our formal system that does not depend on our having as a metalanguage a language so strong that we can already in that metalanguage express all the ideas we want to express in the formal system. If we could isolate a part of the English language, and could defend the claim that this part of the English language was *observational*—i.e., could serve to express any state of affairs that could be observed—then we could say that we want our interpretations of formal systems to be expressed exclusively in the observational part of English. But for reasons that will become clearer and clearer as we go on, if they are not already sufficiently clear, we cannot plausibly isolate any such part of the English language, and we cannot therefore stipulate that the interpretations of our formal systems be expressible in observation language.

There is one case, however, in which we can come close to meeting a requirement like this: and that is when we have to deal with proper names of certain kinds of individuals (individuals that stand out distinctly from their surroundings, that are capable of being pointed at, and so on). We can say "Venus" designates *that*, and point to Venus; "John" designates *him*, and we can point to the individual man John. Such rules I shall call ostensive naming rules, because they can be given as ostensive directives, and they can only be used for giving the interpretation of names or definite descriptions.

A rule of designation next in order of complexity is a rule for giving the meaning of a collective term such as "man", "star", etc., of some of whose *instances* one may be as directly aware as one is the denotation of "John" or "Venus". One can point to men, and to stars. The sort of designation rule involved here has been regarded as fairly simple by some writers, but in fact it is not altogether simple. To say that "red" designates those things that are red, is very different from saying that "John" designates John. In a simple sense we can be directly acquainted with John ("How do you do, John,"), but we cannot be directly acquainted with all red things. The only things we can see are particular red things: this red apple, that red apple, that red barn ...; we are never confronted with bare or abstract redness, nor the color red in itself. The rule of interpretation we require in a formal system employing the term "red" is a rule of the form: this, that, and the other thing, are instances of redness; that, that, and still another thing are instances to which the term "red" does not apply; things like the first group and unlike the second are things to which the term "red" applies. John, Peter, and Susan are things to which the term "man" is to be applied; Fido, this house, and that statue are things to which the term "man" is not to be applied; in general "man" is a term designating things like the first group mentioned and unlike the second group. There are many problems which can be raised about this approach to the interpretation of such ordinary-language terms as "red" and "dog" but I shall suppose that the general idea is clear enough: there are some terms that we can more or less adequately learn the meaning of by being shown (or put in some form of sensory contact with) instances to which they apply, and instances to which they do not apply. The detailed analysis of this fact we can leave to the philosophy of language.

The matter can be put generally as follows. Although some writers appear to have supposed that the interpretation of a general term like "man" or "red" could be given by rules of designation of the same type as are used to give the meaning of terms like "John," "Susan," or "the sun," this would be to suppose

[44]

that one could be confronted with the whole class of men (past, present, and future) or the whole class of red things. If one could be, then the answer would be simple: the general term "red" designates any of these red things; the general term "man" designates any of these human things. But in fact, it must be on the basis of a knowledge of a proper subclass of the class in question (together with a proper subclass of its complement), that the application of the term can be made. Thus on the basis of my acquaintance with John and Peter and Susan, I learn how to apply the general term "man"; the interpretation of the term "man" must be such that I can apply it on that basis. It cannot be such—not if the term "man" is to be one of the "down-to-earth" terms of our system—that it requires for its correct application an acquaintance with the whole class of men. The same is true of the term "red": the interpretation of the term "red" must be such that I can apply the term on the basis of my familiarity with a few apples and a barn, and not such that I must be on speaking terms with the whole past, present, and future class of red things.

It is this fact, that general terms must be somehow, in real life, applicable on the basis of a small finite amount of experience, that I think has led people to feel that there is a serious element of generalization already involved in the use of general terms. There is indeed an element of generalization and uncertainty. For each of us, the sample of red things that serves as a basis for applying the term "red" to other, new, objects, is a different sample. Even the relational term "is similar to" will be based, for each of us, on a different sample.

Just as there are certain properties, which, more than other properties, are ostensive in the sense that we can detect their presence or absence in a fairly simple, straightforward, and direct manner (like redness and humanity), so also there are relations, like being heavier than, being to the right of, being longer longer than, that can be regarded as relatively ostensive. Thus we may interpret the term "heavier than" as applying to this class of pairs (ordered pairs) of physical objects, with which you are familiar, and all ordered pairs which are like them, and unlike those ordered pairs of things which are not included in that class. And the same goes for three and four argument relational predicates, like "gives (x,y,z)" and "x does y before z does w" and so on. Thus we may have relatively ostensive interpretations of terms standing for properties of individuals, properties of pairs of individuals (two-term relations) properties of triples of individuals (three-term relations), etc., where we can observe that the individual, the pair of individuals, the triple of individuals, and so on, has the property in question, and therefore where we can base our understanding of the term of our direct knowledge of a subset of the set of individuals (pairs, triples, etc.) that have that property.

We shall have more to say about the concept of relative ostensiveness later on, and about its relation to interpersonal uniformity. At this point my concern is primarily to contrast rules of interpretation of either the preceding sorts (rules of

[45]

designation for proper names or rules of designation for relatively ostensive predicates, relation terms, and so on) with rules of interpretation that are embodied in the system, but that are not taken to contain any of the empirical content of the system. Such rules are represented by statements in the system (as interpreted), which are held to be true by virtue of the *meanings* of the terms that occur in them. Clearly such statements cannot be part of the calculus, because the terms of the calculus are regarded as lacking meanings. They must be taken as *axioms* or *meaning postulates*, as Carnap has called them. These statements may function as premises in the proofs of theorems, quite as well as the ordinary axioms of the system.

Let us begin by considering rules of interpretation for terms expressing relations that we cannot observe to hold, but which apply to the individuals that we can be acquainted with. Thus we can be acquainted with John and Sally, and we can observe them, but we cannot observe that they stand in the brother–sister relation. Nevertheless, we know something about the relation: we know that it holds only between pairs of people one of whom is male and the other of whom is female. We know that (in the strong sense of the relation) it holds a pair of people only if those people have the same parents. It is the same with such relation-expressions as "married to", "older than", "father of": we cannot observe them to hold in the same way that we can observe the relations *longer than*, *heavier than*, *gives birth to*, to hold, and yet they hold between objects that are fairly directly accessible to us, and there are things we can say about the pairs of objects they characterize that we can say on the basis of the meanings of the relation terms. (E.g., if x is father of y, then x is a male.) The same is true of derivative property expressions ("is a brother", "is married", "is forty years old"). And in general it holds for single-place (and hence for many-place) disposition predicates, such as "soluble" and "flammable". All of the terms we have been considering here apply, like "red" and "man", to objects with which we can be fairly directly familiar; but unlike those terms, they cannot generally be applied directly and simply on a similarly ostensive basis.

The first step we can take in providing interpretations for such terms as these is to provide explicit definitions for some of them. Thus "x is a brother" can be defined in terms of the relation of being a brother of: "x is a brother" holds if and only if "there is a y such that x is brother of y" holds. Similarly, "x is brother of y" holds if and only if "x is male" holds and "there is a z and there is a w such that z gave birth to x and z gave birth to y and w begot x and w begot y" holds. When we can give such explicit definitions as these, we can rest easy regarding the interpretation of the term defined. Since the explicit definition is available, we need not even regard the defined term as an official part of our formal system. In view of the definition, the term is everywhere eliminable (if we choose to use it anyway, that is a matter of convenience, and of no philosophical import). But it is, if not obvious, at least pretty clear, that in useful scientific

[46]

formal systems we are not going to be able to define all the occurring terms except those for which we can provide fairly clear ostensive interpretations.

Even such simple-sounding terms as "soluble" and "married" do not lend themselves to explicit definition in terms that can plausibly be taken as ostensive, even though they apply to things that we can have presented to us (*this* sample of sugar is soluble; the man and woman here in our living room are married). These terms are like "red" and "man" in that they apply to objects of our acquaintance, but they cannot, as those terms can, be applied directly and simply on the basis of what we *see* or otherwise sense. We have to know something more about the object (pair) in question. To say that x is soluble is to say that if it is put into water it will dissolve; but although the truth of the conditional follows from the truth of "x is soluble," "x is soluble" by no means follows from the truth of the conditional, "if x is put in water, then x dissolves". We cannot take the conditional as providing a definitional reduction of "soluble" to the relatively ostensive terms "is put in water" and "dissolves." (Observe that it is no help at all to replace the truth functional conditional by some modal connection such as "if x is placed in water than x *must* dissolve", for the latter modal conditional is no more ostensive than the original "soluble"—indeed, rather less!) Nevertheless, although we do not have a definition, we do have a connection between the non-ostensive "soluble", and the relatively ostensive "is put in water", and "dissolves", and indeed a connection that may be said to hold in virtue of the meanings of the terms involved. The following compound conditional may be regarded as providing a *partial* interpretation of the term "soluble"; it is the sort of thing that Carnap, Kemeny, and others have called a *meaning postulate*.

$$x \text{ is soluble} \supset (x \text{ is put in water} \supset x \text{ dissolves})$$

Such a statement could occur as an axiom in the calculus of a formal system for chemistry. It could also be added to the axioms as part of the interpretation of the expressions (predicates) of the calculus. In either case, the conditional is not taken to embody part of the empirical content of the system, but, as interpreted, merely to elucidate the meanings of the terms of the system. In particular, this statement would be taken as giving a connection between the term "is soluble" and the terms "is put in water" and "dissolves". The latter, in turn, are taken to have relatively ostensive interpretations.

In a similar way, we may elucidate the meaning of the term "married" (in our society) with the help of a number of compound and simple conditionals. If x is married to y, then x and y have been through a valid marriage ceremony, and have not since been divorced. If x is married to y, then x and y signed a marriage license. If x is married to y, then x and y uttered certain words before a minister or magistrate. Whether this procedure could give rise to an explicit definition of

[47]

"married to", however, may be seriously questioned on the ground that a marriage license is not a piece of paper, but a permission granted by society, and that marriage ceremony is not just a sequence of acts and speeches, but a ritual that is taken to serve a certain function. (A marriage on a stage is not really a marriage; a common-law marriage is really a marriage.)

In a certain sense these terms whose interpretation is given partially by meaning postulates are already *theoretical* terms. Their interpretation cannot be given directly by relatively ostensive rules, but must be given indirectly by meaning postulates which relate their meanings to the meanings of other terms that in turn can be given relatively ostensive meanings. But there is one more step we may take to arrive at an interpretation for terms that are theoretical in a yet deeper sense. There are many terms in science that are not even directly related to relatively ostensive terms by conditional statements of the form we have already considered. "Electron" and "gene" are extreme examples; less extreme examples are "chemical compound", "species", "molecule", and so on. "Electron", for instance, is a term related directly to no observational or ostensive terms by semantic rules. It is only in the context of a whole theory, a whole interlocking framework of axioms and meaning postulates and rules of interpretation, that we can construct conditionals that involve both the term "electron" and also relatively ostensive terms. There are indeed certain statements that relate the term "electron" to terms that are closer to the ostensive level, and which themselves may be related by meaning postulates to terms that we might classify as ostensive. But we shall see that there are difficulties in trying to classify such statements (e.g., relating "electron" to "electric current") as either semantic rules of interpretation, yielding partial specifications of the meanings of the terms involved, or as empirical postulates embodying part of the content of the theory. The point here to be observed is merely that in contrast to "is soluble", "is an electron" is not directly related, through meaning postulates, to relatively ostensive predicates. We shall come back again (indeed we shall come back again and again) to the question of these truly theoretical terms, and their relation to so-called observation terms. And as I have been indicating all along, ostensiveness itself will turn out to be a matter of degree.

But for the time being, and subject to all the provisos and complications indicated, we may take the semantic interpretation rules that provide the interpretation for the calculus of a formal scientific system to comprise rules of interpretation of the following types:

A. Relatively Ostensive Rules:
   1. The interpretation of names: "John" denotes *him*. *That* is "the Sun". "North" is *that* way.
   2. The interpretation of predicates: "Red" does not apply to those things, but to these things, and things like them.

[48]

B. Definitions:
1. If a term of our calculus admits of explicit definition, we may regard the term as a mere convenience, on the ground that it is always eliminable. We would not take as part of the basic vocabulary of our calculus a term that was definable and thus eliminable.

C. Meaning Postulates:
1. Direct Conditional Interpretations: "If x is soluble, then if x is put in water, x will dissolve." Here we take the consequent of the conditional to involve only terms that admit relatively ostensive interpretations.
2. Indirect Systematic Interpretations: In this class we would put any primitive statements of the system which are interpreted in such a way that they are understood to express part of the meanings of the terms of the system, rather than to express part of the content of the system.

Both statements falling under C.1. and those falling under C.2. will ordinarily be classified as axioms (primitive statements) of the system. We may, on occasion, wish to distinguish between *axioms proper*, which embody the empirical content of the system, and *meaning postulates*, which are axioms that express part of the interpretation of the system. As we shall see, however, there is no easy way to draw a sharp boundary between axioms proper and meaning postulates, and we shall therefore often lump both groups of statements under the heading "Axioms".

IV

Let us now return to our miniature sociological theory. The three primitive nonlogical terms are "P" (person), "M" (member of), and "C" (club). "P" we may take to be the kind of a general term whose interpretation can be given by reference to individuals with whom we are directly acquainted (A.2.). Thus our interpretive rule is of the form:

> "P" is to apply to the people in this society; there's one, there's one, and there is another. That thing isn't a person; and the man over there on the next island isn't a member of this society.

Observe that this way of introducing terms depends on a fact about the world —namely, that it consists in large part of groups of things that are very like one another and very different from things in other groups. If the world were not so, it would be very difficult to learn a language. And, in fact, when it comes to learning the language appropriate to a part of the world (e.g., the part consisting of gilled fungi) in which this is not true, we are confronted with a difficult job. To learn this language requires much experience and much training. But this does not mean that any facts are presupposed by the existence of language or science in any significant and interesting sense of "presuppose". The rule does not *express* any facts about the world.

[49]

The term "C" is to be correspondingly interpreted, but there are new difficulties, because we cannot be directly acquainted with a club, as such, although of course we can be acquainted with the members of a club, and for that matter, the members of several clubs. Similarly, the expression "Mxy" is to be interpreted to mean that x is a member of y, and it expresses a relation that holds between persons and clubs. All of this, that M is a relation, that it holds between persons and clubs, is semantical knowledge about the term "M" that has not been stated explicitly in the sociological system. It was not stated there, because it wasn't needed—we could prove all the theorems of the informal system without any premises to this effect. Now it is true that (under this interpretation),

(6) $(x)(y)(Mxy \supset Px \,\&\, Cy)$
(7) $(x)(Px \supset \sim Cx)$

We may express the fact that "M" is a relation term either (as we did) through the agency of the formation rules ("M" followed by one variable, followed by another variable is a well formed formula), or by treating all predicates (relational and otherwise) on a par, and exhibiting the fact that "M" is a relation term through meaning postulates:

(8) $(x)(Mx \supset (\exists y)(\exists z)(x = y;z))$,
(9) $(x)(Px \supset \sim(\exists y)(\exists z)(x = y;z))$
(10) $(x)(Cx \supset \sim(\exists y)(\exists z)(x = y;z))$

where "$y;z$" will be our notation for the ordered pair, y-first and z-second.

All of these statements are true under the interpretation contemplated, and furthermore true (as we say) on *semantical* grounds alone. They are semantically true, in virtue of the meanings of the terms. It is perfectly possible that we can provide an interpretation of the calculus of our strict formal system, in which these relations do not hold in virtue of the meanings of the terms. It is easy to do this in a trivial way, and that should suffice to make the point: interpret "Mz" as: either z is mad, or there are entities x and y such that x and y are numbers and x is greater than y, or else x is a person and y is a club and x belongs to y. Interpret "Px" to mean that either x is a person, or else x is an ordered pair of numbers $y;z$ of which the first is greater than the second; interpret "Cx" to mean x is a club, or x is an ordered pair of numbers $y;z$ of which the first is greater than second, or that x is a person who does not belong to a club. Under this interpretation the above five statements all turn out to be false in the domain of persons, clubs, and numbers.

To return to the relational term "M": it is unlike "P"; we cannot suppose that there is a basis in direct observation for the interpretation of "M". We give an interpretation for the relational term "M" by giving examples, just as we do for the relational term "bigger than", but whereas in the latter case pairs that satisfy the relation in question are pairs of objects each of which we can be directly acquainted with, in the former case the pairs that satisfy the relation are such that only one of them can be an object of our acquaintance; the other (the club) is an abstract object. The fact, however, that clubs are abstract objects, or theoretical objects (in the broad sense in which I am using the term "theoretical" here) does not mean of course, that we cannot know about particular individuals belonging to particular clubs. We do. But it is not a matter of any kind of direct observation that a given individual belongs to a given club. What we directly observe (in a straightforward sense of "directly observe") are groups of people meeting together regularly, exhibiting a certain kind of overt behavior toward each other, and the like.

But there is no difficulty in telling that a person belongs to a club: we can ask him, we can ask to see the membership list, we can observe the way he behaves toward other members of the club, and so on. It is true that we may sometimes have trouble; and this fact is one that we would have to take account of in a full-blown theory of club membership. But here we have no full-blown theory to deal with, and we need ask no more with respect to the primitive term "M" than that,

(1) any aspects of its meaning that are relevant to the theory are codified and exhibited as meaning postulates;

(2) there is a relatively high degree of uniformity in the application of the term.

Both of these conditions are met here, so there is no need here to go into the grounds that we might have for saying in a particular case that a given individual belongs to a given club, as there might be need in another theory.

In the same way, the term "C" is an abstract predicate term. It is interpreted as "is a club"; but there is no set of familiar objects in the world around us which are such that those things and things like them are clubs. A club is a group of people (which indeed are familiar objects of our environment) satisfying a certain relationship. Again, the particular social relationship that holds among the members of a club doesn't concern us here and now, nor does the problem of how we ascertain in a particular case that such a relationship obtains. All that we need be concerned with here is that the phrase, "is a club" is one that we and others can apply with a reasonably high degree of uniformity, and that whatever elements of its meaning are involved in the theory be embodied in meaning postulates.

What we require of an interpretation is that there be a group of terms of the theory that can be given ordinary language meanings that can be reliably applied independently of the theory. We demand only that any relevant relations among the meanings of these terms, or among the meanings of the special (non-ordinary) terms of the theory, or between meanings of special terms and ordinary terms, be expressed explicitly as meaning postulates or axioms of the theory.

[51]

It does not matter that some of these ordinary terms are more or less *theoretical* terms of ordinary language in the sense that they have meanings that are not given purely ostensively; we are under no obligation to reduce all the terms of every formal system to terms that can be explained ostensively. It seems reasonable to suppose that all terms, ultimately, must be related (in the ways listed on page 49) to terms that are ostensive in the sense that they can be interpreted according to semantic rules of the sort that allow us to interpret "red"; but this supposition is certainly not necessary to an understanding of scientific formal systems, or of the activity of science; and indeed to insist on it is very often distracting and draws attention away from simpler and more relevant matters, such as: How is such and such a theoretical term related to other terms in the formal system? How is it related to the terms of ordinary discourse? The latter question may be asked quite independently of whether those terms of ordinary discourse to which it refers are relatively ostensive ones or relatively theoretical ones.

V

It is often the case that a given calculus admits of more than one interpretation. The calculus presented toward the beginning of this chapter, for example, is one often used to illustrate the axiomatic method, and the symbols "P", "C", and "M", are ordinarily interpreted as: "is a point", "is a line", and "lies on". In that light the calculus now becomes part of a completely different formal system, for a formal system, you recall, is a calculus *together with an interpretation*. Under this new interpretation the axioms of the system will read:

(A1) Every point lies on at least one line.
(A2) There are at least two points.
(A3) Given any two points, there is one and only one line to which they both belong. (Or: two points determine a line.)
(A4) All points do not lie on the same line.
(A5) Given a line and a point not on that line, there is exactly one line through that point which is parallel to (has no points in common with) the given line.

Here we have a familiar portion of Euclidian Geometry!

Given this new formal system, in which the primitive nonlogical terms of our calculus are interpreted as points and lines and the relation of lying on, do we have a bit of empirical science? That depends on the meaning we assign to "point" and "line". In general points and lines are not objects of our ordinary experience; and so the terms "point" and "line" function is much the same way as "P" and "C" function in our pure calculus; that is, they have no meaning for us until they are given meaning. There are various ways in which these terms can be given empirical meaning. We may interpret a point as a spot of chalk actually existing on a blackboard; a line as a streak of chalk on a blackboard (a streak drawn with a straight edge). Under these interpretations of "*P*" and " *C*" and the obvious interpretation of "lies on", we can perfectly well have a system of points and lines on a blackboard which satisfies the axioms, and which is perfectly ostensive, in the sense that we can take "*P*" to apply to this thing and that thing, and " *C*" to apply to that thing and the other thing, and " *M*" to apply to such and such pairs of things. The formal system may then be descriptive of a certain configuration on a blackboard, and all the terms of the system may admit explicitly ostensive interpretations.

Yet another interpretation of the system would consist in taking "point" and "line" as they are sometimes taken in empirical geometry, to stand for "intersection of light rays" and "path of a light ray". This interpretation is also empirical—it could be falsified, in a system of physical geometry—and yet none of its terms is interpreted ostensively. Indeed the terms "point" and "line" under this interpretation are relatively abstract physical entities, which only come to have empirical meaning through their indirect connection in a system of laws with other terms that in turn do have empirical meaning. The interpretation in this case is of type C.2.

Under all of these interpretations the structure of the system remains essentially the same. The semantics of the system changes, but the syntax does not. Since a formal system consists of a calculus plus an interpretation (a syntax plus a semantics), we have here not *one* formal system, but several. One of the advantages of the formal approach is that the same calculus can be part of a number of systems; the form can be separated from the content, and the form common to two distinct systems of similar structure can be treated as a thing in itself and studied independently. Such study is generally mathematics or logic, and we shall do little of it here; we shall always have one eye on an interpretation, for the sake of which we are developing the formalism.

BIBLIOGRAPHICAL NOTES TO CHAPTER 2

The calculus around which this chapter is built comes from Raymond Wilder, *Introduction to the Foundations of Mathematics* (New York: John Wiley and Sons, 1952), Chapter One; it is used there as an introduction to the axiomatic method, and employs the terms "point", "lies on", and "line" as its primitives. These are given various interpretations in the discussion of the system, including the clubs-in-a-community interpretation taken as fundamental here.

The problems surrounding the interpretation of formal systems have been dealt with in a large, varied, and complex literature. Rudolf Carnap, *Introduction to Semantics* (Cambridge, Mass: Harvard University Press, 1948), provides a general introduction to the formal semantical issues involved in interpreting nonlogical calculi. For a detailed treatment of meaning postulates, see his paper,

"Meaning Postulates," *Philosophical Studies* **3** (1952); this paper is reprinted, together with much other relevant material, in *Meaning and Necessity* (Chicago: University of Chicago Press, second edition, 1956). John G. Kemeny's views appear in "A New Approach to Semantics," *Journal of Symbolic Logic* **21** (1956).

For a strikingly different approach to many of the same issues, one which takes as fundamental the relation between language and experience rather than the relation between language and metalanguage, see W. V. O. Quine, *Word and Object* (New York: M. I. T. and John Wiley and Sons, 1960).

Chapter **3**

QUANTITIES

I

The popular image of the scientist in action (white-coated, spectacled) is that of a man measuring something, generally with the aid of complicated machines whose lights flash and whose needles waver across the faces of dials. Many people tend to think that the distinguishing mark of *real* science or *hard* science is its quantitative character. Surely one of the distinctive characteristics of modern science is its concern with such quantities as length, age, density, hardness, I.Q., mass, time, etc. All of these quantitative concepts fit into the formal systems in which they occur in much the same way; and they each lead to similar problems in interpretation. I shall therefore consider in detail one such concept, *length*, as it might occur in part of a formal system of physics; I shall then generalize on the properties of length and consider other quantities that are

[55]

like it, as well as quantities which do not obey all the simple rules of manipulation that length does.

Consider a man measuring a table. He takes a foot rule, lays it off four times along one edge of the table, and announces, "The table is three and a half feet long." There are two quite different ways of taking this assertion, and indeed any quantitative assertion. We may take it as attributing a certain property (being three and a half feet long) to a certain object (the table). Or we may take it as asserting that the real number value of a certain function (length-in-feet) applied to a certain object (the table) is 3.5. There are advantages and disadvantages to either way of looking at the matter. The former approach seems simpler, but it does require that we somehow account for an infinite number of length properties (being one foot long, being two and a half feet long, being two and a quarter feet long...), as well as an infinite number of weight properties, temperature properties, duration properties, etc. The latter approach requires only a finite number of entities (the functions, length-in-feet-of, weight-in-pounds-of, length-in-centimeters-of, etc.), but the entities it requires are more complicated than the properties required on the first approach. Since I think that the former approach better serves to clarify certain facts about systems of quantitative concepts in the sciences, I shall adopt it in the remainder of the book, but here, for the sake of illustrating the similarities and differences of the two approaches, I shall consider the assertion in question under each of the two interpretations.

Let us begin by taking "The table is three and a half feet long" to mean, "The length-in-feet-of this table is 3.5", or more explicitly yet: "The value of the length-in-feet-of function, for the argument *this table*, is 3.5". Let us introduce "F" as a notation for the distance-in-feet function, and use the subscript "L" to indicate the direction (lengthwise) in which the distance is being measured. Our original assertion then is "F_L(this table) = 3.5". Observe that the "3.5" denotes simply a real number; it has no dimensions. The dimensions (feet, rather than inches or centimeters or degrees centigrade) are represented in the function symbol "F_L" itself. We do not say that the length of the table is (equals) 3.5 feet, but that the value of the length-in-feet function, applied to the table, is the dimensionless number 3.5. We have interpreted length here as a *function* that maps objects (or objects-at-a-time) into real numbers. To talk about the length of an object is to talk about the value that this length-in-feet function has when it takes this object as its argument; i.e., to talk about the length of an object is to talk about a real number. (Real numbers will be discussed in Chapter 8.) In general we have

A1.   For any object x, if $F_L(x) = r$, then r is a real number.

It is an important characteristic of many quantities, including length, that we have a way of combining the objects that have such quantities in such a way that

[56]

the combination has a determinate new value of that quantity. To put the matter simply: there is often a way of combining objects that correspond to the adding of quantities; under the interpretation we are considering, adding quantities is simply adding pure numbers. In measurement of the table, we combined footrules (or footrule distances) in such a way that three and a half of them were the same length as the table. Two conditions must be satisfied if the combination of three and a half footrules is to be three and a half feet long. First, they must be colinear—they must lie in a straight line. In measuring a rectangular table this is often insured by measuring along one edge. Second, they must be juxtaposed: we must have no gaps between our footrules, nor may we allow them to overlap. But given colinearity and juxtaposition, the length appropriate to a combination of footrules will be the sum of the lengths of the footrules.

Because we are dealing here only with lengths, we can simplify matters by ignoring all but one dimension; we may speak of line segments, as they are represented by the distances between marks on a measuring instrument. We shall say that two line segments x and y are colinear, if they lie on the same straight line; let us use the abbreviation, "$Col(x,y)$". "$Col(x,y)$" expresses a relation between the line segment x and the line segment y. Similarly, juxtaposition, symbolized by "J", is a relation that may hold between line segments. Two line segments x and y are juxtaposed if they meet, but do not overlap. In that case, we have, in symbolic, abbreviated form: "$J(x,y)$". In addition to the two relations of colinearity and juxtaposition, we require the operation of combination, abbreviated "$Comb$". "$Comb(x,y)$" is not a sentence asserting that x and y stand in a certain relation, as is "$Col(x,y)$" for example, but is the name of a new entity—the entity we get by combining x and y when they are colinear and juxtaposed. There are a number of meaning postulates that hold for these terms. These are statements whose justification depends only on the meanings of the terms. Among them are

$$\text{MP-1} \quad Col(x,y) \equiv Col(y,x)$$
$$\text{MP-2} \quad J(x,y) \equiv J(y,x)$$
$$\text{MP-3} \quad F_L(Comb(x,y)) = F_L(Comb(y,x))$$
$$\text{MP-4} \quad (\exists z)(Comb(x,y) = z \supset (Col(x,y) \,\&\, J(x,y)).$$

The first two of these statements express the fact that colinearity and juxtaposition are symmetric relations. The third expresses the fact that the operation of combination is commutative, i.e., that we get the same entity whether we combine y with x or x with y. The last statement stipulates that if the combination of x and y exists, then x and y are colinear and juxtaposed.

Now we can express the general property of additivity of length as follows:

A2. $(Col(x,y) \,\&\, J(x,y)) \supset F_L(Comb(x,y)) = F_L(x) + F_L(y).$

That is to say, if x and y are line segments standing in the relation of colinearity and in relation of juxtaposition, then the length-in-feet of the combination of

[57]

x and y is just the ordinary arithmetical sum of the length-in-feet of x and the length-in-feet of y. (If x and y are *not* colinear and juxtaposed, $Comb(x,y)$ does not exist.) One of our concerns, of course, is to be able to express relations among quantities—indeed, this is why we introduce quantities so much: because so many interesting relations can be discovered to hold among them. At this point we don't care whether area and length are logically independent concepts, or whether in fact one is defined in terms of the other; in either case we come up with the following formula for the area of a rectangular shape: $A = B \times S$, where B is the length-of-the-base-in-feet, and S is the length-of-the-side-in-feet. The formula gives the area-in-square-feet of the rectangular shape; just as length was interpreted as a function from objects to real numbers, so area will be interpreted as a function from objects to real numbers. Thus we have

A3.   For any object x, if $A_P(x) = r$, then r is a real number,

where "A_P" represents area-in-square-feet-in-the-plane-P. Now let "$Cop(x,y)$" mean that x and y are coplanar, and let the meaning of J be slightly extended; then, corresponding to A2, we have

A4. $(Cop(x,y) \ \& \ J(x,y)) \supset A_P(Comb(x,y)) = A_P(x) + A_P(y)$.

But we also have, relating the distance function to the area function, the following formula:

A5.   If x is a rectangle, then $A_P(x) = F_S(x) \times F_B(x)$,

where the subscripts "S" and "B" indicate that the linear functions are to be understood to apply to the direction of the side and the direction of the base.

The approach to quantities which takes length to be a property of objects, according to which we say, *not* that the length-in-feet of a body is fifteen, but that the body has a fifteen-foot length, takes length in the abstract to be a kind of predicate of predicates—what logicians call a second-order concept. The instances of *length* are "ten feet", "five feet", "ten centimeters", etc., and it is these instances that in turn apply to objects. Thus having a given specific length is a quality, a property of a particular object. We may still use functional notation, but $F_P(x)$ is no longer simply a real number; it is an abstract length. If we write "L_R" for the set of all real number lengths, we have

A1'.   If $F_P(x) = r$, then r belongs to L_R.

Except for obvious typographical difficulties, an even better notation would be

$$_rL(x),$$

which would hold of x when and only when (in the previous notation) $F_L(x) = r$.

The latter notation brings out clearly that *having a length r* is a property of the object, rather than the result of doing something to the object. It might be

[58]

thought that in a sense, having a given length *is* the result of doing something to the object—namely, measuring it. But I think this is a mistake, because one then tends to identify the measurement with the thing measured, and this raises serious problems when it comes to speaking of the accuracy of measurements, and particularly of the relations between different methods of measuring what we consider to be the *same* quantity. For example, we may measure the mass of an object weighing it or by measuring its volume and using our knowledge of the density of the material it's made of to calculate its mass or we may measure its mass by seeing how much force is required to produce a given acceleration. In each case we do something different to the object, but in each case we are measuring the same quantity. Furthermore, the quantities that enter into the equations of physics and chemistry and engineering, are not regarded as pure numbers. They are generally taken to be *quantities*—so and so many feet, or pounds, or foot-pounds, or feet per second per second. They have *dimensions* which the engineer ignores at his peril.

The operations that we perform on quantities are usually perfectly parallel to the operations that we perform on real numbers. But there is no reason for making this a complete identity; and indeed there are advantages to leaving the question open as to whether the particular quantity we have at hand can be made to fit a calculus of real quantities which is perfectly parallel to the arithmetic of real numbers. For example, there may be circumstances under which it is perfectly clear and natural to speak of combining two entities, x and y, in such a way that the quantity applicable to their combination could be spoken of as the *sum* of the quantities applicable to x and to y separately, and yet in which we would not want this *sum* to have all the properties of arithmetical summation. (We might have reason to give up commutativity, the principle that the *sum* of x and y is the same as the *sum* of y and x, for example.) This option is open to us, if instead of A2, we write

A2.′ $(Col(x,y) \,\&\, J(x,y) \supset (F_L(Comb(x,y)) = F_L(x) \,_L{+}\, F_L(y)),$

where "$_L{+}$" represents not the addition of real numbers, but a corresponding operation on length quantities. The formula reads, "If x and y are colinear, and x and y are juxtaposed, then the length of their combination is equal to the length-sum of their individual lengths." Or, using the more suggestive property-notation,

A2.″ $(Col(x,y) \,\&\, J(x,y)) \supset ((_rL(x) \,\&\, _sL(y)) \supset _{r+s}L(Comb(x,y))).$

In the special cases in which the properties of combinations of objects are additive, the formula says that if x and y are colinear and juxtaposed, then if x has the property of being r feet long, and y has the property of being s feet long, then their combination will have the property of being $(r + s)$ feet long.

[59]

If we are concerned with a quantity R which is not additive, we may still perfectly well have

$$(_rR(x) \,\&\, _sR(y)) \supset {}_{f(r,s)}R(Comb(x,y)),$$

where there is a theory that tells us what the function f is. If "R" represents electrical resistance, for example, the resistance of a *combination* of two resistors will depend upon the mode of combination. Let us write "*P-Comb*" for the operation of connecting the resistances in parallel, and *S-Comb* for the operation of connecting the resistances in series. Then we have the two formulas:

(1) $\quad (_rR(x) \,\&\, _sR(y)) \supset {}_{(r+s)}R(S\text{-}Comb(x,y)),\quad$ and

(2) $\quad (_rR(x) \,\&\, _sR(y)) \supset {}_{f(r,s)}R(P\text{-}Comb(x,y)),$

where

$$f(r,s) = \frac{1}{1/r + 1/s}.$$

Furthermore, the relationship between a quantity such as area, and the quantities in terms of which it seems to be defined, now become clear and explicit and the dimensional relations between them are also exhibited. In A2′ we used a special form of addition appropriate to the quantity length: $_L+$ is an operation that is performed on pairs of length quantities to obtain a new length quantity. It is perfectly natural, if one has such a notion, to introduce a notion also for an operation $_L\times$, which will be an operation performed on pairs of length quantities to obtain, not a new length quantity, but an *area* quantity. And it is perfectly natural to *define* rectangular area as

DA $\quad _{r\times s}A_\square(x) \quad$ *if and only if* $\quad Rect(x) \,\&\, _rL(S(x)) \,\&\, _sL(B(x)),$

where $S(x)$ and $B(x)$ are the side and base of the rectangle x. And of course it is an easy matter to define area in general in terms of rectangular area, if we have enough machinery in the calculus of lengths.

In this formulation it is clear that the units of $_rA_\square(x)$ are square inches when the units of $_sL(B(x))$ are inches, square meters when the units of $_sL(B(x))$ are meters, and so on.

The matter of clarity concerning the dimensions with which we are dealing becomes even more important when we deal with "artificial" quantities, such as entropy. In science to forget the dimensions of the quantities that you are calculating with is to court serious error; and yet the very ease and simplicity of the calculations we make (which we make as if the quantities with which we were dealing were not quantities at all, but real numbers) can lead us to forget that there are dimensions attached to them.

Finally, the technique that is suggested by the analysis of "length" and "area" for dealing formally with quantitative concepts in science gives a clear picture of

[60]

how such concepts can be developed in a natural way, and of how they can be based on properties which can be given fairly straightforward and relatively ostensive semantical interpretations. It does this with all quantitative concepts, including not only those that are *extensive*, or additive in a natural way, like length and mass, but also those that are *intensive*, like temperature, and even those which strike some commentators on science as wholly artificial, like the quantities measured by psychological tests.

II

We now turn to the general characteristics and requirements for the introduction of quantitative terms of all sorts into the terminology of scientific formal systems. What is required first of all is an ostensively interpretable relational predicate, "L", such as "longer than", of which the following two statements are true.

(1) $(x)(y)(L(x,y) \supset \sim L(y,x))$

(2) $(x)(y)(z)((L(x,y) \ \& \ L(y,z)) \supset L(x,z))$.

Statement (1) says that if x and y stand in the relation in question, then y and x do not stand in it; a relation of which (1) is true is called asymmetric. Statement (2) says that if x bears the relation in question to y, and y, in turn, bears that relation to z, then x bears the relation to z. A relation satisfying (2) is called transitive. "Longer than", "heavier than", "greater than" (applied to numbers), are examples of asymmetric, transitive relations.

These two statements do not have to be *accurately* true of the predicates that we begin with. Even the prescientific term "longer than" fails to satisfy them, in some cases. Thus my pipe is longer than the column of mercury in my thermometer; and so from (1) it should follow that the mercury in my thermometer is not longer than my pipe. But that is not *always* true, for the length of the column of mercury will vary with temperature. Nevertheless, when we begin to be scientific, we are not averse to making minor alterations in our predicates—restricting their scope, for example, or adding time parameters. Thus if we restrict the range of the predicate "longer than" to rigid bodies, then it is not the case that my pipe is longer than the mercury column; or if we include a time parameter, it is certainly true that at a given time if one is longer than the other, the other is not longer than the one. In the same way it is easy to imagine being presented with three sticks, two at a time, in such a way that one would judge stick number 1 to be longer than stick number 2, and stick number 2 to be longer than stick number 3, and yet *not* judge stick number 1 to be longer than stick number 3. But these two statements (1) and (2) *do* have to be true, if we are to regard the relation in question as a quantitative one. To treat length as a quantity (or to decide to treat length as a quantity) is precisely to decide that (1) and (2) are to be

[61]

true; it is to decide to treat apparent falsifications of (1) and (2) as *merely* apparent—as error, as inappropriate application, as depending on a change in one of the quantities involved.

All of this holds even of concepts that are quantitative only in a much weaker sense than length. Thus consider the concept of creativeness. We have a perfectly good predicate, "is more creative than" applicable to pairs of people. And there is a fair amount of stability in our application of that predicate, so that we do indeed, in some measure, regard creativeness as a basic personality trait. If we are psychologists, planning to work with this concept, and to explore the relationships between creativeness and other personality characteristics, we will quite naturally want to treat it as a quantity. And thus we will accept analogs of (1) and (2); we will stipulate that they be true of our new scientific concept, though of our preanalytic (prescientific) concept of creativeness they will only be true roughly and approximately.

(3) $(x)(y)(Cr(x,y) \supset \sim Cr(y,x))$ asymmetry

(4) $(x)(y)(z)((Cr(x,y)\ \&\ Cr(y,z)) \supset Cr(x,z))$ transitivity

It is worthwhile exploring, for a moment, the similarities and differences between the concepts of creativeness and length. In the first place, the natural and prescientific concept of relative length more nearly satisfies (1) and (2), than the prescientific concept of creativeness satisfies (3) and (4). In one respect the situation is the same: (1) and (2) fail to hold when there is a change in length in one of the bodies—that is, when the length at one time is greater than the length at another time. And it is often quite easy to establish this change in length, even though we might not be able to account for it. In the same way (3) and (4) fail to hold when there is a change in creativeness of one of the people—that is when his creativeness at one time is greater than his creativeness at another. It is often quite easy to establish this change in creativeness, even though we might not be able to account for it. But there is another difficulty that enters with creativeness; it is easy to think of two people such that one is more creative than the other in one respect and the second more creative than the first in another respect. The question of respect enters into our account of length, too; the length of an object depends on the direction in which it is measured—i.e., its orientation with respect to the axis of the measuring instrument. But (a) it is much easier to stipulate in what respect we are considering length than in what respect we are considering creativeness, and (b) given the stipulation, it is much easier to agree on the *amount* of length than on the *amount* of creativeness present in that respect. As in many matters in the philosophy of science, the most important and relevant distinctions are distinctions of degree.

Another difference lies in the degree to which people can agree about the applicability of the prescientific concepts, or, as I would prefer to put it, the *degree of interpersonal uniformity* in the use of the two expressions, "longer than", and "more creative than". In any group of ordinary people of good will, there will be a great deal of interpersonal uniformity in the application of the predicate "longer than" to most pairs of objects; there will be some pairs of objects about which opinion will be more or less divided, some people maintaining that a is longer than b, and others maintaining that it is not the case that a is longer than b. But if questions of orientation and variability can be settled, the number of such disputed pairs of objects will be small. On the other hand, although there will certainly be a large measure of agreement in a similar group about the applicability of the predicate "more creative than" applied to pairs of people, there will also be disagreement, and there will no doubt be more disagreement in this case than the former. Thus the degree of interpersonal uniformity in the second case is less than that in the first. This does not preclude the possibility of using creativeness as a useful psychological quantity; all that is involved here is a matter of *degree* of interpersonal uniformity, which indeed could perfectly well be expressed statistically, as we shall see later.

The most significant difference between the two cases, however, is that the concept of length has turned out to be of fundamental importance in a wide variety of natural laws—it is extraordinarily useful in science—while the concept of creativeness has been found useful only in some psychological generalizations, and has not been found to be at all as useful as the concept of length. A part of this difference may be due to the fact that length is a quantitative concept that exhibits far more internal structure than does creativeness—that is, there is a simple physical operation that is correlated to the mathematical operation of addition; we can consider arbitrarily great and arbitrarily small lengths; we can assert that between any two lengths, there is a third; that given any two lengths, there is a multiple of the one that is a length greater than the other, etc. Furthermore, the changes in length that are needed to account for failures of (1) and (2) are well understood, and indeed these failures can be predicted and controlled, and thus are not really failures at all. On the other hand, changes in creativeness are not at all very well understood, and any hypothesis accounting for apparent failures of (4) or (3) will have an aroma of the *ad hoc* about it.

Given that we have an asymmetrical and transitive relation, the next step in arriving at the underlying quantity is to establish some way of assigning numbers to the entities in the field of the relation that can serve as *indices* of the values of the quantity that we take to underlie that relation. We want these indices to *fit* the relation L, in the sense that x will have a larger number assigned to it than y does if and only if x bears the relation L to y.

Let us consider first the field of the relation longer than; an object belongs to the field of the relation L if there is an object to which it bears the relation L, or which bears L to it:

(5) $\qquad \hat{x}(\exists y)(L(x,y) \lor L(y,x)) = $ Field of L.

[63]

(I am using "$\hat{x}$" as an abstraction operator, "$\hat{x}Fx$" stands for the set of entities x such that Fx.) We can assign numbers to these objects in the following arbitrary manner, because in experience these objects are presented to us seriatim:

(a) Assign the number 1 to the first object.
(b) If the second object is longer than the first, assign to it the number 2; if the first is longer than the second, assign to the second the number $\frac{1}{2}$; if neither is the case, give it, also, the number 1.
(c) And in general, if the nth object is longer than all of the preceding $n-1$ objects, assign it a number halfway between the largest number assigned and the number 3; if it is shorter than all of the preceding $n-1$ objects, assign it a number halfway between the smallest number assigned and 0; if there are two objects such that there is no object assigned a number between the numbers assigned these two, and if the nth object is longer than one of these objects and shorter than the other, assign it a number halfway between the numbers assigned to the two objects mentioned; and finally, if none of the preceding clauses apply to the nth object, assign it the number assigned to the first (earliest) object in the sequence which is neither judged longer nor judged shorter than the nth object.

What this rule amounts to in general is this: if there is no object already encountered such that it is to be neither judged shorter nor judged longer than a new object (i.e., which is indistinguishable in length from the new object), then the new object is assigned a number in the obvious way; if there is at least one such an object, the new object is assigned the same number as the *first* object of the sequence indistinguishable in length from the new object. To be sure, we can devise a much better way of assigning numbers to objects to represent their length (see Section 3); one natural objection to the present method of assignment is that it makes the numerical length of an object depend on where that object occurs in the sequence of objects. But we are trying to see what we can do if we assume no more than that the relation longer than is transitive and asymmetric; in particular we are not assuming that "neither longer nor shorter" means the same as "is the same length as", and has the convenient property of transitivity.

On the supposition that the relation L is truly transitive and asymmetric, we will, of course, never find that our assignments of numbers fail to satisfy the requirements of transitivity and asymmetry. But this does not insure that our assignment of numbers will *fit* our judgments of relative length; we may still find certain cases in which we have neither $L(y,z)$ nor $L(z,y)$ despite the fact that we have assigned different numbers to y and to z. Thus we may find objects x and y such that we judge (1) that x is not longer than y, and (2) that y is not longer than x. Then we might find an object z such that we judge (3) that z is longer than x, and (4) that the first object of the sequence is longer than z. But on the basis of direct comparison we might also judge (5) that y is not longer than z

and (6) that z is not longer than y. We might, for example, assign lengths of $\frac{1}{2}$ to x and to y, and a length of $\frac{3}{4}$ to z, despite the fact that z and y are indistinguishable in length. This assignment of numbers under the rule is perfectly possible, and perfectly consistent with our stipulations of transitivity and asymmetry, even though the numbers fail to reflect our relational judgements. Of course we can patch things up; there are three things we can do:

(i) We can reject one of our immediate judgments: we can either reject one of the original four judgments, or we can reject the sixth judgment, that z is not longer than y.

(ii) Or we can reject the rule for assigning numbers, or modify it; and indeed we must modify it if the numbers are to reflect our intuitive relational judgments.

(iii) Another line of attack would be to reject the refinements of our relational predicate—i.e., reject the general applicability of the transitivity law and the asymmetry law, in order to clear up the difficulties of our rule for assigning numbers.

Our course is fairly obvious. In the interest of having precise and manipulable quantities to use in the development of our sciences, we hang fast to the refinements of our relational predicate "longer than" (or "more creative than"), and we even impose the following additional restriction on the use of our relational predicate, in order that the numbers assigned to objects will fit our intuitive judgments. The condition will be this:

$$(6) \qquad (x)(y)(z)((\sim L(x,y)\ \&\ \sim L(y,z)) \supset \sim L(x,z)).$$

This condition (we need one which is slightly stronger than that suggested by the preceding problem), might be called the transitivity of indifference or of indistinguishability. It, more than any of the other rules, is plainly false to fact when applied to relational terms like "longer than" when they are regarded as purely ostensive. It is simply not the case that if you can't tell whether or not a is longer than b, or vice versa, and you can't tell whether b is longer than c or vice versa, then you will never be able to tell whether or not a is longer than c. We attribute this fact to the inaccuracy of our observations, which is a perfectly appropriate thing to do; all I wish to bring out here is the fact that it reflects a change from the original ostensive "longer than" to a new, somewhat theoretical "longer than", which is no longer purely ostensive. But although it is not purely ostensive any more, it is still largely so: in most cases, "longer than" is a relation that we can simply *see* holds of a given pair of objects. The problematical cases are in the very small minority.

There is another fact that underlies this procedure: a problematical triplet of objects x, y, z, can very often be found not problematical after all, by making more careful observations. Here again is a phenomenon pervasive in science:

[65]

terms are useful partly because they are capable of refinement—the techniques that we use for deciding whether or not the term "longer than" applies to a given pair of objects are techniques that can be progressively refined. (I am not speaking, at the moment, of what one might call theoretical refinements, such as, for example, the use of optical devices for measuring lengths to within the order of wavelengths of light. I simply mean: more careful and controlled observation.) As the technique of decision becomes more refined, the class of problematical cases becomes smaller and smaller—there are fewer and fewer instances in which we have to do violence to some of our immediate judgments in order to maintain (1), (2), and (6). It is less and less often that we must reject one of our length judgments.

With respect to creativeness, we are in the same realm, but at the other end of the country. Here there are a great many problematical cases even in the casual application of the term. It is easy indeed to find oneself saying that x is more creative than y, and then, in another context, saying that y is more creative than x. It is easy indeed to find oneself committed to the assertions that x is more creative than y, and that y is more creative than z, and then to discover that one does not, after all, regard x as more creative than z. And it is easier yet to deny that x is more creative than y, and that y is more creative than z, while it is quite patently obvious that x is far more creative than z. But if we are to treat creativeness as a quantitative concept at all, as I have already pointed out, we must disallow these situations. If we have accepted the assertion that x is more creative than y, then we must not accept the assertion that y is more creative than x. Similarly for the transitivity law: we must simply reform our usage—even arbitrarily—so that it reflects and does not violate that law. All of this is entailed by the proposal to regard creativeness as a quantity. (It might be felt to be sufficient—indeed there may be many readers who already regard it as sufficient—to cause us to reject the notion that creativeness is a quantity; or to reject at any rate its one-dimensionality. But this is another matter. I am assuming that we are going to regard it as a quantity.) When it comes to satisfying the analog of (6), the problems and unrealities are even more intense, but not essentially different in kind. Where (4) reflected the commitment to the transitivity of judgments of the form "x is more creative than y", (6) merely reflects the commitment—only slightly stronger—to the transitivity of judgments of the form "x is *not* more creative than y".

The analog of (6) is the only additional thing we need in order to apply a rule like the one suggested above; indeed the rule can, in view of (6) be given a slightly simpler form:

(a) Assign the number 1 to the creativity of the first individual.
(b) If the first person is more creative than the second, assign the number $\frac{1}{2}$ to the second; if the second is more creative than the first, give him the number

2; if neither is the case (i.e., if neither is more creative than the other) give the second also the number 1.

(c) In general, if the *n*th is more creative than all of the preceding people, give him a number halfway between the largest number already assigned and the number 3; if every other person is more creative than he is, give him a number halfway between the smallest number assigned and 0; and if there is somebody already examined who is such that we wish to say neither that the *n*th person is more creative than he is, nor yet that he is more creative than the *n*th person, give the *n*th person the same number as the mentioned individual; and finally, if there are two individuals already examined, such that there is no individual whose creativeness falls between theirs, but the *n*th individual, then assign the *n*th person the average of the numbers assigned to these two people.

This is simpler than the preceding rule, because we can (in view of (6)) rule out the possibility that we can have a number of distinguishable objects (persons) each of which is indistinguishable from the *n*th object (person).

The development that has just been described both for length and for creativeness is common in the growth of scientific systems (except that it employs a scale with limits 0 and 3). It may be described as the creation of a set of equivalence classes, or indifference classes, or indistinguishability classes, or as a partition of a given set, under the somewhat artificial relation, "is neither longer than nor shorter than" in the first case, and "is neither more creative than, nor less creative than" in the second. Let us use the phrase "equivalence class". An equivalence class produced by a relation R satisfying analogues of (3), (4), and (6), is a set of objects no two of which bear R to each other. That is, if x and y belong to a given equivalence class of lengths, say, then we have both $\sim L(x,y)$ and $\sim L(y,x)$. Observe that we do *not* need to say that "has exactly the same length as", nor "has exactly the same degree of creativeness as", are relations that hold among the elements of a given equivalence class. We can satisfy the preceding axioms for length (1), (2), and (6), even if we are so blunt-headed that we can only distinguish three lengths in all the world. Length might be still a perfectly fine quantitative concept, although, naturally, it would not serve us quite so well in the formulation of physical laws. The fact that creativeness has merely (if at all) the limited quantitative aspect that I have outlined so far may indicate why it does not serve any useful function in quantitative laws.

Each equivalence class corresponds, now, to a numerical predicate: having creativeness of such and such a degree, or having such and such a length. We can define the sequence of *quantitative* predicates: "has length $\frac{1}{2}$", "has creativity $\frac{3}{4}$", and so on in terms of these equivalence or indistinguishability classes. In accordance with the notation suggested earlier, we would have, for any number r, $_rL(x)$ if and only if x belongs to the set of objects to which the rule

[67]

assigns the number r. "$_rL(x)$" means that x has the length r. Note that the "r" is simply a part of the predicate, like the "cat" in "predicate". It would be dangerously misleading to write "$L(x) = r$". The "L" in this expression represents the function described in (a), (b), and (c); and that is quite a different thing from a length. We do not want to substitute "$L(x)$" for example, into contexts appropriate to substitution of real numbers; far less into contexts appropriate to the values of other kinds of functions, such as temperature or mass functions. All this is taken care of (and there are other advantages as well) by the proposal to regard quantities as quantitative predicates.

"$_rL(x)$" means that x-has-length-r; "$_rCr(y)$" means that y-has-creativeness-r. There is no mention of units, such as feet; the numbers are simply indices, so far, that reflect the relationships (longer than, more creative than) involved. In practice, of course, one would want to (and need to) identify the sequence in which the creativeness of y was s—in a different sequence of individuals, y might very well have a different number. But I have been supposing here that there is only one series that we need to take account of; and the rule for assigning numbers is such that we never have to renumber an individual in a given sequence.

The next step in the approach to a useful quantitative concept, consists in the choice of a standard series. We have finally, with the introduction of a *standard* series, arrived at concepts of the sort that are actually used in science. Hardnesses provide a fine example of quantitative predicates whose values are determined by comparison with a standard series. The standard (Moh) series, together with the numbers assigned to each member of it is:

Substance	Hardness
Talc	1
Gypsum	2
Calc Spar	3
Fluorspar	4
Apatite	5
Feldspar	6
Quartz	7
Topaz	8
Sapphire	9
Diamond	10

The numbers assigned to each of these substances are perfectly arbitrary, except insofar as they indicate relative hardness: a substance having a higher number than another will scratch the other, but will not be scratched by it. Thus diamond will scratch anything else in the list, sapphire will scratch quartz, but will not be scratched by quartz, and so on. Given any new substance, we fit it into the standard hardness series by testing it against various substances in that series;

[68]

and then it takes its place in the series in accordance with rules of just the sort previously described. But even this is a weak quantitative concept. It is weak because there is no structure, other than order, in the sequence of quantitative predicates corresponding to places in the series; there is an order relation, and that is all. In a certain sense, then, it is even misleading to correlate the places in the series with numbers, because we expect to be able to add and subtract and multiply and calculate with numbers, and there is no such possibility with the numbers representing places in a series.

It is still useful and convenient to use numbers to represent those places; we could use any ordered set of objects at all, provided there were enough of them for the case at hand. For hardness, we could just as well use $A, B, C, \ldots, I$, as the number 1–10; but for creativeness and certainly for length, we want to be able to create an arbitrarily large number of predicates. Numbers have one very great advantage over some other sequences of things, and that is that we can always find a number that fits between any two given numbers. This property makes it possible to apply the rules suggested above and thus avoid changing numbers once they have been assigned. For example, to use natural (whole) numbers, we should have to (1) order the objects in a finite set by the relation in question, (2) assign numbers to the objects in that order, and then (3) go through the same process again every time we wanted to consider a larger set. Every new individual might require the readjustment of some of the numbers that had already been assigned to individuals.

The concept of length that has been defined, like the concept of creativeness, is a concept that admits of an infinite number of values. In the way it has been defined, there may be lengths such that, if we kept on comparing the lengths of things, we would in the limit have used up all the ratios between 0 and 3. The same is true of creativeness. I have just pointed out that we need not end up with this many equivalence classes of lengths or of creativeness; but even if we do we are still some distance from the concept of length that enters into the physical sciences in such an important way.

III

To arrive at quantities in the best and most useful sense, in which we can calculate with them in interesting and useful ways, and in which we can formulate quantitative laws which make use of the structure of the number system, we need one quite new thing: it is a way of combining objects of experience to yield new objects that still belong in the field of the relation. Thus in the case of the lengths of sticks, an operation such as putting two sticks end to end in a straight line generates a new object which is (in fact) longer than either of the objects that compose it, and which is comparable in size to the objects that compose it.

The same thing is true of mass, and in fact the same thing is true (but in a more complicated way) of temperature. That is, although temperature is not simply additive in the way that mass and length are, there is nevertheless often a way of combining bodies that have certain temperatures to yield a new body with a new temperature; and in fact we can calculate that new temperature, given knowledge of the masses and specific heats of the original bodies. What we do is not in any theoretical way different from what we do when we combine bodies of given lengths to get a compound body of a new length. The arithmetic happens to be easier in the latter case. But it is easy to imagine a universe in which this was not the case: it might be the case that the temperature of every body was proportional to its mass (so that when two bodies of equal mass at 100°F are combined, juxtaposed, or intermixed, the resulting body has a temperature of 200°F) and it might be the case (perhaps as a correlate of this physical phenomenon) that when two bodies are juxtaposed, the length of the resulting combination is only calculable by reference to a complicated formula that depends on parameters characteristic of the particular kinds of substance involved, like specific heats, though in this case we would speak, say, of length-combining constants.

What is the nature of the act of combination? In the case of weight, it is simply a matter of treating the two objects as one complex object: putting them both on the pan of a balance, or lifting them both at once, or dropping them both at once. In the case of length, it is a matter of putting the two objects end to end in a straight line, and regarding the result as a single object. In this context "straight line", like "end to end", is simply a predicate that we know how to apply on the basis of ostensive familiarity. The semantic rules that govern its application are ostensive rules; here it has no serious geometrical connotations.

Now both of these modes of combination—the end-to-end-juxtaposition-in-a-straight-line, and the simple handle-as-one-thing—are modes of combination that allow iteration: we can put two sticks end to end, or three, or four..., and the same is true of weights. To begin with, suppose that we have a large equivalence class (indistinguishability class) of objects with respect to length, and let us call the property they have in common, *having-length-one*. We can combine any two of these objects, and discover that the resulting combination is indistinguishable in length from the combination of any other two of these objects. This is an empirical discovery about length and juxtaposition. (It might not be so, as the temperature example shows. In fact it is not quite so, even for lengths; the kitchen matches in a box might be regarded as indistinguishable in length, and yet two pairs placed end to end might quite clearly differ in length. The individual matches might differ in length by at most 1/64 of an inch, which we might not be able to observe; but the end-to-end pairs could then differ by as much as 1/32 of an inch, which we could observe.) Furthermore, it is true of combinations of three, and of four, and indeed of any n we happen to have tried. In assigning numerical lengths to objects we can arrange to take the length of the first object we encounter as one—i.e., we can pretend that that standard object was the first we encountered. But beyond this there is no telling what the length (in the sense

[70]

of our previous assignment of numbers) of the combination of two of these one-unit objects will be, or of three of them or of any number. It might just happen for example, that the length of one of the unit objects was $_1L$, that the length of two of them put together was $_2L$, that the length of three of them was $_{2.5}L$, of four of them $_{2.75}L$, and in general of a combination of n of them, $_{3-(1/2)^n-2}L$. It might fall out this way. But of course that would be rather fantastically unlikely. And it still wouldn't give us the kind of length measurement that we find most useful.

Therefore, let us abandon the rule expressed by (a), (b), and (c) and try an altogether different rule. If we have a method like this of combining lengths, then the following rule might quite naturally suggest itself, for measurements of a given general order of magnitude:

(a') Choose a convenient sized object as a unit; assign to it, and to all the objects having the same length as it the number 1—i.e., take "$_1L(x)$" as the predicate truly applicable to all the members of the equivalence class determined by that standard object.

(b') Take the length of any object that is the same length as a combination of n of these unit objects to be $_nL$.

Since we have discovered as an empirical fact that the combination of any n of these unit objects is the same length as the combination of any other n of them, and since we earlier (6) decided on the transitivity of the relation *being the same length as*, we know that the length of any object which is the same as the length of a combination of any n of the standard objects, will be the same as the length of any other object which is the same as the length of any other n of the standard objects.

This takes care of all the lengths that are integral multiples of the standard length. It also partially determines the numbers that may be assigned to the intermediate lengths, since we wish to hang on to the original fact that if $_sL(x)$ and $_rL(y)$, then x is longer than y if and only if s is numerically greater than r. But we can be more precise than this. We can very likely find an object such that it and another one of exactly the same length, combined, yield a compound object that is the same length as the standard object. What more natural than to assign to it the length $\frac{1}{2}$? And the same thing that is true of the standard objects will be true of the set of objects of length $\frac{1}{2}$: that they will all be equal in length, and that the length of the combination of any two of them will be equal to the length of any one of the standard objects, etc. All of this is expressed in this version of the third part of the rule:

(c') In any equivalence class of objects, suppose that the combination of m of them is the same length as the combination of n of the standard objects. Then assign the predicate $_{n/m}L$ to the members of this class.

[71]

As before, we observe that it doesn't matter which m or which n objects you choose from the respective classes. In principle, the technique I have outlined takes care of the problem of rational lengths of ordinary size, and this is the basic problem of quantity here. Indeed it is only in the context of a theory—such as in a geometry of physical objects—that one can even begin to consider the question of irrational lengths. Every ordinary measurement yields a rational number.

Three problems may come to mind; lengths that are very large relative to our unit (e.g., the distance to the sun, relative to our meter-stick); lengths that are very small relative to our unit (e.g., the wavelength of a certain color of light relative to the meter-stick); and irrational lengths (e.g., the circumference of a circle whose diameter is 1 meter, or the length of the hypotenuse of a 45° right triangle with unit legs). The solutions to all three problems are similar. They involve the use of geometrical or physical theories, into which these quantities enter. We calculate the distance of the sun with the help of Euclidean geometry, on the assumption that light travels in Euclidean straight lines. We calculate the wavelength of a certain color of light with the help of a whole body of physical theory (concerning diffraction gratings, interference, and so on), as well as with the help of geometry. The calculation of π, the circumference of a circle one unit in diameter, also takes place within a Euclidean geometric framework, but involves as well the mathematical theory of convergent series.

What this chapter has described does not purport to be historically true, of course, except perhaps in a kind of schematic way. It is laid out the way it is in order to exhibit the relation between terms, such as "longer than", that may be given ostensively to begin with, and quantitative terms, derived from them, that are given only partly ostensively, the other part being conventional. There is also an empirical element involved: the technique last given for assigning numbers to lengths would not work—would not yield numbers satisfying the relations that we wanted to exhibit in the first place—were it not for the fact that the combination of any three units has the same length as the combination of any other three units. And this is already an idealization: the length you get by combining 10,000 foot rules is not (probably) the same as the length you would get by combining 10,000 other foot rules. It is only within limits that our judgments may be regarded as dependable. But in the transitivity of the relation "longer than", we already find idealization: regarded as a purely ostensively defined relation, "longer than" is only transitive most of the time; some of the time it may fail to be transitive. Nevertheless we find it more profitable to incorporate transitivity in its *meaning*, through semantic rules (meaning postulates), than to take "longer than" as being approximately transitive and completely ostensive.

Transitivity is important—indeed perhaps the most important aspect of all quantitative predicates. It is in virtue of transitivity that we can compare things indirectly. The primitive predicate "longer than", which we learn ostensively, is only ostensively applicable directly to things lying side by side. Next, it can be made to apply directly to things that can be placed side by side. But (discounting memory, which is both fallible and indirect) it gives us no way of telling that the stick in the next room is longer than the stick here in this room, except by moving one or the other. When we have guaranteed transitivity, we can take a light, easy-to-carry stick, which is the same length as the telephone pole in this room, and carry it into the next room to compare with the telephone pole there; we know that its length will bear the same relation to the length of the telephone pole there, as the length of the telephone pole in this room bears to the length of that telephone pole. We know this, because we know that physical objects do not change size as they are carried through space (at moderate speed); this is a fact about the world—in fact, a rather sophisticated one—just as is the fact that any two one-foot sticks will combine to have the same length as any other two one-foot sticks. How we know this fact and how this fact fits into our body of physical knowledge are complex questions we leave to one side, for the moment. Once we have introduced a unit and a concept of combination that allows us to use rule (a')–(c') to generate numerical length predicates, then all we need is a yardstick to compare the lengths of the two things that cannot be brought together—as for example, the depth of a well in China and the height of a boulder in Colorado.

IV

Let us consider, briefly, derivative quantities. They can only be treated fully in the context of some sort of theory; but we can deal with them here in a rough way. Consider, for example, area.

We have a primitive basic ostensively introduced relation, "has greater area than" applied to the surfaces of flat objects. It isn't as nice a predicate as "longer than", because the shapes of the areas involved are often so confusing that it's hard to form a judgment about whether area A is bigger than or smaller than area B. Certain types of shapes are easier to deal with than others: squares and rectangles are simpler than pentagrams. And these are also easy areas to combine, because they have straight edges, and fit together nicely. (Hexagons would also fit together nicely, but they cannot be subdivided into smaller hexagons neatly and evenly; equilateral triangles fit together and can be subdivided, but they would be much harder to relate to length.)

It is easy to compare the areas of two squares, and thus easy to make such areas satisfy a transitive, asymmetric relation ((1), (2), and (6) above), *has more area than*. Furthermore, as in the case of length, there is a natural and simple way of combining squares. If we have two squares of the same size (neither has more area than the other), we may combine them by placing them edge to edge. Thus, if the fundamental unit of area is a square, we can consider areas of one square,

[73]

two squares, three squares, etc., just as we considered objects of length one, of length two, of length three, etc. (Fig. 1a). Fractions of squares are a little

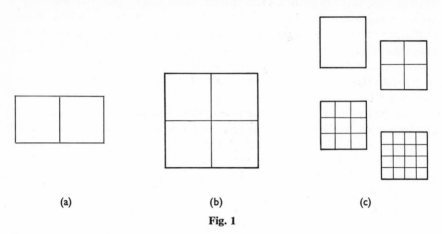

(a)   (b)   (c)

Fig. 1

more complicated, however, than fractions of length; for if we divide a square in two, we don't have objects of the same shape any more; if we divide it twice (once each way) we can get square-shaped objects, but it takes four of them to make up one square (Fig. 1b). We can determine certain fractions of squares this way: quarters, ninths, sixteenths, twenty-fifths, and so on (Fig. 1c).

Having done this, it is easy to use the transitive and asymmetric properties of "has greater area than", together with the additive property of square-shaped areas, to construct a set of equivalence classes of any areas at all. For we can find two areas compounded of square-shaped areas one of which is larger than, and one of which is smaller than, any oddly shaped area we choose (Fig. 2), and which are as nearly the same in area as we choose. Note that we can do this quite independently of any way of constructing or talking about squares of any dimensions other than units, quarters, ninths, and so on.

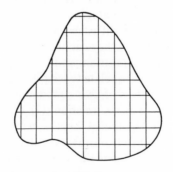

Fig. 2

[74]

We have now a general way of treating area as a quantity: we have a set of quantitative predicates of area, all defined in terms of the unit square. But we have no connection, as yet between squares and our unit of length. The natural point of connection is to take the side of our fundamental unit square to be one unit of length.

To see clearly where we go from here it might help to consider, first of all, triangles, rather than squares; it is often easier to focus on details in the unfamiliar than in the familiar. Suppose we measure areas in equilateral triangles, just as we measured areas in squares. Take the unit triangle to have a side of one length unit. Then an equilateral triangle 2 units on a side will have an area of four triangles; one of n units on a side will have an area of n^2 triangles (Fig. 3). A

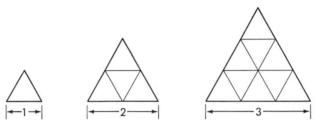

Fig. 3

rectangular area that is $(\frac{1}{2}) \sqrt{3}$ units high and b units long, will have an area of $2b$ triangles; in general a rectangular area that is a units high and b units long will have an area of $[2b \times a]/[(\frac{1}{2})\sqrt{3}]$, or $(\frac{4}{3})\sqrt{3}\, ab$ triangles (Fig. 4). But

b=3

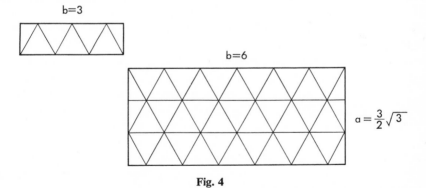

b=6

$a = \frac{3}{2}\sqrt{3}$

Fig. 4

what does it mean to multiply these a's and b's? What does it mean to say that a triangle that is a feet on a side is $a \times a$ triangular feet in area? In order to understand this clearly, we must go back to the fundamental units we have been considering: to say that the equilateral triangle x has an area of four is to say that it

[75]

has the property $_4TA$; thus it is to assert "$_4TA(x)$". Let $E(x)$ be the edge of the triangle x. To say that it has a length of two, is to say "$_2L(E(x))$". Now we have the assertion: if x is an equilateral triangle, then $_4TA(x) \equiv {}_2L(E(x))$; and in general, we have this relation between subscripts: If x is an equilateral triangle, then $_{n^2}TA(x) \equiv {}_nL(E(x))$. In the case of rectangles, if we denote the height of a rectangle x by "$H(x)$" and its width by "$B(x)$", we have, correspondingly,

$$(_aL(H(x)) \text{ \& } _bL(B(x))) \supset {}_{4/3\sqrt{3}\,ab}TA(x).$$

What we have is a way of calculating the subscripts which indicate the magnitude of the quantity in question. How much area? The answer is indicated by the subscript; and the subscript may be calculated by the preceding algorithm. It is simply a fact that there is a multiplication involved; but the multiplication, as it stands, has nothing to do with the quantities; we are not multiplying two lengths to get an area—indeed, observe that even if it made sense to multiply the two lengths, we would not get the number that represents the area in triangular units. All we have is an algorithm for calculating subscripts, where the subscript is an index representing the area.

In the case of squares, the relation is definitely simpler. Let "$_rA_\square(x)$" mean that x has square area r units; then if x is a square,

$$_{n^2}A_\square(x) \equiv {}_nL(H(x));$$

and for a rectangle,

$$(_aL(H(x)) \text{ \& } _bL(B(x))) \supset {}_{ab}A_\square(x).$$

To get the area of a rectangle in this system, one need merely multiply the index of the width by the index of the height. But of course one is not (not on this interpretation, as it stands) multiplying a width by a height, but two pure numbers; and what one gets is not an area, but simply another number, which serves to indicate the magnitude of an area.

Now let us introduce something quite startlingly new, the idea of *abstract quantity*. The abstract quantity of length may be construed in either of two ways: as the class of things of such and such a length, or as the property of being such and such a length. The abstract quantity *two feet long*, for example, may be taken to be the set of all things that are two feet long, or it may be taken to be the property of being two feet long. For our purposes here, either construal will do. Let the set of all these abstract quantities be denoted by "L_R", where we have chosen our unit of length to be the foot. The members of L_R—the particular quantities—will be denoted by "2 feet", "1.5 feet", etc.

Let us now define an operation, length-addition, (denoted by "$_L+$"), on these abstract objects. This length-addition of abstract objects corresponds to the physical operation of combining physical objects. We shall say that a feet $_L+ b$ feet $= c$ feet, if and only if there is an object with the property a feet and one

[76]

with the property b feet, and their colinear, juxtaposed combination has the property c feet.

Definition:

 a feet $_L+$ b feet $=$ c feet *if and only if*

$$(\exists x)(\exists y)(\exists z)(_aL(x) \ \& \ _bL(y) \ \& \ _cL(z) \ \& \ z = \text{Comb}(x,y)).$$

Observe that this would be a useless definition if physical combination did not have the properties that it in fact has. It is a fact about the world that length-addition has the following properties:

 (1) *Existence:* if $x \in L_R$ and $y \in L_R$, then there is a z such that $z \in L_R$ and $z = x_L+ y$.

This is somewhat abstract and hypothetical, but certainly true if we construe "objects" broadly enough.

 (2) *Uniqueness:* if $x \in L_R$ and $y \in L_R$ and $z = x_L+ y$ and $w = x_L+ y$, then $z = w$.

Since $x_L+ y$ is the equivalence class determined by the physical combination of an element of x and an element of y, this amounts to the stipulation that all such pairs of objects yield a combination of the same magnitude; and we can make this stipulation only because of the empirical fact that all such combinations are (essentially) indistinguishable.

 (3) *Commutativity:* $x_L+ y = y_L+ x$.

This reflects the empirical fact that it doesn't matter how you regard a combination; or, it doesn't matter which end you start measuring from.

 (4) *Associativity:* $(x_L+ y)_L+ z = x_L+ (y_L+ z)$.

In combinations of three or more things, it doesn't matter what you regard as components.

 We can also consider the sum which results when a quantity is added to itself m times, where m is a natural number. It is natural to think of this sum as m times the unit quantity. Consider the ratio r/s. We may consider a quantity such that it, added to itself s times, is the unit quantity; add together r of these quantities, and we have a quantity r/s times as big as the unit quantity. Finally, consider a sequence of rational quantities, (r_1/s_1) feet, (r_2/s_2) feet, ... (r_i/s_i) feet, ... If the limit of the ratios (r_1/s_1), (r_2/s_2), ... (r_i/s_i), ... exists and is q, then we may naturally suppose that the limit of the sequence of quantities exists and is q feet; and it is also natural to think of this quantity as q times the unit quantity.

 We may thus define the (scalar) multiplication of a quantity by a real constant, and think of the quantity k feet as k times the unit foot, or $k_s \times 1$ foot.

 I have supposed here, as we in fact do suppose, that it is reasonable to have in science a continuum of lengths. However, I initially introduced quantities as equivalence classes of objects indistinguishable in length. In proceeding from equivalence classes of objects encountered in experience (for which we do not, obviously, need more than a finite number of equivalence classes) to a set of equivalence classes which is nondenumerable, we are passing from a realm of actual objects to a realm of possible objects. Possible in what sense? In the sense that (1) any or all of those objects (equivalence classes) may consistently be supposed to exist; and (2) the existence of any finite subset of these objects conflicts with no empirical knowledge that we have. These conditions are clearly satisfied here: there is no logical reason why the universe should not contain objects of all sorts of sizes—where "all" means "a nondenumerable number of" —and no finite set of quantities will conflict with any empirical data, or any theoretical consequence that we accept, for no direct measurement need be regarded as yielding anything but one of a finite number of lengths. Much the same considerations apply to other quantities regarded as continuous. We may, in some cases, have theoretical grounds for assuming a continuum of magnitudes, but in general our assumption is one of convenience, not conflicting with what we know.

One very useful principle is the distributive principle. It is this that makes it possible to do so much of our calculation, not in quantities, but in pure numbers:

(5) *Distributive law:* a feet $_L +$ b feet $= a {\,}_s \times$ feet $_L + b {\,}_s \times$ feet $= (a + b) {\,}_s \times$ feet.

This law merely embodies the facts that we based our construction of lengths on, that were embodied also in A2″, but it enables us to do most of our calculations with pure numbers.

We can also, in a perfectly natural way, define multiplication for these abstract quantities. Let us use $_L \times$ to denote length multiplication. According to the preceding discussion,

$$a \text{ feet } _L \times b \text{ feet}$$

is the same as

$$(a {\,}_s \times \text{ feet}) {\,}_L \times (b {\,}_s \times \text{ feet}).$$

It is natural, since multiplication by a real number, $_s \times$, distributes over length addition $_L +$ by the distributive law (5), to take it also to distribute over quantity multiplication; this yields:

$$(a \times b) {\,}_s \times (\text{feet} {\,}_L \times \text{ feet}).$$

But what is the quantity (feet $_L \times$ feet)? Even independently of the use of such products in computing area, it seems perfectly reasonable to call it square feet. And "feet $_L \times$ feet $_L \times$ feet" will be cubic feet, and there is no reason why we should not continue into quadratic feet, and quintic feet, and so on.

All this has been done purely abstractly. There is no physical characteristic of anything that corresponds to five quintic feet; and similarly, there is no need for anything that corresponds to four square feet. But in fact, there is something that corresponds to the latter—area. Consider the earlier discussion of area: we uncovered the connection:

$$(_aL(H(x)) \ \& \ _bL(B(x))) \supset \ _{ab}A_\square(x),$$

where ab is just ordinary numerical multiplication. This was a way of calculating the subscripts that indicated the magnitude of the quantity, area. But in view of the fact that the unit of area has been taken to be the square foot (square if whatever length unit we have), why not regard this as a genuine multiplication (of quantities), which naturally yields precisely the same unit? That is, why not take feet times feet to be the same as square feet? For a rectangle x of height $H(x)$ and base $B(x)$, we now have the formula (using L as the function *length of*):

$$\begin{aligned} A_\square(x) &= L(H(x)) \ _L\times \ L(B(x)) \\ &= a \text{ feet } _L\times \ b \text{ feet} \\ &= ab \times (\text{feet } _L\times \text{ feet}) = ab \text{ feet}^2, \end{aligned}$$

which is just the formula we learned at school. Similarly, volume, cubic feet, comes out to correspond to feet $_L\times$ feet $_L\times$ feet. And there the chain, with ordinary experimental properties, comes to a halt. But there is no reason for us not to have at our disposal (should we want them) such quantities as feet^4, feet^5, and so on, despite the fact that they correspond to nothing in experience.

There is one more step to be made with the quantities derived directly from feet. Just as the notion of multiplication in mathematics brings in its train the notion of division, so here, where we have in general the relation

$$a \text{ feet} \times b \ Q = ab \ _s\times (\text{feet} \times Q),$$

where "Q" denotes any quantity whatever, we get the idea of solving such an equation by dividing by bQ. The subscript "s" in "$_s\times$" still serves to remind us that the multiplication is scalar—i.e., that the expression to the left of "$_s\times$" denotes a pure number; but the quantity-multiplication has dropped its subscript: the resulting unit is indicated by the units whose product it represents. In general, this form of multiplication of quantities satisfies the following laws:

$$Q_1 \times Q_2 = Q_2 \times Q_1$$
$$Q_1 \times (Q_2 \times Q_3) = (Q_1 \times Q_2) \times Q_3.$$

(There may exist multiplications of quantities for which we wish to deny one or both of these laws, but usually they hold.) Given these laws, we may use the quantity "reciprocal feet" to solve the preceding equation:

$$\begin{aligned} (a \text{ feet})^{-1} \times (a \text{ feet} \times bQ) &= (a \text{ feet})^{-1} \times [(ab) \ _s\times (\text{feet} \times Q)] \\ &= a^{-1} \times ab \ _s\times (\text{feet}^{-1} \times \text{feet} \times Q) \\ &= bQ. \end{aligned}$$

[79]

Thus, in addition to the positive exponents, we may perfectly well deal with quantities involving negative exponents. One particular way in which negative exponents come up is in connection with converting quantities expressed in one unit to quantities expressed in another unit. Thus if our original unit is feet, and we decide to have a special name for twelfths of a foot (inches), we want to be able to convert a quantity in feet to a quantity in inches, and *vice versa*. Thus we want to say:

$$a \text{ feet} \times 12 \, \frac{\text{inches}}{\text{feet}} = 12a \text{ inches.}$$

We can get at the matter directly by writing: 12 inches = 1 foot. This equation expresses the identity of two classes:

$$12 \,_s\times \text{ inches} = 1 \,_s\times \text{ feet.}$$

The abstract quantity 12 inches, is just the same as the abstract quantity 1 foot. But this is just to say (in accordance with our convenient policy of writing quantities as pure numbers multiplying a dimensional unit) that $12 \,_s\times$ inches $= 1 \,_s\times$ feet. As multiplication is well understood, so we can take again division as the inverse of multiplication, and divide by one foot or twelve inches:

$$1 = \frac{12 \,_s\times \text{ inches}}{\text{feet}}, \qquad 1 = \frac{1/12 \,_s\times \text{ feet}}{\text{inches}}.$$

Since multiplication by the number 1 alters neither numbers nor quantities, we have a convenient method of changing units.

Now we have quantitative concepts corresponding to length, and corresponding to length raised to any power, positive or negative. We can complete the picture by speaking of a quantity (any quantity) raised to the 0 power as being a pure number, viz., 1.

There are many quantities whose analysis will be nearly the same as that of length. Weights, for example, are additive in just about the same way as lengths are additive (i.e., there happens to be a simple and natural way of combining massive bodies), and gives rise to a family of quantitative predicates; and thence to a pure quantity, abstract weight. This quantity also leads to other quantitative concepts corresponding to weight raised to a power (often -1), or multiplied by another quantity (e.g., feet), or both. But just as in the case of quantities related to length, the beginning lies in ostensive comparative judgments of the form "x weighs more than y."

V

One quantity whose analysis must be slightly different, is *time*. Can one directly compare two time intervals? If they are about the right size—neither too long nor too short—and occur close enough together, we can indeed compare two time intervals. And if nothing terribly interesting or terribly dull is going on during those time intervals, our judgments will conform fairly well to the basic quantitative postulates of asymmetry and transitivity. The most immediate difference between time intervals and other quantitative concepts that we have talked of, is that we cannot move time intervals around at will, as we can move sticks (for lengths) and squares of paper (for areas) and rocks (for weights). Furthermore, an immediate logical difference is that we do not ordinarily speak of the time interval of a *thing*. We speak of the time that a certain process or a certain change takes. Most primitively: the time that it takes an object to move a certain distance.

The difficulty engendered by the fact that we cannot move time intervals around as we can move sticks and stones is not an insurmountable one. To speak of the weight of a mountain, or to compare the height of a barn in Minnesota and a pagoda in China, we cannot generally make a direct comparison, any more than we can make a direct comparison in the case of a time interval today and a time interval last year. But what we can do is to compare the duration of a process last year with the duration of a *repeatable process*; then we can repeat that process this year, simultaneously with the occurrence of a process today, and thus *indirectly* compare the duration of today's process and the duration of last year's process. Standard processes—like heartbeats, revolutions of the sun about the earth, movements of moon and planets—such things serve precisely the same function in the measurement of time as standard sticks serve in the measurement of length.

One difficulty in the measurement of time intervals, which is new in degree, but not in kind, is that the standard objects are not as easy to find. An ordinary meter stick is pretty rigid; a high-quality, steel meter stick is only slightly more accurate. But there are few regular and convenient processes in nature that can serve as standards of time intervals. Pulse beats and respirations, we know perfectly well, are irregular: we can simply judge them to be irregular. The diurnal movement of the sun seems to be regular, but it is not convenient for comparison with relatively short intervals. To construct a convenient, portable process that can be compared with other processes of various durations, is to construct a watch, which in turn embodies physical theories in which time appears as a variable. But there is no greater difficulty in principle here than in the construction of range-finders or micrometers: we use the instruments we have in order to build instruments that are better.

Congruence of time intervals raises many of the same problems, ultimately, as congruence of lengths. We can often tell, simply by looking (or enduring), that one length or time interval is greater than another, if they differ enough in magnitude; but we cannot always tell when they are the same. We thus have a little leeway for theoretical adjustments (e.g., between sidereal time and solar time), and we adopt that time as *true* which gives rise to the best or simplest physical theories. This is not the whole story—it doesn't deal with universal dilations of time or space, for example—but it will do for this time and place.

The *individuals* that a period of time or a quantity of time is a predicate of, are events or processes, rather than solid objects; but note that there is nothing untoward about this: we have already dealt with the quantitative concept of creativity, which is applicable to people, not (like length) in their role as concrete objects, but in their role as living and thinking human beings.

To begin with, then, we have

$$(1) \qquad D(x,y) \supset \sim D(y,x),$$

where "$D(x,y)$" means that the duration of event x is greater than the duration of event y, and

$$(2) \qquad (D(x,y) \ \& \ D(y,z)) \supset D(x,z).$$

As in the case of length, these principles of asymmetry and transitivity are to be understood as holding, almost always, for the relatively ostensive concept. It is generally the case that when we judge that x lasts longer than y, and that y lasts longer than z, then we judge that x lasts longer than z. But there might be circumstances in which we would make a series of three judgments that would contradict this. When we begin to treat duration as a quantity, we take (1) and (2) to hold generally, and to hold in virtue of the *meaning* of "greater than" applied to durations. "Having greater duration than" is not, at this point, a purely ostensive concept, though it still has powerful ostensive roots.

As in the case of weights and lengths, we impose on our natural concepts of duration the condition which is reflected in the transitivity of indifference:

$$(3) \qquad (\sim D(x,y) \ \& \ \sim D(y,z)) \supset \sim D(x,z).$$

Once we have a standard unit of duration, such as the day, for example, we can subdivide it into equal parts, just as we subdivided the stick. For the purpose of future comparisons, however, we can't put a half a day in our pockets as we put a half a stick in our pockets, and so the problem remains of finding a standard, recognizable process which occupies just half a day. Well, noon is recognizable, and marks the middle of the daylight day; dawn and sunset mark a couple of other boundaries. For shorter periods of time, we are pretty well stuck (since the duration of most natural processes is rather variable) until we invent a water clock or a sundial. For quite short periods of time, we can take pulse beats as a standard. The idea is that although the practical difficulties of constructing clocks are a lot more difficult than the practical difficulties of constructing yardsticks, the process is not different in principle.

The next requirement that must be met before we have a good and useful quantitative concept of time is that there be some way of juxtaposing the individuals to which the concept applies so that we can speak of the application of the concept to their combination. This is easy in the case of time, so long as we deal with processes at least one of which we can initiate: just as in the case of sticks, we need merely make the *end* of one process coincide with the *beginning* of the next, and regard the two processes as a single process. Thus there is a simple and natural form of combination of processes, such that we can consider the duration of their combination as the sum of the durations of the individual processes.

Given a unit, we thus have a way of describing, quantitatively, the duration of processes: "$_rD(x)$" means that the duration of x is r units. Furthermore, where x is the combination formed by the juxtaposition in time of the processes y and z,

$$(_rD(y) \text{ \& } _sD(z)) \supset _{r+s}D(x).$$

Just as we compounded quantitative concepts based on the concept of length, so we could compound quantitative concepts of time: we could speak of square seconds, cubic seconds, and quartic seconds. We have no call to do this; there is nothing that could be measured by such quantities in our experience. But curiously, from an abstract point of view, there are things that occur in our experience which involve units of time raised to negative powers. Consider speed.

Speed is a roughly ostensively definable concept. We can tell when one thing is moving faster than another. "Travelling faster than" is a predicate that satisfies (closely enough) the transitivity and asymmetry requirements for a quantitative relation, and it isn't hard to make it satisfy the transitivity-of-indifference requirement, too.

But there is a difficulty in the way of making this a fully quantitative concept on a direct ostensive basis: there is no natural way of combining moving objects so that the speed of the combination is the sum of the speeds of the individual objects—that is, there is no obvious way of selecting a unit speed, and referring all other speeds to that unit. But there is an alternative open to us: we may observe that the faster an object moves, the shorter the length of time it takes to cover a given distance; or, since distances are easier to measure, we can say that the faster an object moves the greater the distance it will cover in a given period of time. Thus we can take our properly scientific concept of speed to be given by *definition* as the ratio between two other quantities: distance traveled and duration of travel. Take the quantities in the form already suggested, as the product of a number and a unit. Then the ratio in question is, say

$$\frac{a_s \times \text{ feet}}{b_s \times \text{ seconds}} = (a_s \times \text{ feet}) \times (b^{-1}_s \times \text{ seconds}^{-1})$$

$$= a/b \text{ feet/second.}$$

Thus the scientific concept of speed, the defined concept, is fully quantitative, and has as units feet^1 × second^{-1}. What is the connection between this scientific concept (quasi-scientific, because the true scientific concept, which we shall come to in due course, is not speed, but instantaneous velocity) and the ostensively defined term "moving faster than"? It is perfectly straightforward: in

[83]

point of fact, almost always x is moving faster than y (in the largely ostensive sense) if and only if the speed in feet/second of x is greater than the speed in feet/second of y. As long as this relation holds, there is no conflict between our intuitive ostensively given concept of speed, and the introduced scientific one. But of course they are not precisely the same thing, as many philosophers from Bergson on have pointed out.

In a similar way, we may define the rate of change of a velocity. In ordinary language: we may distinguish between the rate at which x goes faster and faster, and the rate at which y goes faster and faster. We cannot do this often, but there are cases in which we can say (using a term which is only defined scientifically, because there isn't much use for it in ordinary observation) that x is accelerating faster than y. And we can define this (over a small period of time) as the rate at which the speed of a body is changing. The natural units of this will be (feet per second) per second; or (feet^1 × seconds^{-1}) × seconds^{-1}; or feet^1 × seconds^{-2}.

Note, finally, how the units cancel out. Suppose that x is moving at 7 feet per second for 10 seconds. To calculate the distance moved in that period, we perform the following computation with quantities:

$$\begin{aligned}
(7 \text{ feet}^1 \text{ seconds}^{-1}) \times (10 \text{ seconds}^1) &= (7 \text{ }_s\times \text{ feet}^1 \text{ seconds}^{-1}) \times (10 \text{ }_s\times \text{ seconds}^1) \\
&= (7 \times 10) \text{ }_s\times ((\text{feet}^1 \text{ seconds}^1) \text{ seconds}^{-1}) \\
&= 70 \text{ }_s\times \text{ feet}^1 (\text{seconds}^1 \text{ seconds}^{-1}) \\
&= 70 \text{ feet}.
\end{aligned}$$

To sum up, the conditions under which a quantitative concept can be based on a relatively ostensively defined relation R are

(4) $R(x,y) \supset \sim R(y,x)$ the relation must be asymmetric.

(5) $(R(x,y) \,\&\, R(y,z)) \supset R(x,z)$ the relation must be transitive.

It is not difficult to find ostensively defined predicates that have very nearly these properties; and it is a simple matter to make them conform by stipulation. But before we can have truly quantitative concepts, we must also have transitivity of indistinguishability, which is a different and more complex matter. The best observable relations fail to satisfy this relation; therefore it must always be imposed axiomatically. This amounts to saying that to call a relation quantitative means that in addition to (4) and (5), it satisfies

(6) $(\sim R(x,y) \,\&\, \sim R(y,z)) \supset \sim R(x,z)$.

Any relation that satisfies (4), (5), and (6) can give rise to equivalence (or in-difference) classes, and is thus a relation that may lead to quantities. We can identify the abstract quantities with the equivalence classes that they characterize; and we can define quantitative predicates in terms of these relations as well. We can always do this. If this is all we can do with the quantitative relation at hand the numbers we assign to the quantities are relevant only in the sense that they reflect the relations of greater or less of the original quantitative concept. This is

[84]

to say that they serve little more than an indexical function. The numerical values of these quantities do not enter into any kind of arithmetical relation with each other, except the order relation.

The best quantitative concepts satisfy another condition as well: there is a way of combining the objects (processes, individuals, events) to which the concept applies, which is such that the quantity applicable to a combination of individuals can be regarded as the sum of the quantities applicable to the individuals from which the compound is constructed. In the case of length, we have colinear juxtaposition; in the case of squares of the same size, coplanar juxtaposition; in the case of time, immediate temporal succession. When this is the case, we can define the scalar product of an ordinary number with the basic unit of the quantity, and express all values of the quantity in these terms. We can then multiply and add and divide these quantities, just as if they were numbers, making use of the distributive and commutative and associative laws of arithmetic, and keeping in mind that there is no reduction of units of one dimension to another: thus we can take feet^2 to be the product of feet and feet, feet^2 seconds^{-1} to be the product of feet, feet, and the reciprocal of seconds, and so on. Every defined quantity—area, velocity, acceleration, and as we shall see, force, work, and so on—carries with it its appropriate units. We can even define quantitative concepts that have no known application, such as quintic feet, and square seconds.

Measurement has been taken to be the central activity of science, and quantities its content. The old-line, hard-headed, materialistic scientist was the man whose constant challenge was: if it's knowable, it must be measurable; if it can't be measured, it can't matter. If we construe measurement simply as assigning numbers to things, we might well be able to make a case for this old-fashioned viewpoint; we might still be able to make a case for it if we demand in addition that the numbers reflect some perceived order among the entities to which they are applied. But as I hope the foregoing has made clear, there is a great gap between merely assigning numbers (even in some significant order) to objects of experience, and measuring them in the sense which gives rise to real quantities which can be multiplied, divided, added, subtracted, etc. In the sense in which time, mass, and distance are quantities, there are few quantities in science. But here, as so often, there is a continuum ranging from bare nonquantitative classification, to simple judgments of more and less (creativeness) to similar judgments making use of measuring instruments (I.Q.) to judgments yielding numbers that figure in general laws (temperature), to fully quantitative judgments (measurements of mass or area or velocity or duration). Sciences that employ quantitative judgments of the last sort are no doubt more powerful and more useful (they provide quantitative predictions) than sciences that do not; but we should not regard them as different in basic characteristics. This will become clearer as we explore, in the next chapter, the question of scientific terms in general.

[85]

BIBLIOGRAPHICAL NOTES TO CHAPTER 3

Good general treatments of quantity and the problems of measurement are to be found in N. R. Campbell, *Physics: the Elements* (Cambridge, England: Cambridge University Press, 1920) (republished as *Foundations of Science*, New York: Dover Publications, 1957), and in Morris R. Cohen and Ernest Nagel, *An Introduction to Logic and Scientific Method* (New York: Harcourt, Brace and World, 1934). For a detailed analysis of the problems of measuring space and time, see Adolf Grünbaum, *Philosophical Problems of Space and Time* (New York: Alfred Knopf, 1963) and Hans Reichenbach, *Philosophy of Space and Time* (New York: Dover, 1958) (German edition, 1928).

Chapter 4

SCIENTIFIC TERMS

I

This chapter will consider the general question of the nature of the terms we encounter in scientific formal systems, how they are related to each other, and how they are related to the observations on which the system is based or by reference to which it is justified. There is in any scientific system a wide variety of terms. Any sharp classification of these terms with respect to their degree of ostensiveness is difficult, for reasons which will be apparent shortly. Even the particular class of terms, the quantitative terms, that we considered in such detail in the last chapter are difficult to place in a hierarchy between *theoretical* and *observational*. We shall see that many other scientific terms share this characteristic.

One class of terms that can be isolated with relative ease and precision: the logical and mathematical terms. With respect to logical terms—the sentential connectives, like "or", "and", "if... then...", and quantifiers like "for every x..." and "there is a y..."—there is no problem. Their logical characteristics are fully determined by the formal systems which characterize their technical counterparts, "$\vee$", "$\&$", "$\supset$", "(x)", "$(\exists y)$", etc. There is nothing in the world to which these signs refer, by themselves, although of course they function as essential components of statements which do refer to the world. It is a matter of taste, or perhaps a matter of opinion, whether mathematical terms are regarded in this same light or not. I shall suppose that they are, and lump them together with the logical signs here; but I shall reopen the question in the chapter devoted to mathematics, Chapter 8.

Geometrical terms may or may not be included among the logical-mathematical terms. If the geometrical terms are regarded as *uninterpreted*, as they often are in abstract treatments of geometry, no question can arise as to whether they are empirical or not; this question can only be raised with respect to *interpreted* terms. Geometrical terms admit of two relatively standard interpretations, one empirical and one nonempirical. If geometrical terms are interpreted by reference to other mathematical entities, as is done in analytical geometry where we take a point to be a pair of real numbers (coordinates), and where we take a straight line to be a linear equation in two variables, and so on, then the geometrical terms are nonempirical, and are to be classified with the mathematical terms. On the other hand, if the geometrical terms are given physical interpretations—i.e., if they are intended to apply to "physical space"—then they must be treated like other empirical scientific terms, and their connections with entities of ordinary experience (lines drawn on paper, flat surfaces, beams of light, or whatever) must be spelled out. Because geometrical terms admit a number of interpretations, a whole chapter (Chapter 9) will be devoted to geometry.

Leaving geometry to one side, what is far more interesting and problematic than the interpretation of the logical and mathematical signs in the general consideration of scientific formal systems is the interpretation of the nonlogical signs. I have in mind such terms as "electron", "mammal", "compound (chemical)", "mass", "oviparous", and so on, as well as such common terms as "red", "lightbulb", "dog", and "rat", and such designating expressions as "John W. Smith", "New York", "this crow", "that thermometer now", and so on. I shall consider three classes of nonlogical terms, but it must be remembered that the classification is a very rough one. The three classes are: (1) observational terms, like "red", "hot", "smooth", which can generally be applied veridically on sensual grounds (as we saw in the last chapter some of the most important observational terms are relations, like "longer than", or "heavier than"); (2) ordinary language terms, or terms closely related to them that are not purely observational, but exhibit some theoretical meaning, in the sense that more is implied by the application of the term than meets the eye or ear (thus when we attribute *anger* to a person, we mean to do more than characterize his facial expression or his tone of voice; we imply that he will react in certain ways to certain kinds of stimulation, or even that he is in a certain mental state); and (3) technical and specialized terms like "magnetic field strength", "electric current", and so on, that are introduced only into an abstract theoretical framework.

One reason that this classification is not a hard and sharp one, is that science, by its very nature, is in a state of change and flux. A science claimed to be in its final form would not be science, but dogma; the crucial characteristic of science is its sensitivity to experience and experiment, its susceptibility to modification. A classification of the sort suggested can only hold good (if it can hold good at all) for a particular formal system at a particular time. Thus at a certain stage in the development of natural history, the term "bear" is simply an observational term—or at any rate, more of an observational term than a theoretical term. To say of something that it looked, smelled, and acted like a bear, but was *really* not a bear, would be to invite (quite properly) ridicule. To cut it open subsequently and find a lot of springs and gears and cogs would show that you were right, after all; and this in turn shows that the word "bear" even at an early stage of the development of natural history, was already a word bearing some theoretical import. But nowadays it makes perfectly good sense to speak of something that looks and smells and acts like a bear, being in reality something quite different: a different species of animal, in fact.

The theoretical content of a term is hard to specify exactly; roughly it amounts to what you would know *a priori* about an object to which the term correctly applied—i.e., what you would know on the basis of the *meaning* of the term, and not on the basis of empirical knowledge you might have connecting that term to other terms. Thus it is part of the theoretical meaning of the term "bear", that anything that is a bear is flesh and blood, and not clockwork. More technically, it is part of the meaning of "bear" that its young are nourished within the maternal uterus until they are highly developed; that it is capable of digesting meat; that in normal locomotion its heel rests upon the ground. No creature, no matter how bearlike in appearance, that lacked these characteristics could be classified in the family *Ursidae*. To put the matter dramatically: twenty-five hundred years ago it was a matter of *fact* that bears did not lay eggs; it was no part of the *meaning* of the term "bear" that it applied only to placental mammals. Now the meaning of the term has changed; now it is a matter of meaning alone that bears do not lay eggs. Anything that laid an egg would be incorrectly classified as a bear.

Pursuing this will eventually lead us to the knotty biological or philosophical (as the case may be) problem of speciation. At the moment, it should merely be noted that the burden of theory that a given term of science carries varies with the state of the system in which it occurs; and that since scientific systems constantly change, that state will vary with time. This is not to say that

[89]

it is not worthwhile getting clear about just what the theoretical content of a given term is, or might be, at a given time; it is to say that there is a certain arbitrariness in such a theoretical content; and it is also to say that ordinary usage—even scientific usage in the past—is not a sure guide in itself to this content in the present. This is true not only of ordinary language terms, but also of technical terms and observational terms. It is also true of the classification of given terms: "water" is an ordinary language term having some theoretical meaning; at an early stage of science it was a relatively observational term; in physics or chemistry it is now a theory loaded term: water is the oxide of hydrogen, and it fits into a system of physics, physical chemistry, etc., in a certain way.

Every scientific system contains ordinary language terms. Even such a fancy system as physics, which can talk, in its theory, primarily about quantities and other such abstract entities, must descend to ordinary language terms when it describes experiments, and when it is concerned with specific events in the real world. All scientific systems, in the beginning, are simply codifications in ordinary language of ordinary observations about the subject matter in question. Ordinary language terms do not, of course, retain their ordinary meaning unchanged when they enter into a scientific system. And of course there is, properly speaking, no time at all when a given word is not part of a scientific system. To know how to use a word is to be familiar enough with its applications to know something already about the way the objects to which it applies behave, for example, and this is already science. But as the formal scientific system develops, there is a constant change in the meaning of the word. The meaning, then, cannot be given as ostensively as it once could. A term which is observational (or very nearly observational) is one whose meaning is given largely by ostensive means. An observational term is the kind of term that was once said to be defined ostensively; the word "defined" is an unfortunate one in this context, however, because one ordinarily defines by means of words rather than by means of things or qualities, whereas ostensive definition (so-called) is very often partial, and is accompanied by partial verbal definition: "*This* is longer than *that*, and that *means* (implies) that *that* is not longer than *this*." Instances are *exhibited* at the same time transitivity (for example) is *stipulated*. Clearly there is a sense in which the whole enterprise of science depends on, is hung onto, the meanings of terms of this relatively ostensive or observational sort which provide the most direct connection between (verbal) knowledge and observational experience.

II

To illustrate the way in which terms are adapted from ordinary language to serve in scientific formal systems, let us examine some typical examples in detail. The preceding chapter was concerned with quantitative terms, and, illustratively,

[90]

with the development of quantitative length terms out of the observationally given, relatively ostensive, relation, *longer than*, already present in ordinary language. But there is a whole complex of terms in ordinary language that involve the same concept as "length": "shorter than", "long", "very long", "short", "very short", "small", "large", and so on. These terms (with the exception of "shorter than") are *systematically ambiguous*, as well as ambiguous in a *nonsystematic way*. They are systematically ambiguous, in the sense that the term that is modified by an adjective determines, to some extent, the meaning of that adjective: thus a small elephant is an object of greater length (say) than a large dog. The ambiguity here is systematic, in the sense that no one who knows the meaning of the terms involved is going to think that because he can lift a large dog with difficulty, he can lift a small elephant easily. The terms of ordinary language, "large" and "small", "long" and "short", have ordinary language meanings that vary systematically with the context in which they are used. This systematic ambiguity of these terms is one of the things that makes them broadly useful, and the language in which they occur powerful. If it were not for this ambiguity, we would need different adjectives to describe a short man and a short blade of grass. ("Short change" is something else again.)

But they also are ambiguous in a less felicitous way. They are idiosyncratically ambiguous. What you mean by "large" in the phrase "large dog" may be quite different from what I mean by "large" in that same context. This idiosyncratic ambiguity, the fact that no two people use any ostensively defined term in quite the same way, infects all of the empirical terms of ordinary language, and continues, as we shall see, to infect the observational terms of a scientific language. Nevertheless, the scientific length concept can be made to do the work of all of the above terms (or a part of their work, since a term like "large" involves or may involve mass or volume as well as any one of several linear dimensions) without recourse to systematic ambiguity, and with a minimum of idiosyncratic ambiguity. We shall say then that the scientific term has greater *interpersonal uniformity* than the ordinary language term. This concept of interpersonal uniformity is one that we shall find very useful in what follows; it is worthwhile to give it an explicit definition here.

One term t has a greater degree of *interpersonal uniformity* than another term t', when there is less variability (not merely less variation) in its application by different individuals. It is possible to spell this out quasi-scientifically: term t has greater interpersonal uniformity than term t', if there is a large number of possible circumstances under which people who understood both t and t' would apply both terms, if there is a number of possible circumstances under which people would agree in their application of t, but under which there would be much disagreement about the application of t', and if there is no significant number of circumstances under which people would agree in the application of t' but disagree concerning the applicability of t. "Significant disagreement" about the application of a term t might be defined statistically as: 25 per cent of the group of people would apply t (withhold t) in instances in which 75 per cent would withhold t (apply t).

Now we cannot, of course, replace the "short" of ordinary language with a particular length term. What we can do, however, is, whenever there is question about the meaning of a particular occurrence of the word "short", replace it by the corresponding length term. And this indeed is what is done in a scientific context: "The ears of the XXX-rabbit are short (averaging 3.7 cm.)." There is no reason, therefore, to include such ordinary language terms as "long", "short", ... etc, in our scientific formal system, once we have included the set of length terms. The ordinary language terms are used in scientific work and discourse only where their meaning is clear, and even in such contexts they are usually explained parenthetically, as above.

Of the family of related length terms, not all can be eliminated in favor of real number length properties, or real number quantities. In particular, the relational terms: "shorter than", "longer than", "the same length as", cannot be replaced by quantitative terms in all contexts. All of these terms can be defined in terms of one another: we want to say that x is longer than y if and only if y is shorter than x; and that x is the same length as y if and only if x is neither longer nor shorter than y. Therefore we need consider only one term, "longer than". "Longer than" is a fine example of an observational term in science, or at any rate, a term that is at least as purely observational as any other, barring such psychological terms as "looks longer than". We cannot dispense with it, for immediate judgments of the form "x is longer than y" are required for measurement, and measurement in turn is required for the replacement of the simple qualitative terms "long", "short", etc. On the other hand, as soon as "longer than" has any logical properties at all—such as transitivity (not to mention transitivity of the relational complement, "not longer than")—it is no longer strictly speaking a purely observational predicate. Any immediate judgment of the form "X is longer than Y" may some day come into conflict with a pair of judgments, just as immediate, of the form "Y is longer than Z" and "Z is longer than X". It is this fact which already introduces uncertainty into measurement, and thus, in turn into the application of the numerical correlates of the ordinary language terms "long", "short", etc.

Observe what has happened. We began (hypothetically, illustratively, but not historically) with a large family of length-type predicates, interpreted relatively ostensively, and therefore relatively incapable, in themselves, of being misapplied. (I am not sure this is altogether true; but the state of Arcadian innocence that I am describing is so foreign to our experience that it might perfectly well be true.) The fact that one person might apply such a predicate in a case where another might withhold it, is simply due here to the ambiguity of the terms themselves: "long" means different things to different people, even in the same

[92]

context. Now we replace all of those terms by a single relational term, "longer than", which is such that there is a great deal of uniformity in its application: i.e., we replace these terms by a single term of vastly increased interpersonal uniformity. There is a price, of course. The term that we replace the others by is a term that is both partly ostensive and also forms part of a formal structure in which certain stipulations must be satisfied. In the new language "longer than" has a number of logical properties (e.g., irreflexivity) which hold not merely almost always in point of fact, but always in virtue of its (new) meaning. These properties can only be supposed to hold in virtue of the meaning of the term, if we give up the claim that applications of the term can be made with certainty. The term is no longer ambiguous—and neither are the terms that it replaces, which used to be ambiguous. (There is nothing at all ambiguous about having a length of 7.5 cm.) In place of ambiguity, however, we have uncertainty. We could be perfectly certain that Rover's tail was long; we cannot be perfectly certain that Rover's tail is exactly $14\frac{1}{8}$ inches long. One advantage of suffering uncertainty, rather than ambiguity, is that the uncertainty can be measured and controlled, and even in many cases, reduced, by mechanical procedures. We have traded ambiguity for uncertainty, and interpersonal variation for interpersonal uniformity. We have obtained a system with a powerful and useful internal structure, but we have lost the direct connection to observational experience. Notice that we have really, altogether, lost this connection. There is no observation that can insure that x is the same length as y. What we observe can serve as a strong indication that x is about the same length as y; but both the "strong indication" and the "about" need to be spelled out at length; to do so (as we will later) is to look into the theory of errors.

III

Temperature is a quantitative concept occurring in our scientific formal systems that has many properties in common with length, but it is significantly different in one important respect: temperature is not easily additive in the sense that length is. Out of two objects of lengths m feet and n feet, we can some-sometimes construct an object of length $(m + n)$ feet merely by juxtaposing the objects. But out of two objects of m degrees and n degrees, there is no ordinary way in which we can construct an object of $m + n$ degrees. (There are unusual ways of combining objects in such a way that the temperature of the combination is the sum of the temperatures of the components: one, suggested by Wesley Salmon, is to take equal amounts of water at 50°C, put them in a pot over a fire, and let them come to a boil.) Observe that we cannot always physically add two lengths—in fact, it is fairly rare when we can. The physical addition of two lengths depends on the fact that the objects can be manipulated; that they are rigid enough to be moved about; that juxtaposing them does not cause any untoward reactions: chemical or physical or biological. But although we can never

[93]

add temperatures as simply as we sometimes do lengths, temperature is still one of the most stable and useful quantitative concepts we have; and it is worth reviewing its development from, and relation to, ostensively defined predicates.

The basic relations from which the concept of temperature is developed are those of "warmer than" and "colder than". These are terms familiar to everyone, and come readily into the language on an ostensive basis. It is generally true that "warmer than" is irreflexive: nothing is warmer than itself. (There are exceptions: put one hand in hot water and the other in cold, then both into lukewarm water: it will feel warm to one hand and cool to the other, and thus, in a sense, warmer than itself.) Furthermore, within the limits of ordinary ambiguity and vagueness, the relation is transitive: if x is warmer than y, and y warmer than z, then x will generally turn out to be warmer than z. Just as in the case of judgments of the form "x is longer than y," these relational judgments suggest taking as a theoretical relation, a "warmer than" which is irreflexive and transitive in virtue of its meaning.

Even in the most ordinary of parlance, there are two standard reference temperatures: boiling hot, and freezing cold. These do not lead to equivalence classes of temperatures, because there are all kinds of temperatures above and below them that we can recognize. In special contexts, we do have equivalence classes: for baking, cookbooks distinguish just four degrees of hotness: very hot, hot, moderate, and slow. For frying on a griddle, there are two or three degrees of hotness. But in order to construct general equivalence classes of warmths, we need to do more than suppose that "not warmer than" as well as "warmer than" is transitive: we need some permanent way of identifying particular equivalence classes of warmths.

In the case of lengths we found certain kinds of objects that were fairly resistant to change and fairly rigid, whose length appeared sensibly constant regardless of the environment about them. In the case of warmth, we have a few such things, but very few. The temperature of certain springs, for example, seems to stay constant; the temperature of a large body of water stays constant over fairly long periods of time (weeks or months; some places indefinitely); boiling and freezing water each seem to be always about the same temperature; the human body maintains a constant temperature. But these few points don't suffice to construct a scale of temperatures, because we can neither find nor construct objects with permanent intermediate temperatures. This is not a problem of additivity, notice: we could construct a fine temperature scale if we lived in a region, for example, with a hundred springs of water, each of a sensibly different temperature, whose temperatures did not vary with the seasons. To live near such a set of springs would not make temperature easily additive.

In point of fact, we do not have a temperature *scale* until we relate temperature to some other quantity: length or time or volume or force. We standardize oven temperatures by measuring the time it takes to bake a standard sample of standard dough, making use of the generalization already present in the ordinary use of temperature concepts, that the hotter the oven, the less time it will take for the dough to turn brown. We measure the heat of a griddle by the time it takes for a drop of water to evaporate, again making use of a generalization: the hotter the griddle, the faster the water will evaporate. We could use the force with which a bimetallic strip pushes on a spring (measured in turn by the deformation of the spring); we could use the volume of a standard quantity of gas under standard pressure; we could use the length of a steel bar, if we had constructed some machine that would serve to magnify the changes in length to the point where they are easily observable; we could use the length of time that it takes a standard block of ice to melt. Historically, the most important scheme for measuring temperature is the liquid thermometer. Let us take for our purposes a mercury thermometer. I do not pretend to anything like historical accuracy here: remember that we are concerned not with the actual sequence of events, but with a possible and natural sequence of ideas. In point of fact, of course, the development of the mercury thermometer goes hand in hand with the development of an increasingly useful temperature scale. Here (as is usual) instrumentation and theory develop simultaneously; but I shall suppose that we have the instrument, ready made, and consider the development of the corresponding conceptual structure.

Here is a glass bulb, let us say, with a long smooth neck. The bulb is full of mercury.

A. We notice that the length of the column of mercury in the neck varies as our judgment of temperature. Within the ranges we can judge, if a is warmer than b, then the juxtaposition of the bulb with a will eventually be followed by the mercury climbing to a higher point in the neck than it does when the bulb is juxtaposed to b. In other words, height of mercury corresponds to temperature, at least so far as our ostensively given transitive relation, "warmer than", is concerned.

B. "Not higher than" corresponds to "either lower than or not noticeably different from in temperature". This suggests already that we can use our thermometer to establish equivalence classes. The transitivity of indifference will not be perfectly satisfied here (any more than in the case of length) but it comes close. And we can always blame any failures on faulty judgment of the height.

C. Furthermore, we notice that definite points on the thermometer correspond to the colloquial "freezing cold" and "boiling hot": when our instrument is put into a bath of ice and water, the mercury always falls to about the same point, regardless of the surrounding temperature, the proportions of water and ice, or indeed whether the ice is melting or the water freezing. Similarly, when it is put into boiling water, the mercury climbs to about the

[95]

same point, regardless of whether the water is boiling fast or slowly. The same thing is true of other substances: boiling alcohol, for example, or acetone, or a solution of nitric acid of given concentration, etc. Observe, however, a kind of harmless circularity: for we do not have alcohol (pure alcohol) or nitric acid, or acetone, until we have a fair amount of chemistry; and we cannot have this amount of chemistry without a relatively sharp concept of temperature. This is not a vicious circularity: all we really want is pure water to freeze and boil, and rainwater, snow, often spring water, is quite pure enough for our present purposes. There are variations in boiling point according to the barometric pressure (i.e., according to the weather), according to impurities, according to altitude above sea level, and so on. Nonetheless, the boiling point is constant enough that we can form the idea that water boils at a fixed temperature.

D. The next idea is to divide the length of the tube between the freezing and boiling points into equal intervals, and to let these correspond to equal increments of temperature. That this is plausible can be established merely by the fact that it does not conflict with our intuited temperatures: boiling is too damned hot, and freezing is too damned cold; if you mix equal quantities of water at these extremes, they ought to average out, and sure enough the resulting mixture is neither too hot nor too cold, and does make the mercury rise about halfway between the lower point and the upper point. This is a pleasant coincidence—but note that having a temperature scale does not depend on this fact: it might be that the specific heat of water varied greatly with its temperature, so that it takes as much heat to raise a quantity of water from 90°C to 100°C, as it does to raise it for 0°C to 90°C. Indeed this is suggested by the length of time it takes to boil water over a fire: it quickly gets to steaming; needs much longer to get to boiling. Even if this were the case, the simple and natural thing would be to divide the interval between the freezing and boiling points into equal segments.

E. We can extend the markings below the 0 point and above the boiling point. This is quite sufficient to provide a basis for a theoretical concept of temperature. (Heat, remember, is something else again.) Within a certain range, mercury thermometers agree with each other pretty well, just as, within a certain range of lengths, the results of laying down footrules over and over again, generally agree within reasonable limits. The range is limited, of course; it is limited at the extremes by changes of state of mercury, its boiling point and freezing point. And as these extremes are approached, the behavior of thermometers becomes a little erratic. But as long as we stay well within this range, not only do all thermometers agree pretty well, but the numerical laws to which we are led are many, simple, and interesting. We can determine the existence and value (within this range) of coefficients of thermal expansion for various substances, including (important for our

[96]

measurement of temperature) the self-same glass of which thermometers are made. We can determine what we now call the specific heats of substances, so that we can predict the temperature of a mixture of components of given substances at given temperatures, e.g., equal parts of water at 10°C and 30°C will yield a quantity of water at 20°C. We can determine heats of crystallization and of vaporization, so that we can predict the temperature that will result from mixing given quantities of ice and water at given temperatures, or the temperature that will result from mixing given quantities of water and steam at given temperatures. All of these laws will be expressed in terms of the abstract quantity, temperature, which will have been defined in a manner similar to that in which the abstract quantity length was defined, as an equivalence class of (possible) bodies at the same temperature.

Before going on to the next development of the temperature concept, let us pause to notice that we have been able to discuss it in the same way as other quantitative concepts: we begin with a relation that is given quite ostensively ("warmer than"), together with a number of cognate terms ("hot", "cold", "lukewarm"), which are also given ostensively; all these terms are ambiguous and vague. We have a set of temperature-type terms that are highly variable in their use from person to person; they have little interpersonal uniformity. We take one of these terms ("warmer than") that has a relatively high degree of interpersonal uniformity. We discover a way of making even this term far more precise, by finding a related term, "makes the mercury rise higher in the thermometer", that has an even higher degree of interpersonal uniformity, on the basis of which we arrive, by idealization if you will, at the abstract idea of temperature as equivalence classes of objects of the *same* temperature. This term, "having a temperature of n degrees centigrade", is a term that cannot be applied directly on an ostensive basis; we can never be certain that a given body has the property denoted by that term—i.e., belongs to the equivalence class we think it belongs to. But the uncertainty involved in the application of the term is made up for by the very high degree of interpersonal uniformity of related terms: the temperature is 24°C, A is hotter than B, X melts at 48°C, C is the same temperature as D. Furthermore, the uncertainty can be reduced, if we wish, by using better thermometers, by using more of them, by using thermometers with bigger bulbs and tubes with finer, more uniform holes in them, by taking a number of comparable readings. At the same time, we have replaced the vague and general theoretical dimension of these temperature-type words by a vast and intricate theoretical framework. The new theoretical term "temperature" becomes the *standard* of all the ordinary, once ostensive terms.

F. The next obvious improvement in the temperature concept is to break the hold of the traditional mercury thermometer. There is no reason why the

[97]

abstract quantity cannot be defined for all kinds of ranges: for arbitrarily low temperatures and arbitrarily high ones. Even though we only know how to test for sameness of temperature in the range suitable to mercury thermometers, there is no reason why we cannot talk of temperatures of 10,000°C, or −200°C, or (at this point) −1000°C. To say that a body is at −1000°C is to say that it belongs to a certain equivalence class of objects. Whether there is any physical object ever in that class, and how we would tell if a given object were in that class, is unknown, at this point. We break the hold of the traditional thermometer, by accepting as true certain laws that relate the behavior of substances to temperature changes: thermoelectric effects, for example, can be correlated with changes in temperature; the differential expansion of two bonded metallic strips produces measurable stresses and strains that can be correlated with temperatures; the pressure of a fixed volume of gas (provided it is not too dense) varies with the temperature. Many of these things can be rendered neatly linear within the range of the mercury thermometer. What more natural than to stipulate that they are (ideally) linear elsewhere too? And this gives us means of measuring temperatures well outside of the mercury thermometer range. Indeed, as the network of laws involving temperature expands, we can find within this network the means of measuring temperatures from absolute 0, −273°C, to the temperature of the interior of the sun. These are perfectly good temperatures: they are derived from computations involving laws no more and no less than the temperatures that we attribute to the interior of a pizza oven or a deep-freeze; it is merely that the particular temperatures involved are considerably more removed from our own sensations of heat and cold.

Absolute 0, the rock bottom minimum temperature, figures in a number of laws. The simplest and most important of these are the gas laws which lead to the gas thermometer. In the mercury thermometer range, we find that for nondense gasses at constant volume, a change in pressure (in pounds per square inch, say) is a linear function of a change in temperature. The neat linear equation at which we arrive is one that predicts no pressure at −273°C. Below that temperature, pressure becomes negative; but this doesn't make any sense. The same is true of the temperature–volume relation: if temperatures could go below −273°C, we would have to tolerate negative volumes. Of course we *could* say simply that these particular equations (they are in fact really just one equation) don't hold at such low temperatures. But there are other equations—relating temperature to the difference of electric potential between two metal strips, relating radiation and absorption of heat between black bodies, relating electrical resistance to temperature, etc.—that have this same curious property: they imply, if they are regarded as holding generally, that there is an absolute minimum of temperature at −273°C.

IV

Consider a different kind of term, "intelligent". This is the sort of term, like "long", that is learned more or less ostensively: you simply learn by observation that John and Peter are intelligent; that June is stupid; that Mary is smarter than Joe. All of these terms: "intelligent", "stupider", etc., can be learned and used on a relatively ostensive basis. Again, as in the case of length, in real life things are not quite so simple: there is no theory-free use of any term, and thus no *purely* ostensive use; this is particularly the case with complicated terms, like "intelligent", that refer to whole patterns of behavior. Thus we can't really tell that John is intelligent by looking at him, though at this stage of inquiry, we can tell with reasonable accuracy that he is intelligent by being acquainted with him. Now just as in the case of "longer than", "more intelligent than" has some of the properties of a quantitative relational term: it is irreflexive (nobody, alas, is more intelligent than himself); it is generally transitive: if we judged x more intelligent than y, and y more intelligent than z, but judged x as *not* more intelligent than z, we would be rather surprised that our judgments had come out this way, and we might even have a tendency to withdraw one. At the extremes of intelligence (barring deviant cases such as geniuses and idiot-savants) there is a high degree of interpersonal uniformity: there is a wide variety of cases in which teachers agree uniformly that Johnny is smarter than Susan. There is also a wide variety of cases in which the difference is not pronounced: some teachers think Alice is smarter than Peter, and some think the opposite, and some don't know. There is even, perhaps, some vague theoretical framework supporting the details of ordinary usage: it may be noticed that children of intelligent parents are intelligent; that a pupil who is judged intelligent in one field of endeavor is generally (not always, to be sure) judged intelligent in other fields of endeavor; that a student who is intelligent at the age of five will also be intelligent at the age of fifteen and at the age of twenty-five. (After this, of course, occupational senility may set in; but even now we have no theoretical account of this phenomenon.)

This is the kind of situation in which the introduction of a quantitative term is often constructive and useful; and it was to do just this that intelligence tests were developed. In the picture that I have given of the development of scientific language toward interpersonal uniformity, note that the test cannot be simply *proposed*; not any old test will do. It must be one which satisfies two general criteria: First, where the old relation "is more intelligent than" is almost universally agreed to hold (e.g., between Tom, who is at the head of his class, although he doesn't work hard, and is very naughty, and Peter, who is very hard-working and really does the best he can, but who is still in the bottom quarter), the test must reflect this relation; and in the case of instances that are *generally* held to satisfy the relation denoted by "more intelligent than", we want most of them to test appropriately, although if there are a few exceptions, we won't discard the test. Second, we want the test results to fit in with the vague theoretical background of the vague ordinary language term," more intelligent than". Thus (since we are quantifying intelligence) we of course make the demands that are required for any numerical predicate: transitivity, transitivity of the relational complement, and so on. But we also would like such vague, general, observations as "the children of intelligent parents tend to be intelligent," "a child's position on the intelligence scale, relative to his contemporaries, does not generally change with age," to continue to be confirmed.

Intelligence tests do satisfy these criteria: children who are smarter in the ordinary language sense (by whatever criteria people apply who try to teach them things) generally turn out to be indeed smarter by the tests. If person A is very definitely and obviously smarter than B, in an ordinary language sense, or in the less ambiguous sense in which teachers use "smarter than", then A's I.Q. will definitely be higher than B's. In the majority of cases in which A is just generally judged to be smarter than B, his I.Q. will still test out higher. And often, in cases of conflict between test result and observation, we have an explanation: the individual concerned has a complex which causes him to become rattled when he sees paper, or he is unfamiliar with the language, or he has a personal dislike for the tester, or he comes from an economically (and thus culturally) deprived segment of the population, or.... These causes of discrepancy reflect further vague theoretical generalizations concerning the relation between intelligence and test-taking ability.

The theoretical criterion that was taken most seriously in the development of intelligence tests, in point of historical fact, was the invariance of intelligence with age. It was supposed that knowledge is acquired in a more or less linear fashion for the first fifteen years of life, and tests were constructed to measure knowledge; divide by age, and we get I.Q. And in fact, tests have been developed which do satisfy the criterion of invariance with age very well. Furthermore, it does turn out (generally) that intelligent parents have intelligent children.

It has been said by some psychologists that "intelligence" is just that which I.Q. tests measure. In a certain sense that is true: just as length is that which yardsticks measure. It is certainly true that, so far as the technical vocabulary of psychology is concerned, we can replace the whole cluster of vague ordinary language terms: "intelligent", "unintelligent", "smart", "more intelligent than", "stupider than", "average", etc., by terms defined by reference to I.Q. But just as length expressions became precise at the cost of uncertainty in their application, so I.Q. is precise, but uncertain in its application. It makes perfectly good sense to say of a given person that his I.Q. is 110, though he has been tested five times, and always scored between 67 and 73; but what is said is very improbable. The concept of intelligence, like the concept of temperature and like the concept of length, has become theoretical, and thus lost all of its direct ostensive connection to ordinary experience: it is a theoretical and probabilistic question, whether a given individual does or does not have a given degree of

[100]

intelligence. The new terms, the terms defined by I.Q., are terms that have very precise meanings: there is no vagueness in their application.

We have replaced terms which have a low degree of interpersonal uniformity by terms that have a very high degree of interpersonal uniformity. Although the application of these terms is infected with uncertainty, just as the application of precise length terms or precise temperature terms is infected with uncertainty, it is an uncertainty that can be measured and controlled, as we shall see later, and that moreover is essentially the same for all people. Although people may disagree very much about how intelligent (in the ostensive sense of the word) John is, there is not much room for disagreement about his score on an intelligence test. (There is some room because mistakes can be made in counting; a blurry mark may be taken as a correct answer, an incorrect answer, or no answer at all, and so on.) The relation between the test score and the I.Q. is one that admits error; just as in measuring a table we must distinguish between the result of a particular measurement and the actual length of the table, so here we must distinguish between the test score and the actual I.Q. Nevertheless, the measurement provides strong probabilistic evidence concerning the length, and similarly, the test score provides strong probabilistic evidence concerning I.Q. The technical term, "I.Q.", has a very high degree of interpersonal uniformity, in the sense that (1) people can agree very easily and very closely on the outcome of a given measurement of I.Q., and (2) the I.Q. that it is reasonable to attribute to a given individual generally depends only on the result of such measurements.

Intelligence thus *is* what intelligence tests measure; but some tests are better than others, the result of no test is infallible, we can look forward to better tests of intelligence than we have now (which will not necessarily require that we have a different concept of intelligence), and perhaps we can even look forward to physiological tests of intelligence. But all this is merely to say that intelligence is a theoretical concept, like length.

Although length, temperature, and I.Q. are all quantitative, and all have a very high degree of interpersonal uniformity, and all have a theoretical background that makes them important and interesting quantitative concepts, there are important differences among them. As we have already noticed there is an important difference between temperature and length: there is a natural way of adding lengths (and weights); there is no natural way of adding temperatures. There is therefore less theoretical structure connected with the concept of temperature in itself, than there is connected with the concept of length. But there are many other quantities that vary linearly with temperature, just as there are many quantities that vary with length (or volume or area). If we consider not merely the concept itself, but the framework of physical laws that it is employed in, we find that the quantitative concept of temperature is a very rich and fruitful one. The simplest physical law is this: there are many instances in which change in length and change in temperature are directly proportional.

[101]

As there is no way of adding bodies so that the temperature of the combination is the sum of the temperatures of the parts, so there is no way of adding people so that the intelligence of the combination is the sum of the intelligences of the parts. (Indeed, it is well known that it works the other way about: the collective intelligence of a committee is inevitably and necessarily less than that of the least intelligent member.) But more than this, there is no large network of simple laws in which I.Q. enters, as there is in the case of temperature. The only thing that is directly linearly related to I.Q. is performance on I.Q. tests. Even here, there are instances in which performance on tests is held not to indicate intelligence—e.g., in the special cases I mentioned before. There are a number of things that are statistically correlated with intelligence: success in school, success in later life, marital discord, bastardy, ability to learn, etc. But in almost every case there are a number of other factors than intelligence that are also important. There is no body of psychological laws that have the form $X = k(\text{I.Q.}) + c$, where k and c are constants, and X is some other quantitative concept.

Observe, furthermore, that while "length" and "temperature", as defined in relation to measuring operations, can replace all of the cognate terms of ordinary language for the purpose of scientific discourse, the same thing is not true of the defined "intelligence", which is defined for people only. It would not make sense to apply the same sort of criteria to a dog or a rat or a horse, though it makes perfectly good ordinary language sense to distinguish between intelligent dogs and not-so-intelligent dogs, and the same with other species. As for cross species comparisons, things get a little foggy. They are made, but there is very little uniformity of opinion about them. Perhaps they are pointless: if a particular rat was as slow in learning a maze as a dog that we judge to be intelligent, we would take the rat to be retarded; but conversely, if a particular dog were as hard to train to retrieve as a particular rat that we classify as "very intelligent", we would regard that dog as hopelessly stupid.

To sum up the discussion so far: length, temperature, and I.Q., all have a certain amount of theoretical structure built into them, although they vary greatly both with respect to internal structure, and with respect to theoretical fruitfulness. But they have one supremely important thing in common: they all have a very high degree of interpersonal uniformity compared to the relatively ostensive, ordinary language terms that they replace.

V

Not all technical scientific terms are quantitative; indeed by far the greatest part of them are not. Nevertheless, the same analysis in terms of theoretical fruitfulness and interpersonal uniformity can be applied to them. The same replacement of ostensiveness and ambiguity and vagueness, by clarity, precision, and uncertainty, takes place with nonquantitative terms as takes place with quantitative terms.

[102]

Sometimes we are lead to quantitative replacements for qualitative terms. Consider color terms, for example. There is nothing more firmly based on ordinary language than the usage of color terms; nor anything more clearly ostensive in definition. And yet they are subject to quite a variation among people: the degree of interpersonal variation for color terms is fairly high. But just as "has the same length as" has a high degree of interpersonal uniformity, so does "has the same color as"; and this leads to the use of samples as standards for comparison: color swatches. This is what is used in judging colors of fabrics, for example, and even in certain quantitative chemical tests. These are not always the best and most desirable tests, because there may be more variation about matching colors than there is about counting, for example, or reading a buret, which is essentially a length judgment, and some people are left out of account by the color matching test, because they happen to be color blind.

The replacement of a direct color judgment by a color matching judgment is already essentially quantitative. Indeed, in many industries, the replacement of a descriptive name by a number (color 317, color 218) satisfies some of the criteria for quantitative judgments. Assigning numbers to the colors is arbitrary, and this has been said to render such an assignment not really quantitative. But observe that the assignment of numbers to lengths is arbitrary too; even if we accept the principle that if x and y have the same length m, their juxtaposed colinear combination will have the length $2m$, the choice of a unit is still arbitrary. It is true that there is a natural order among lengths; but we can find a natural order among colors, too: for the dyer will find it advantageous, if he has many colors, to group them so that 100s are shades of gray, 300s are shades of blue, 500s are shades of green, 700s shades of yellow, 900s shades of red, and so on. In this scheme, the number of a color is no more arbitrary than the number of an I.Q., and certainly does give some information about the color. We only know what it really means, in a sense, when we see the color that corresponds to the number; but we only know what a temperature of 146°F *really* means when we have felt warm water of that temperature. For that matter, we only know what a yard really is when we've seen a yardstick. The order of colors is not very significant, and if significant order is taken to be of the essence of quantities, these numbers are *merely* indexical. Another way of saying the same thing is simply that the numbers enter into no laws at all. They are thus merely one degree less useful than the numbers associated with intelligence.

With the help of physical theory, however, we can go much further. We can in principle analyze monochromatic light into wavelength and intensity; and we can analyze any given light into a combination of monochromatic components We can then define the true color of a surface to be characterized by the light reflected from the surface by white light of a standard intensity and orientation. This yields us a true (multidimensional, numerical) characterization of color. And this is what we would take as the ultimate standard in our present state of knowledge. We seldom refer to this ultimate standard—even in scientific contexts. We do not expose a woodpecker to white light of standard intensity, and then analyze the intensity of the monochromatic components of the reflected light, in order to arrive at the conclusion that it is red-headed. Nevertheless, the existence of this standard has a profound effect on the meaning of the color terms we do use, both in ordinary language and in science. One profound effect is that it renders the color terms (which we learn ostensively) theoretical rather than purely ostensive terms. In the scientific framework we can *observe* that *X* is red, only in the sense that our observation makes it very highly probable that it is red. In the scientific language, it makes perfectly good sense to say: It *looks* red, but is it *really* red?

Of course, our current ordinary language is a mixture of languages, and it is true that as we use the expression "red" in ordinary everyday discourse, it is quite open to question whether (or to what degree) it is being used as a primitive, ostensive, observation predicate, or as a scientific theoretical term. There is, as we noticed earlier, a theoretical element even in the so-called ostensive meanings. Thus a given area cannot be all red and all green at the same time: everything extended has some color; there are conditions concerning the existence of normal illumination, and the like, implied in the most ordinary conceivable language of color terms. (Is that really mauve? It's hard to tell in this artificial light.) Our concern here is not, however, to try to reflect the mixture of usages common in ordinary language, nor to expose the semantic framework undergirding the coherent use of color terms in ordinary usage, but to reflect the peculiar characteristics of the scientific and relatively formal uses of color terms. In this sense, the standard of redness is something that we never see: namely, the wavelengths corresponding to red light.

To verify this, let us suppose that we were to wake up tomorrow, to find that all the things we were used to seeing as red looked green, and vice versa. Our red necktie now appears green, the green skirt appears red, peas look red and cherries green. The simple-minded, natural thing to do, is simply to suppose that red things and green things have changed color. And indeed, on an ostensive interpretation of color words, this is the only thing we can do. But in point of fact, we would not be sure at all (as contemporary, scientific-minded persons) whether indeed things had changed color, or whether our perceptions of things had changed. This is a perfectly good question, given our scientific, theoretical orientation, and it would be answered by the perfectly straight-forward and feasible procedure of analyzing the light reflected from the startling cherries and apples and skirts and shirts and ties. If the light is the same (according to our spectographs and calculations), then it is our percepts that have changed. If the wavelengths have altered, we will infer that the microstructure of the surfaces of the objects in question have changed, and that the things have indeed changed color.

[104]

Such a thorough experiment as this should make it quite clear that color words are relatively theoretical words in the formal systems of science. How is it that we judge colors directly on the basis of observation? Under ordinary "good" light. If even color terms are not purely observational, but partly theoretical, what remains to be observational? We shall see the answer in Section VII, which will be concerned with "observation terms" in formal systems.

VI

Let us next consider a term which might occur in a biological formal system, "dog". This term is perhaps a bit uncomfortable scientifically, because there is such a tremendous variation among dogs; but there is some variation among the members of any species with respect to size, coloration, conformation, etc., and the fact that it is pronounced in the case of dogs, as well as the fact that dogs are familiar to us all, will make the term a good one for our analysis.

Since we have here nothing that can by any stretch of the imagination be termed a quantitative term, our analysis is considerably simpler than any we have been concerned with before. "Dog" is a term that occurs in ordinary discourse, and its meaning is given quite ostensively there, together with a certain commonsense general background of vague generalizations (Dogs bark, usually; they don't purr; they are not kept to be milked by farmers; they are not generally ridden in Central Park...). There is considerable uniformity in the use of such a term as "dog", but it is largely accidental. We can easily see that the usage would not be uniform, if we turned loose coyotes, wolves or Australian dingoes, or hyenas; some people would say that they were dogs, others would not. Furthermore, and more important, as scientists, we want to be prepared for as much as possible: we want to be prepared for the discovery of a species of beast on a hitherto unknown Pacific island, and we want to be able to classify the beast as a dog or as some other kind of thing. For this reason, and for the reason that we want to be precise in the rules of our system, we would not conduct lexicological inquiry, but would formulate criteria which would allow people with great uniformity to classify the beast as either a dog or a nondog. Again: we seek interpersonal uniformity.

It is in the interest of interpersonal uniformity that the taxonic criteria have been selected—that interest, and the interest of having many important and interesting generalizations available and well confirmed. Thus for the term "dog", defined more or less ostensively in ordinary language, we substitute a scientific term "dog" which is defined explicitly by certain taxonomic features. Some of these features are observable under fairly ordinary circumstances (quadruped); others are observable only under rather special circumstances (young born with hair); others are observable only by destructive analysis (the olfactory nerve is larger in diameter than the optic nerve). And finally, since dogs are supposed to be a species there is the general speciation problem: is this object a member of

[105]

the species *dog*, or is it a member of a new species? And this question, which must be answered before we can say that the beast in question is or is not a dog, is one that cannot be answered definitively by any amount of observation. Cross fertility is perhaps the best and most observable criterion; but it is certainly not definitive when present—consider that tylons may rarely be produced by crossing tigers and lions—and far less is it definitive when absent: any individual may be sterile; or there may be simple mechanical difficulties that preclude testing the hypothesis.

It is easy to see then, that in the biological formal system in which the term "dog" plays a part, the part that it plays is theoretical. Though the term is ostensive in ordinary language—more or less ostensive: remember that most terms of ordinary language drag with them a haze of vague generalities some of which may be regarded as expressing part of the meaning of the term—it is a theoretical term, only indirectly related to direct observations, in the scientific formal system. Of course, the best and simplest test of whether an animal is a dog in the scientific sense, as in the ordinary sense, is that it looks like a dog. But if the word "dog" were purely ostensive, one would not need to say "looks" like a dog: looking could not be in error. The same thing is true here as was true of the more complicated quantitative terms we considered earlier. The ordinary language term was in important respects vague and ambiguous—it would be easy to construct in imagination objects that some people would call dogs and that other people would deny were dogs. The more scientific term is one which reduces this variation: it is a term with a greater degree of interpersonal uniformity. The cost of this, as before, is uncertainty in application: we can no longer be sure that a given object is a dog; we can only be *sure* that it *looks* like a dog. But this uncertainty is controllable and reducible. (If worse comes to worst, by destructive analysis.) In addition, the scientific term enters into various laws and generalizations that are interesting and significant, and, most important in this particular sort of study, laws and generalizations that relate dogs to other animals through the very taxonomic features that are used for its classification. Thus: no quadrupeds whose young are born hairless are carnivorous. This applies automatically to dogs through the scientific, taxonomic definition of "dog". Dogs are classified as carnivores, and it therefore follows that their young are not born hairless. But it would apply only by special notice to "dog" understood in the ordinary language sense, since it might be doubted that all kinds of dogs were carnivores.

There are many words in ordinary language, some or even many of which, find their way into scientific formal systems, and which are at no stage in their careers ostensively defined terms. Such a term is "atom". In traditional, ordinary-language talk, an atom is simply a simple, an indivisible. It is a word that comes into the language from a philosophical or scientific background; its definition would be theoretical and ideal: you can saw up wood, and smash rocks, and make smaller ones out of bigger ones; but you can't do this in-definitely, and what you would come to, were you able to carry out this ideal process of subdivision ideally far, is something that can't be further divided: and that something is what we mean by "atom". This definition is clearly packed with theory: a whole theory about the constitution of the universe. It is, as it stands, an incomplete theory: for it says nothing about the nature of the atoms. There may be an atom for each kind of thing; there may be only one basic atomic substance, and the atoms of different things may differ only in shape; there may be atoms only for a small number of substances—e.g., earth, air, fire, and water—other things being made by combinations of such substances. Or there may be no atoms at all. It is easy to see how the concept of the atom lends itself to a wide variety of scientific theories. The meaning of the term, equally clearly, varies according to the theory in which it occurs. In contemporary atomic theory, atoms are no longer altogether indivisible: their feature is that they are indi-visible by *chemical* means; where of course "chemical means" is defined by the body of contemporary chemical theory.

So far I have tried to trace in some detail, in a few selected instances, the semantic relations between relatively ostensive terms of ordinary language, and homonyms of them that occur as relatively theoretical terms in scientific formal systems. Needless to say, the semantical rules that govern the scientific use of the terms are seldom spelled out explicitly in a formal system; but they are there in the sense that should dispute concerning the use of a technical term of the formal system arise, it would and could be settled by citing, or inventing, the appropriate rules. The line between the formal systems of self-conscious science and the vague theoretical generalities of ordinary life and language, is not a sharp one; we would not, after all, expect it to be sharp. In particular the se-mantical distinction between a scientific, theoretical term, and an ostensively given term of ordinary language is not always sharp. It is generally a matter of degree, for generally the development of scientific knowledge and scientific formal systems is a gradual and continuous development of ordinary knowledge and tradition, a development that involves two profound and important changes correlated with the semantic changes in the meanings of the terms of the language:

A. A change in the use of terms that promotes interpersonal uniformity. This occurs both through the definition of new terms on the basis of the old ones (as particular length predicates on the basis of the relation "longer than" and a standard unit), and through the out-and-out change in meaning of an old, largely ostensively defined term ("dog") to a new, theoretical term ("dog"). With this increase in interpersonal uniformity—i.e., the decrease in vagueness and ambiguity—goes increased uncertainty. Ostensively interpreted terms can be applied with certainty, because we can go no further than the simple recog-nition that the term applies. Theoretical terms can only be applied on the basis of

[107]

criteria which are never definitive: we can always look for additional criteria, or more telling ones; we can always entertain the possibility that we have made a mistake, an error in the application of the theoretical term. But this uncertainty can be measured, controlled and reduced, while the antecedent vagueness and ambiguity cannot. Remember that I am speaking of degrees here: no term is purely ostensive; probably no term with its roots in ordinary language is purely theoretical.

B. A change in the number, richness, significance of the relations that are known to hold among the things signified by the terms. This is reflected in axioms in the formal system from which laws and generalizations are derived. Very few interesting laws (perhaps no laws at all except statistical ones) can be formulated in relatively ostensive terms; in the new (theoretical) terms, many such laws can be formulated, and confirmed, made acceptable by the evidence. Some of these new laws may be regarded as merely meaning postulates, which are not confirmed by evidence, but are acceptable in virtue of the theoretical meanings of the terms involved. They may nonetheless be interesting. The distinction between these generalizations, and those having empirical content that are really about the world, is one that can be hard to draw; for the time being, we shall leave open the question of drawing such a line.

VII

However much we remold ordinary language and render its ostensive terms theoretical in the interest of interpersonal uniformity and richness of generalization and structure, we must still have some connection between the sentences of our scientific formal system and our experience of the world that the scientific system is about. There must be an observational basis for science. And this is already entailed by our desire for interpersonal uniformity; for there can be no interpersonal uniformity in the application of a theoretical term, unless that term is somehow related to the experiences that different persons may have. For example, "I.Q." was cited as a term that has a higher degree of interpersonal uniformity than "intelligence", because it is easier for two people to agree (within a small margin of error) on the I.Q. of an individual, than it is for them to agree on the use of the various ordinary language cognates of the term "intelligence". The reason that it is easy for them to agree (within this margin of error) is that there are instruments (tests) for measuring I.Q. and to read one of these instruments involves, primarily, counting. Counting is the sort of operation that people can perform with a high degree of agreement and consistency—i.e., a high degree of interpersonal uniformity. Thus we replace one judgment—that of intelligence—which is hard to achieve a high degree of uniformity about, by another judgment which is easier to achieve a high degree of uniformity about. As we have repeatedly observed, this is typical of the development of scientific language. But just what are these judgments that are basic? What are the kinds

[108]

of judgments that it is initially possible to achieve a high degree of uniformity about, and to which other judgments are to be reduced?

Counting is one such kind of judgment. While it is true that people sometimes make errors in counting, these errors are controllable and reducible (by being careful; by counting several times; by having several people count). Counting is furthermore just the same in ordinary language as in the formal system. To count 84 correct answers on a test is to go through a process of correlating the first correct answer with the number one, the second correct answer with the number two, etc. The number which is correlated with the last correct answer is the number of correct answers. What is ostensive here? The correlation of the correct answers with numbers. *This* corresponds to 1, *this* corresponds to 2, and so on. Some of the judgments may be in error—i.e., the correspondence may not be truly one-to-one. Yet two ordinary human beings of our culture will generally come to very close agreement in counting. Furthermore, that agreement can often be reached, even when it hasn't been reached the first time, by counting over, or by counting together.

This universality of counting is one thing that makes it so fundamental in science. We not only reduce judgments of intelligence to counting but also judgments of other personality traits (through tests), including judgments that are based on projective tests like the Rorschach, where the actual scoring and interpretation is done by counting the numbers of responses of various categories. In biology and sociology, counting is obviously central to any theory that involves statistics, such as genetics, theories about population movements, characterizations of social groups, etc.; it is also involved centrally in taxonomy and thus in the theoretical structure of many of the terms of biology: "four-winged", "multi-foliate", "two-legged", "six-legged", etc.; it is involved in physics, for example, in measuring radioactivity by scintillations or clicks.

Counting is also involved in length-measurements, which are the next most universal kind of primitive observational judgments. Length judgments are made even more uniform by printing numerals on our scales. It has been said that what we are concerned with in science is the coincidence of a pointer with a mark; but the marks still help to make our counting easy. The difficulty is that the pointer almost never does coincide with the mark. A straight length measurement is also essentially a counting process: we count the number of units that seems to correspond to the length of the object. By "units" I do not mean meters or light years; but whatever is the smallest unit appropriate to the measurement: miles, if we are measuring the distance between two points far separated on the earth's surface; microns, if we are measuring the distance between two points on a chromosome. But of course we hardly ever measure such distances directly: what we measure directly are distances (usually) on the order of two or three inches—distances, that is, on the faces of dials.

A measurement with a footrule of the edge of a table will illustrate the

[109]

principles: we lay off the footrule along the edge of the table. Say that we can do this four times—but then there is some table left over; or five times—but then the rule sticks out over the end of the table. If the distance is to be expressed in feet we can say either 4 feet or 5 feet. It doesn't much matter. We can make a comparative judgment of whether the excess of footrule or the excess of table is greater in the two cases, and make our judgment accordingly. If we want the distance in inches, the operation is quite different. We don't use an inchstick, but we count by inches. We lay off the footrule once: that's 12 inches; again: that's 24; again: that's 36; again: that's 48; and now when we lay it off again, we count out along it: 49, 50, . . ., 53 inches, and there is a little table left over; 54 inches, and the inchstick drawn on the footrule sticks out over the end of the table. So: 53 or 54 inches; the judgment can be based on a comparison of the excess in the two cases as before. A finer measurement? That we perform with a yet smaller unit: eighth inches, for example. We don't use an eighth-inch rule, of course (for one thing, every time we pick up and lay down the rule, we know we introduce an error). We use the same old footrule, counting in units of 96 eighths of an inch to begin with; then in units of eight eighths; then in single units. The whole pattern is so familiar as to be trivial and perhaps unnecessary to describe at such length. But it is centrally and essentially a process of counting, and furthermore, just like any other process of counting in whole numbers. In measurement, there is no need for continuity.

Temperature measurements are also quite obviously (being in the first place measurements of length) counting measurements. Measurements of time: again counting, by way of measurements of length or directly as in counting pulse beats, sequences of day and night, sequences of summer and winter, etc. Measurements of weight: first by balance, counting the number of one-unit weights that just overbalances the object being weighed. Or by scale of some sort, which comes down to a measurement of length again. The reading of a dial is the measurement of a length and thus essentially a counting procedure.

It should be noticed that even with respect to counting, instrumentation plays a role. The footrule may be regarded as an instrument for counting inches and fractions of inches, just as the odometer, on which we read numerals representing miles, is an instrument for counting miles, or tenths of miles. To take an eighth-of-an-inch rule and lay it off 73 times is much more errorful (remember that we have ways of measuring errors) than to take a footrule and read off $9\frac{1}{8}$ inches.

Pervasive as the counting procedure is, however, as providing an observational basis for scientific terms, it is not universal. Indeed, it is easy to see that it could not be universal, since it is only with the joint development of scientific theory and of instrumentation (which could not develop without the theory) that various kinds of observations can be reduced to counting. Many observations in science cannot be reduced to counting. This is particularly true if we do not attempt to reduce all sciences to a common basis in physics. Biology, for example, can be developed perfectly well without fancy developments in physics, on the basis of such observation-predicates as "red", "blue", "hair", "scales", "feathers", etc., and other mainly ostensively defined terms from ordinary language. Still, note that we do not have our present powerful formal system of biology, unless some of the terms that are ostensively defined in ordinary language—like "rabbit", "cat", "fish", etc., become transformed into theoretical terms of the formal system.

There are also terms in biology that would be very difficult to reduce to basic terms in physics. Predicates denoting kinds of shapes are pervasive in biology, and are not at all easily reducible to other terms; in particular the obvious proposal to define these predicates geometrically has been found completely impractical. There are certain important shapes that one simply gets to learn: shapes of kinds of animals, shapes of cells as seen through a microscope, etc. This is true in physics, too: we learn to recognize shapes traced on photographic plates by the light reflected from droplets of moisture caused by the passage of a particle in a cloud chamber. We learn to recognize certain shapes in our scientific activity, just as we learn to recognize certain objects in learning an ordinary language. But again notice the increase in interpersonal uniformity in taking certain *shapes* as fundamental, rather than certain *objects*. An object is a substance as well as a shape: to put the object in a category, to give it a name, is to adopt certain beliefs concerning its substance as well as its shape. Should we say that shape is "more objective" than substance? Hardly. The advantage of saying that something is hairlike (hair-shaped), rather than that it is a hair, is that it is much easier for everyone to agree that a thing is hair-shaped than that it is indeed a hair—i.e., has the theoretical properties that hairs have, as well as the shape of a hair. Shape judgments are an important class of observational judgments of high interpersonal uniformity.

Chemistry involves color judgments, which, so far as the chemical formal system is concerned, are straightforward empirical judgments based directly on observation. Color predicates *could* be defined physically, but the point is that at least in many fragments of the chemical formal system they *need* not be so defined. In chemistry, to somewhat less extent, judgments about smells are also basic. They are not basic in the sense that chemical theory as it stands now, embedded in physics, could not be developed except by creatures with a sense of smell; they are basic only in the sense that we do not ever inquire further into whether or not something smells acrid, or has a mercaptane smell. That such and such a bunch of stuff has a certain kind of smell, is simply a datum: it rarely functions as a hypothesis after we have smelled the stuff. Rough and smooth; slimy and dry, are other kinds of observation terms that are found in both biology and chemistry. And perhaps just as certain shapes are taken to be observation predicates, so certain kinds of movements are understood this way.

Psychology is full of ordinary language observation terms: not only "red"

[111]

and "green" (used in the descriptions of test situations), but also "agitated", "emotional", "hungry", "afraid", etc. There is a tendency in psychology to try to replace terms of these latter sorts by "more objective" ones: thus to replace: "is hungry" by "will undergo a shock of 54 volts in order to get food". The suggestion is that there is something subjective and therefore unscientific about "hungry", "afraid", and the like. But this is not the reason for the replacement. (Indeed, the "in order to" in the phrase offered as a substitute for "is hungry" seems just as subjective.) The point is not the comparative subjectivity of "hungry" as opposed to "crosses 54 volt grid"; it is the fact that the application of the term "crosses 54 volt grid" has a much higher degree of interpersonal uniformity. It is (again, as always) infected with a kind of uncertainty that "is hungry" might not be infected with; but not so much so, since "hungry" in ordinary language is already involved in a vague general theory that animals who are hungry are satisfied by food, and that they will undergo dissatisfactions for the sake of getting greater satisfactions. The point is precisely the same point that justifies replacing "intelligence" by "I.Q." It is not that there is any useful and coherent sense in which I.Q. is objective and real, while intelligence is subjective and unreal; it is that the application of "I.Q." is highly uniform among different people. I.Q. and intelligence amount to the same thing in application over many common instances—i.e., they satisfy the same order relationships (and note that it is intelligence, not I.Q., that provides the original standard). The advantage of I.Q. is its interpersonal uniformity in application to the marginal cases. In general we strive to replace terms of low interpersonal uniformity ("intelligence", "hunger", "fear", . . .) by terms of high interpersonal uniformity ("I.Q.", "voltage", "galvanic response", . . .) However, we need not and cannot replace all psychological predicates by "counting" predicates.

We may summarize in this way: in a scientific formal system, certain predicates are taken as observation predicates; these are predicates of ordinary language, with essentially only an ostensively defined, ordinary language, meaning. It is these predicates, fundamentally, which tie the formal system to ordinary experience and scientific experience. These predicates (like color predicates in biology) may be theory laden in the system of scientific knowledge as a whole, but they may function perfectly well as observation predicates *just so long as immediate observation judgments about their applicability are nearly always correct.* Thus we use "red" as an observation term, not because we take our judgments to supercede the physical theory that correlates red light with light of a certain wavelength, but because we know that practically all the time, under ordinary lighting conditions, when we judge something to be red, it really is red, i.e., reflects light in the corresponding part of the spectrum.

In a physiological psychology, for another example, we might have an observation recorded as: "Rat A solved the maze M in t seconds." To call A a rat is to make a serious theoretical claim, but it is one that will not be defended in such a context. And correctly. For it is a very well confirmed hypothesis of biology (if you will) that anything looking a lot like a rat, is a rat. And thus, instead of saying awkwardly and also inaccurately: "The rat-shaped, rat-smelling, rat-behaving object A..." we make a simple biological inference, and say, "Rat A." An unnecessarily accurate way of putting the matter would be to say: "The object A which I judge to be a rat...," where the judgment is not presumed to be infallible, but only highly probable. Indeed, this suggests a way of treating all of the terms which are used in science as if they were observation terms, but which are in point of fact loaded with theoretical baggage: namely, as probabilistic observations. When I say, "I observe the temperature to be 60°C," what I really mean is that my reading of a thermometer is 60°C, and that this reading in turn makes it very probable that the temperature of the object is very close to 60°C (other things being equal—i.e., supposing that I know that the thermometer has been in contact with the object for a reasonable length of time, is not seriously biased, etc.). Just so, when I observe a rat, or a specimen of hydrochloric acid, or a spoonful of table salt, or the expression of fear or love, what I am really doing may be observing a set of physical circumstances, and making a trans- or supra-physical claim (at any rate, a fallible claim), expressed by saying that *this is* hydrochloric acid, or a rat, or the expression of fear.... There is thus a large class of terms in a formal system that can function as observation terms in this probabilistic sense, although in point of fact they are also theoretical terms in the sense that they have theoretical import, as the term "rat" has theoretical import.

In any science there are some terms and predicates that have a minimal amount of theoretical structure: they are the most irreducible observation predicates. The most important and most pervasive of these predicates are the counting predicates: these, more than any others have the desirable quality of interpersonal uniformity. But there are always other predicates as well that are regarded as basic: particularly shape predicates, and in psychology intention and attitude predicates. In general, as a scientific system progresses and changes, the set of (relatively) basic observation terms becomes smaller and smaller. More and more quantities, for example, will come to be measured in terms of the counting predicates, by instruments with dials, or multiple choice tests. The set of observation terms will come to be composed not only of fewer and fewer terms, but in particular of those with the highest degree of interpersonal uniformity. Relations, for example, will occur among these terms after qualities have been replaced; thus "longer than" is a relational term found among observation predicates, after "long" has been banished from science as "subjective".

But observe that we may have to retract some judgments of the form "a is longer than b". We might be able to construct something of a case for regarding even the most irreducible observation terms as probabilistic, too. Even counting, after all, is probabilistic when we say: "There are seven," rather than "I

[113]

counted seven." And it is the physical fact, not the biographical fact, that enters into the formal system. But even though judgments concerning the basic terms may be only probabilistic, these terms are fundamental, provide the fundamental connection between reality and the formal system, simply because there are no other terms to be interposed between experience and these terms.

VIII

There is one further class of terms that occurs in scientific formal systems, and these are technical terms that are introduced *de novo* (*ab ovo*) in the formal system itself. These terms are not (at least not initially) in any sense observational. They are introduced to serve a certain essential function in a formal system. "Gene" in the theory of heredity is an example; "*psi*-function" in quantum mechanics is another. Sometimes these terms stand for entities—i.e., physical objects, sometimes for properties ("recessive", as applied to genes), sometimes for relations ("linked", as applied to genes). Sometimes (as in the case of "*psi*-function") one is not quite sure what they stand for. If they stand for physical objects, we can sometimes come to observe them as we have managed to observe (albeit indirectly) viruses and positrons. But it is not necessary to observe such things, or even to be able in principle to observe them, in order to have good reason to believe in the existence of such objects, properties, relations, and so on. What allows us to believe in them, is having good grounds for accepting the formal system as a whole; or at least for believing that some such formal system represents the facts, and also grounds for taking the terms in question to be essential to the structure of that system.

We shall want later to consider in detail the ontological question of what constitutes adequate evidence for the existence of an entity or property or relation; for the moment, let it suffice to observe that it is a question of the ground we have for accepting a whole system in which terms denoting those entities, properties, and so on, play an essential role. Here we need only observe that it is not at all the case that every term of a scientific formal system must be directly connected to observation terms; nor even that it must be indirectly connected in the sense that there is a particular deductive consequence of axioms involving the term, such that if that deductive consequence were to be refuted, we would be obliged to deny the existence of anything denoted by that term. The term may function strictly internally in the formal system. The question of whether or not a term functions *essentially* in a formal system, when its function is strictly internal in this sense, is a question of what constitutes a crucial change in the structure of the formal system. We shall consider particular cases later.

IX

It has been suggested that science progresses by becoming more quantitative; physics is the paradigm of the highly developed science, while the social sciences are looked down upon because they are not quantitative. In a certain sense it is true: as a science progresses, quantitative terms seem to play a larger and larger role in the formal system that represents it. Yet in another sense the truth is the very reverse. Science progresses by substituting qualitative judgments for quantitative ones. One cannot develop a quantitative physics, for example, in terms of people's quantitative judgments of weight, speed, time, force, and so on. In order to arrive at a quantitative physics, one must replace the quantitative judgments (much time, little weight) by purely qualitative judgments that have a high degree of interpersonal uniformity: the beam balances or fails to balance; the ends of the measuring rod and the object measured coincide or do not coincide. It is qualitative judgments like these that constitute the fundamental observational basis of physics.

It thus appears that it is not the absence of quantities as such that makes the difference between sociology and physics, but absence of sharply interpreted predicates and relations, having a high degree of interpersonal uniformity, and fitting into a rich axiomatic framework. What counts are the interpersonal uniformity of the terms and the richness of the axiomatic framework, which together yield publicly verifiable predictions, explanations, and so on. It is utterly irrelevant whether or not any of the terms of the theory happen to have the internal structure common to masses, lengths, and time intervals.

BIBLIOGRAPHICAL NOTES TO CHAPTER 4

The most important general approach to the interpretation of scientific terms since the 1930's has been *operationism*, first discussed in detail by P. W. Bridgeman, *The Logic of Modern Physics* (New York: Macmillan, 1927). According to this view, the meaning of a scientific term is the set of operations by means of which one would determine whether or not the term applied. For critical discussions of operationism, see Ernest Nagel, *The Structure of Science* (New York: Harcourt, Brace and World, 1961); C. G. Hempel, *Philosophy of Natural Science* (N.J.: Prentice-Hall, 1966). Rudolf Carnap, "Testability and Meaning," *Philosophy of Science*, Vols. III and IV, 1938), proposed that scientific terms that are not to be taken as ostensive be introduced to the formal language by means of *reduction sentences*—i.e., statements giving an observational necessary condition and an observational sufficient condition for the application of the theoretical term. This approach has been modified and generalized over the years (for its current state, see *The Philosophy of Rudolf Carnap*, P. A. Schilpp, ed., Open Court, Illinois, 1963); the views presented in this chapter are not far removed from Carnap's present position, except in their emphasis on interpersonal uniformity as a matter of degree, and on ostensiveness as a matter of degree. These elements of gradualism may be found in W. V. O. Quine's *Word and Object* (New York: Wiley, 1960), in which, however, the emphasis is on natural language rather than scientific formal systems.

Chapter **5**

AXIOMS

I

It is the axioms of a scientific formal system that embody its content. In a metaphorical but nonetheless significant sense, the axioms contain all of the theorems of the system. It is our present task to disentangle these axioms from the statements (meaning postulates) that do not have empirical content, but function in somewhat the same way as premises in deductions in the system. It will also be our job in this chapter to examine the role that each of these kinds of statements plays in the formal system.

In Chapter 2, the sample formal system that we discussed, the sociology of clubs, was presented in a standard way. Some statements (A1—A5) were taken as axioms, characterizing the subject matter; and some statements ((6)—(10), page 50) were taken as meaning postulates, as part of the interpretation, characterizing the terms of the system. It thus appears that there are two kinds of

[116]

statements that we will write down in presenting a formal system: axioms, in the proper Aristotelian sense, that embody the empirical content of the formal system; and axioms which are, properly speaking, not part of the calculus of the formal system at all, but a part of its interpretation. The former we shall call *material axioms*, the latter *meaning postulates*.

Already in Chapter 2 we saw that this was an oversimplification. One of the alternatives we considered was to stipulate as part of the formation rules—i.e., as part of the *calculus* of the formal system, that only formulas of the form "*Mxy*", and not formulas of the form "*Mx*" were to be considered well formed; that is, we considered ruling out a class of statements (those of the form "*Mx*") by stipulating syntactically that no such statement is to be considered well formed. In informal terms, we would say that any such statement was simply ungrammatical, and hence meaningless. (The corresponding ungrammatical English would be: "*x* is a member of".) The grounds on which we want to rule out such statements are not syntactical, however, but semantical: it is our knowledge of the meaning of the membership relation that tells us we can rule out of consideration statements of the perverse form "*Mx*".

Although I do not know that it ever has been asked, there is no reason why we cannot consider the question: can the formation rules be used to rule out all those statements that we wish to rule out—i.e., all the statements that would ordinarily be characterized as nontheorems? Put another way, can the formation rules do the work, in the calculus, that is ordinarily done by meaning postulates, axioms, and rules of inference? This would be possible (in some calculi), but pointless. It would be pointless because the metalinguistic formation rules would then have to embody just those facts about meaning and just those empirical facts that the formal system is intended to codify. To know that S is well formed, in such a system, is to know that it is one of those statements we want to assert; and to know this, in the general case, requires that we have a metalinguistic formula or prescription which will allow us to show, of a given statement, that it is well formed. But it is to serve precisely the function of such a formula or prescription that we propose the formal system in the first place; we construct the formal system because we want some way of characterizing the infinite number of statements that constitute the total empirical content of the theory. To require that we characterize these statements by means of the formation rules alone is to require that the formation rules embody the whole content of the theory, and thus that they be as complicated as the theory they are supposed to be part of.

In most theories complex enough to express part of our scientific knowledge, there would be another difficulty as well. A requirement which is generally adopted for formation rules, is that there can be an effective, mechanical, procedure for discovering whether a given statement is or is not well formed. On the other hand, in any logical system containing so much as a lower function calculus (quantifier theory), there is no effective, mechanical, procedure for discovering whether or not a given expression is a theorem. This fact may very well mean that to take the formation rules as embodying the empirical content of the theory will entail that we no longer have an effective criterion for determining whether or not a given empirical statement is well formed. We therefore have good reason for not wanting to put the whole burden of expressing the empirical content of our formal system on the formation rules.

But we do need some formation rules: we need formation rules even for pure logic. And we also need some formation rules to enable us to construct well-formed formulas out of the nonlogical components of our formal system. In the sociological example, it seems very plausible and natural to use the formation rules also to exhibit the structural difference between the relational term "M" and the predicates "P" and "C".

We may, on the other hand, adopt the following alternative: instead of using the formation rules to eliminate from consideration in the formal system certain expressions, we may use meaning postulates. Thus we may perfectly well allow the formula "Mx" to count as well formed, but reject it as false (rather than meaningless) when x is something other than an ordered pair consisting of a person and a club. We arrange this by adding, as axioms of the system, the following statements:

$$\text{M-1: } (x)(Mx \supset (\exists z)(\exists y)(x = y,z))$$
$$\text{M-2: } (z)(y)(Myz \supset Py)$$
$$\text{M-3: } (z)(y)(Myz \supset Cz).$$

We had best also add a meaning postulate to the effect that nothing can be both a person and a club.

$$\text{M-4: } (x)(Px \supset \sim Cx).$$

Notice how complicated the formation rules would have to be to replace M-4; instead of merely saying that if S and T are well-formed formulas, their conjunction will be a well-formed formula, we have to stipulate that if S is "Px" and T is "Cx" then their conjunction is not well formed; and if S contains "Px" as a conjunctive component and T is "Cx", their conjunction is not well formed, and so on. And then we would have to make corresponding exceptions for negation, the conditional, etc. In fact, we would have to rule out every statement whose denial was a theorem on the meaning-postulate scheme.

These axioms, M-1–M-4, will not be regarded as embodying part of the empirical content of the system; they are meaning postulates, and merely reflect our decision as to the meanings of the terms "M", "C", and "P". As in the case of formation rules, the usual grounds on which we justify such axioms are semantic: it is in virtue of the meanings of the terms, as they are ordinarily understood, that we may incorporate the axioms in our system.

Which of these alternatives we follow is somewhat arbitrary: it depends, among other things, on the interpretation of the system we have in mind when

[118]

we frame the axioms. If we wish to allow for a wide latitude of interpretations of the calculus, then we will want to leave as much of the characterization of the terms of the system as possible to the meaning postulates, which will then become part of the interpretation, rather than the calculus. On the other hand, if we have some definite interpretation in mind, then it is all to the good to make the structural commitments of that interpretation explicit in the calculus itself. Thus, I offered one interpretation of the calculus of the clubs which rendered all four of the meaning postulates false. But ordinarily, one would include them in the calculus. Compromises are possible; thus it would be quite plausible to include the content of M-1 among the formation rules (rendering "Mx" meaningless), and then to include as axioms of the system M-2, M-3, and M-4, so that "Mxy & $\sim Px$", "Mxx", etc., are perfectly meaningful but false.

II

Just as we could conceivably (but inefficiently!) make our formation rules do the work of our meaning postulates, so, it turns out, we can make our meaning postulates do the work of our material axioms. To do so, however, imposes very strong and unrealistic conditions on the possible interpretations of the system. We may do this, roughly speaking, by simply stipulating that the meanings of the terms in our system are to be *such that* the axioms are true (and therefore such that they are true by virtue of the meanings of the terms that they involve). This may not seem plausible, but there are writers whose radical conventionalism would suggest that this is the best analysis of scientific theories. While it may not be implausible to regard the equation "$f = ma$" as a definition of "force" in mechanics, surely it is difficult to regard "Every animal that has a heart also has a liver," as a (partial) definition of "heart". Nevertheless, let us pursue this approach and see where it leads us.

In our sociological example, we might simply stipulate that the terms "P", "C", and "M", are to be such that Axioms (1)–(5), and M-1–M-4 are *to be* true. This is just to say that we take the axioms of the calculus, and the meaning postulates, together, to define implicitly the meanings of the terms that occur in them. But, on the assumption that these axioms are to be "true by virtue of the meanings of the terms they contain," we can construct another and neater theory, using predicates having the same empirical content as the old predicates, and for which the axioms turn out to be logical truths.

Write "$T(P,C,M)$" for the set of axioms (1)–(5) and M-1–M-4 of our sociological theory. Let our variables range over points and lines, as well as people and clubs, and introduce "S" for point, "L" for line, and "O" for the relation of lying on. (I use a geometrical interpretation because it is familiar, but we know, from analytic geometry, how to replace it by a purely arithmetical or logical interpretation.) Now we introduce three new terms "$P*$", "$C*$", and "$M*$", by formal definitions.

[119]

(i)   "P^*x"   for   "$(T(P,C,M) \mathbin{\&} Px) \lor (\sim T(P,C,M) \mathbin{\&} Sx)$"

(ii)   "C^*x"   for   "$(T(P,C,M) \mathbin{\&} Cx) \lor (\sim T(P,C,M) \mathbin{\&} Lx)$"

(iii)   "M^*x,y"   for   "$(T(P,C,M) \mathbin{\&} Mxy) \lor (\sim T(P,C,M) \mathbin{\&} Oxy)$".

Now observe:

(A) That the starred predicates have the same empirical content as the unstarred predicates, on the supposition that conformity to A-1–A-5 is to be regarded as part of the meaning of the unstarred terms.

Proof (for "P^*"):

(1) Suppose that "Px" holds. Then since our interpretation of the predicates is to be such that the axioms hold, "$T(P,C,M)$" will hold as well, and thus also "$T(P,C,M) \mathbin{\&} Px$", and thus, by (i), "P^*x".

(2) Suppose that "P^*x" holds. Then one side or the other of the alteration in (i) must hold; since we take "$T(P,C,M)$" to hold by convention, it must be the left side; and therefore "Px" must hold as well. Therefore, our interpretation of "P^*" is such that P^*x if and only if Px. The proof in the other cases is similar.

(B) "$T(P^*,C^*,M^*)$" is a theorem of (Euclidean) geometry.

Proof (for the part A-1):

"$T(S,L,O)$" simply represents a few of the axioms of Euclidean geometry (and indeed on the interpretation provided by analytic geometry, is an arithmetical truth). We may thus affirm both "$T(S,L,O)$" and "$T(P,C,M)$". The part of "$T(P^*,C^*,M^*)$" that represents A-1 is

$$(x)(P^*x \supset (\exists y)(C^*y \mathbin{\&} M^*xy).$$

We outline a proof of this part of "$T(P^*,C^*,M^*)$":

1. P^*x hypothesis
2. $(T(P,C,M) \mathbin{\&} Px) \lor (\sim T(P,C,M) \mathbin{\&} Sx)$ (i)
3. $(T(P,C,M) \mathbin{\&} Px) \supset (\exists y)(Cy \mathbin{\&} Mxy)$ From A-1 in $T(P,C,M)$
4. $(T(P,C,M) \mathbin{\&} Cy) \supset C^*y$ (ii)
5. $(T(P,C,M) \mathbin{\&} Mxy) \supset M^*xy$ (iii)
6. $(T(P,C,M) \mathbin{\&} Px) \supset (\exists y)(C^*y \mathbin{\&} M^*xy)$ 3,4,5
7. $T(S,L,O)$ geometrical fact
8. $Sx \supset (\exists y)(Ly \mathbin{\&} Oxy)$ from the counterpart of A-1 in 7

9. $(\sim T(P,C,M) \mathbin{\&} Ly) \supset C^*y$ (ii)
10. $(\sim T(P,C,M) \mathbin{\&} Oxy) \supset M^*xy$ (iii)
11. $(\sim T(P,C,M) \mathbin{\&} Sx) \supset (\exists y)(C^*y \mathbin{\&} M^*xy)$ 8,9,10
12. $(\exists y)(C^*y \mathbin{\&} M^*xy)$ 2,6,11
13. $(x)(P^*x \supset (\exists y)(C^*y \mathbin{\&} Mxy))$ 1,12,UG

This procedure has an appealing neatness and simplicity to it. But it is altogether inappropriate for scientific systems. It is a fundamental and important

[120]

characteristic of scientific formal systems that they can come into conflict with experience; indeed, this is just the other side of the coin of their usefulness: for a scientific formal system to be a useful guide it must somehow limit the possibilities we may expect to encounter in the future; but just insofar as the system rules out the possibility of some futures, so far may the future make a liar of the system. If the predicates of our scientific formal system are such that the axioms (both empirical axioms and meaning postulates) turn out to be truths of arithmetic, then it is clear that the system cannot be refuted, and that it therefore does not rule out any future events, and that it therefore has no empirical content!

Let us see how this can be. Suppose that we do reformulate our sociological formal system in the manner suggested above. And then suppose, just for example, that we find somebody who doesn't belong to a club. In the original system, this would be taken as a refutation of the theory: the theory entails that everyone belongs to at least one club; here is somebody who doesn't belong to a club; therefore the theory is false. In the new system, this is not a refutation. Why not? Because the new system entails, logically demands, that our "observation" be in error in this case: either we have no person; or else he does after all belong to some club. One or the other. And this in turn amounts to saying that we can no longer be sure of a given entity that it is or is not a person or a club, or of a given pair of entities, that the one is or is not a member of the other. And, as a final turn, this amounts to changing the rules of interpretation of the formal system. We initially had a relatively ostensive rule of interpretation for the term "P"; and although the rules for the terms "C" and "M" were not quite ostensive in the same sense, still, we took them to be simply recognizable. Which is to say, we took a number of ordinary language semantic relations between "C" and "M", and ordinary relatively ostensive terms, to be patent enough not to need discussion, and to provide, among them, pretty good grounds for the interpersonal use of the terms "C" and "M".

The novel terms "$P*$", "$C*$", and "$M*$", which the new system uses are not in any sense ostensive terms, and therefore neither, on the proposal to regard $T(C,P,M)$ as analytic of the meanings of "C", "P", and "M", are these original terms "C", "P", and "M". To know that "$P*$" applies to an individual, for example, is already to know that he will not falsify the theory. In fact, the move described, whether it is formalized arithmetically, or simply regarded as a reinterpretation of the original terms "P", "C", and "M", is a move that cuts the formal system completely loose from all ostensively defined terms, and renders it completely empty.

We could still salvage some of the content of the system, however, if we wanted to be pig-headed, by the following gambit: we could say that although we cannot tell on an ostensive basis when an object in the field of the theory is a person (i.e., when he has the property denoted by "P" or "$P*$") yet a good statistical generalization is that when an object seems to be a person, he is in fact a person

[121]

(i.e., is such that he has the property denoted by "P") and is also such that "$T(P,C,M)$" is true. This generalization, of course, is not part of the theory itself, but is part rather of the *interpretation* of the formal system. To provide another example: if we make it part of the meaning of the terms "heart" and "liver" that the generalization "all animals with hearts have livers" is true, then what becomes nontautologous and embodies our biological knowledge of the world is the interpretative generalization that practically all the animals that we judge to have hearts, or that seem to have hearts, will also be judged to have livers, or seem to have livers. The predictive content of "all animals with hearts have livers" is nil; but the predictive content of "this thing, and things like it, are hearts" is not nil. The object language statement is empty, but the semantic rule (perhaps we should say, the set of semantic rules) is not empty at all. Even in the conventionalists' book there are statements that are not true by convention. What is novel in the conventionalist's view of the matter is that they are no longer part of the scientific formal system.

By this extreme gambit, the empirical content of our scientific system is not altogether removed (that would have been absurd) but is embodied exclusively in the rules of interpretation of the terms of the system. But just as the proposal to embody the content of the formal system in the formation rules becomes silly when the formation rules become as complicated as the original formal system, so this proposal to regard all of the axioms and postulates of the formal system as true by convention becomes silly when it empties the system of empirical content only to relocate the empirical content in the judgments that are ordinarily regarded as ostensive.

III

If we do not indulge in the "implicit definition" gambit, then there will be some terms in our scientific formal system that will be given ostensive interpretations; and conversely, if we give some of the terms in our scientific system ostensive interpretations, the implicit definition gambit will no longer be completely open to us. In any realistic view of science, we must simply accept the fact that there are some terms that are simply taken to be observation terms in the sense that we do not settle a dispute about the applicability of the terms by performing more tests. Within the given science there is no higher authority than sense. In biology, red feather are feathers that look red in daylight. But in another science, there may indeed be a higher authority for the application of the same term; in physics a body that reflects red light is a body with a certain absorption spectrum.

There are not many observation terms in some sciences; and the general development of a body of science invariably reduces their number, as terms which at one point are purely (or almost purely) ostensive become tainted with theory. But even in cases of this sort there is an ostensive remainder: "looks red" is ostensive, even when "red" is interpreted in wavelengths; "looks like a dog" is ostensive, even when dogs are defined taxonomically. And there remain such perennially highly ostensive terms as "definitely between", "definitely shorter than", "definitely brighter than", etc. (which of course do not satisfy the axioms for quantitative relations; they invariably lack the transitivity of indifference). These terms are ostensive in the sense that there is no higher standard to turn to, other than immediate judgment: "You can see with your own eyes that...." These terms, rather than others, are chosen because they possess a high degree of interpersonal uniformity. No science can exist without such terms, and such terms can only be interpreted by ostensive semantic rules. These rules must be metalinguistic; they cannot be represented in the calculus of the formal system, as, for example, meaning postulates can.

The specific terms that are taken as ostensive in the sense mentioned above may vary from scientific system to scientific system, just as they vary, in a given system, with the state of the art, i.e., from date to date. Thus if we meant our sociological theory to be taken seriously, we would certainly take "person" as ostensive, though in a biological formal system, we would define "person" by means of taxonic criteria. But the reason that we are free to take "person" as ostensive in our sociological theory is that it is very unlikely that it should ever become a serious bone of contention whether or not a given entity was a person; if it did, we would equally certainly turn to biological criteria.

There is another sort of rule, which is also ostensive in the sense that it is a rule of interpretation that cannot (generally) be embodied in the calculus of the scientific system, but which is not taken to be ostensive in the sense that "red" is taken to be ostensive in biology, for example. A typical instance is the relational term "longer than". This is a term that is applied to a pair of objects, often, on the basis of direct and immediate judgment. In that sense, the term is ostensive. And yet, unlike the judgment on the basis of which we apply the term "red" in biology, the judgment on the basis of which we apply "longer than" is not essentially infallible. It is easy to make a sequence of such judgments, and then to discover that (in virtue of the transitivity of "longer than", say) one of them must be rejected. Although many such judgments are fallible, very few turn out to have to be rejected.

There are two ways of taking account of this situation: one is to suppose that there are purely ostensive terms which are fundamental and whose application is infallible, and to insist that the connection between the purely ostensive terms and the ones that have some theoretical content be made a part of the theory; and the other is to allow ostensive rules of interpretation that admit of error. Taking the former approach requires introducing a bit of psychology into every formal system, in the sense that in order to connect the system to purely ostensive terms—i.e., to experience and experiment—we must be able to accept such psychological perceptual generalizations as: "If x looks longer than y, then (probably) x is longer than y," "If z looks red, under normal illumination, then (probably) z is red." In other words, if we want our formal system to be pinned to judgments which are as close as possible to infallible, then we must take account of the probabilistic connection between the subject matter of those judgments and the subject matter of the science with which we are concerned. (The subject matter of physics, for example, concerns relations such as "longer than", rather than relations such as "looks longer than".) The other way of taking account of the fallibility of judgment, and the way that I shall generally adopt, is to suppose that there is a class of ostensive rules of interpretation that are themselves fallible. Thus in physics, on this approach, we introduce the term "longer than" quasi-ostensively: "x is longer than y," means that the pair $(x;y)$ is one of the set of observed pairs R, or very like them, and "longer than" also satisfies the postulates of transitivity, irreflexivity, etc. This is to say that if the set of "longer than" judgments does not satisfy those postulates, something will have to be changed; and that is simply to say that the judgments are not infallible. Because we demand that the judgments satisfy the postulates, they are not completely ostensive, and so I call them quasi-ostensive. On the other hand, since they are not (on this second account) to be regarded as derivative judgments, based on some prior judgments that are regarded as infallible, such as judgments of the form "x *looks* longer than y", they are still to be called ostensive.

Among the interpretative rules for formal systems, then, we have the purely ostensive rules first mentioned, and the ostensive part of the quasi-ostensive rules just described. I shall take the typical scientific formal system to involve both kinds of rules. Although (as I have pointed out above) it is possible to include many other elements in the interpretation part of a formal system, there are good reasons, chief of which is clarity, for incorporating everything we can in the calculus part of the formal system. When we have a calculus for which we wish to provide several interpretations, the situation is otherwise; but from now on, we shall devise our formal systems with particular interpretations in mind; and, that being the case, we shall reflect in the calculus all of the *formal* relations that hold among the terms of the system. All that is left, then, is the ostensive part of the interpretation.

IV

Since we have supposed that some of the terms of the formal system have been interpreted ostensively or quasi-ostensively, we cannot lump the material axioms and meaning postulates together and regard them as constituting an *implicit definition* of the terms that occur in them. Ordinarily, there will be both material axioms and meaning postulates. Certain axioms (meaning postulates) in the calculus will be regarded as giving the theoretical (and quasi-ostensive) terms part of their meaning. Others (material axioms) will be taken to state the characteristics of the properties, objects, and relations denoted by these terms. Sometimes it is quite clear that a given axiom in a given formalization of a scientific theory performs one of these functions, but not the other. Sometimes it is not so clear.

We may ask whether or not there is a criterion that we can use for deciding which role an axiom plays: the role of a meaning postulate or that of a material axiom of the system. Observe that asking the question, "Is there any experience —i.e., any statement that can be phrased in ostensive terms—that will refute this statement?" is not generally decisive. There are such cases, of course. If we give "person", "club", and "member of" their usual, relatively ostensive meanings, then it is easy to see that finding a person who doesn't belong to a club will refute one of the axioms of our system. But if there is any appreciable theoretical content to the terms "member" and "club", then very likely there is an out: we will be able to reject something other than the axiom in question. And when it comes to rich theories, where what is actually tested is far removed from the original axioms on which it depends, and is dependent not only upon the abstract axioms but also on particular assertions (boundary conditions), that in turn depend on general theoretical structures, and indirectly, on many other assertions, a definitive experiment is rare indeed. In the event that experience does not turn out the way in which the system leads us to expect it to turn out, what is refuted is usually not a single statement, a single axiom, but a conjunction of statements. In real life, one might rather say a whole fabric of statements than a conjunction. What must go, in the face of recalcitrant experience, is only some element of this fabric. Sometimes it is quite clear what must go; other times it is open to considerable question; and at times it may be clearly a matter of free choice.

One argument for attempting to make a sharp distinction between axioms and meaning postulates is that we understand that no meaning postulate can be refuted by experience: a meaning postulate merely reflects a resolve concerning the use of language; it doesn't contain any assertions about the world that *can* be refuted. But this is an idealization, too. Just as scientific theories come to be refuted by recalcitrant experience, so scientific terms come to modify their meaning in similar circumstances; and this change of meaning is reflected in a change of meaning postulates. Sometimes we can save the maximum amount of structure of our scientific system by changing the meaning of some crucial terms. It is just as reasonable to suppose that experience can indicate the advisability of changing our scientific vocabulary as to suppose that it can cause us to reject material axioms.

And yet the two procedures are quite different. It is helpful and enlightening, despite the foregoing facts, to classify the basic statements of the calculus of a scientific formal system into two groups: one that we will hang on to very strongly, and one that we are less concerned to hang on to. The first group we may regard as irrefutable; we take them to reflect our decisions about the relations of the meanings of the terms that we employ. If we decide to reject a statement belonging to this group, we should say we had decided to change the meaning of a term, rather than that we had been *forced* to give up a generalization. The other class of statements we also tend to hang on to pretty strongly. We tend to plead inaccuracy of measurement, bias of instrument, or even incompetence of an investigator, when we encounter results that conflict with a popular theory; but fortunately for the development of science, there are pretty well-defined limits beyond which we cannot go in defending theories regarded as having empirical content. We can generally imagine having to give up one of these theories, in the face of certain plausible, imaginable bodies of experience. We regard them as having empirical content, and should we give one up, we should regard it, not as a decision to change our language, but as a course of action forced on us by an intransigent world.

This pragmatic criterion is sometimes clear enough; but is there a formal criterion corresponding to it? How can we distinguish between material axioms and meaning postulates? This question was first brought up by Quine. Quine also solved it: the axioms proper are the statements on the page marked "axioms", and the meaning postulates are the expressions that appear on the page marked "meaning postulates". It is a matter to a large extent arbitrary, and not generally very crucial, whether we list a given statement as a meaning postulate or as an axiom. If we have reason to accept the formal system as a whole, we have reason to accept all of its axioms as true, and it doesn't really make much difference whether a given (axiomatic) statement is true by virtue of the facts of the world, or by virtue of the meanings of the terms that occur in it.

There is none the less good reason to make the distinction clear cut, even though it must always remain to some extent arbitrary. At the point at which experience and experiment cause us to reject the system as a whole, it does make a difference—at least a difference in our analysis of what occurred. No axiom which is true by virtue of the meanings of the terms that occur in it can be rejected, unless we change the meanings of some of those terms. Thus to decide that Axioms A-1, A-2, and A-3 of our sociological system are to be true by virtue of the meanings of the terms they contain, is to say that, barring a change in the language, they will never be rejected; and this is just to say that if an experiment yields a result that conflicts with the theorems of the system, it will be A-4 or A-5 that we reject, or else the observation itself, rather than one of the first three axioms. And it is quite reasonable to make this decision, as to which axioms are to be vulnerable to experiment and which are not, in advance.

The foregoing discussion may suggest that the question of whether an axiom is to be regarded as a material axiom or a meaning postulate is always moot. This is far from the case. The problematic axioms (such as the equation "$f = ma$" in mechanics) are few and far between, though it is true that there is no axiom so obviously true by the meanings of its terms that some philosophical mind cannot build a case for regarding it as having factual content, and no material axiom so obviously material that another philosophical mind cannot build a case for regarding it as true by virtue of the very meanings of the terms that it contains. The claim that is made above is merely that in those relatively few cases where it requires no great exercise of philosophical ingenuity to generate doubts about the status of a given axiom, as in the case of "$f = ma$", the matter is not one of pressing urgency.

V

Let us look at some of the kinds of axioms that we may encounter in scientific systems, beginning with axioms that quite clearly play the role of meaning postulates.

First of all, in every scientific system, there will be a logical framework; and in most, there will be a mathematical framework as well. Although these frameworks may be incorporated unobtrusively in a rule of inference (to the effect that anything that goes in mathematics goes in the system in question), they may also be spelled out more explicitly with their own axioms and rules of inference. Thus we may perfectly well include among the axioms of a system of chemistry or sociology axioms that embody sentential logic and quantificational logic; and we will very often want to include among the axioms some axioms adequate to the development of set theory (axioms of membership), not only for the sake of the mathematics that can be developed only with the help of set theory, but also for its own sake: set-theoretical notions and formulations can be very helpful in the formal system itself. Almost no one would insist on regarding the logical and set theoretical axioms as material; they will amost universally be regarded as meaning postulates unfolding the meaning of such logical and mathematical constants as " $\downarrow$ ", "ϵ", "(x)", etc. (From a dialectical point of view, this is an oversimplification; and yet I cannot believe that even a dialectician could seriously regard such axioms as falsifiable.)

Next, we may have axioms that merely unfold the logical structure of the nonlogical terms they characterize. We have axioms that could naturally be replaced by formation rules—e.g., that "M" is a relation term may be expressed either by including in our system the foregoing Axiom M-1, or by stipulating that "M", followed by anything but two variables, is simply not well formed. We also have axioms that would not be replaced by formation rules, as these are ordinarily understood: axioms characterizing the internal structure of relations —e.g., that "longer than" is transitive and irreflexive, and that even its relational complement is transitive. The axioms that we found we needed in the development of quantitative predicates are all axioms of this sort. All of these axioms are naturally regarded as meaning postulates, for reasons that were mentioned in the discussion of quantities.

[127]

Third, we have meaning postulates in the most direct and natural sense: postulates which relate the meanings of different terms: thus, the "married to" relation holds between pairs of objects only if one member of the pair is a man, and the other member is a woman. (This is on the natural supposition that we do not offer an explicit definition of the term "married to", but merely wish to characterize it axiomatically, by meaning postulates.) Other examples: A postuate concerning the predicate "soluble" might have the form, "(x)(Soluble (x) $\supset$ (Placed-in-twenty-times-its-volume-of-water-and-shaken-for-ten-minutes(x) $\supset$ dissolves(x)))." A postulate concerning the three-termed relation "Gives (x,y,z)" might be: "$(x)(y)(z)$ (Gives (x,y,z) $\supset$ (Person (x) & Person (z)))."

Now we come to axioms that are taken to embody the empirical content of the formal system. These are what are generally presented, in the usual semi-formal development of a body of scientific knowledge as the axioms (although often a few meaning postulates, or what can be taken to be meaning postulates, sneak into the formulation). There are a number of different kinds of axioms that play a material role. Curiously, a type of axiom that is looked upon as temporary and deficient (in most bodies of knowledge) is one that most definitely and obviously and directly has empirical content. This is the statistical axiom: "The proportion of A's that are B's lies between the limits p and q." The better developed sciences attempt so far as possible to replace such statistical generalizations by universal ones. Observe that one may have statistical statements that formulate relations between abstract entities (such as energy states of particles), as well as statistical statements that relate ostensively defined predicates (such as "The proportion of plants grown from this box of seeds that will have red flowers is around a quarter.") And one may also have mixed statistical statements: "The proportion of objects that reflect light in the red range of wavelengths, that look red in daylight, is very close to unity."

A second kind of axiom is the straightforward law-like generalization or theoretical statement. By the term "lawlike generalization", I do not of course mean merely those statements that begin with a universal quantifier and are conditional in form, though this may be the most common case. There are some simple generalizations that merely relate terms that have relatively ostensive meanings—at least at some point in the development of science—such as, "All creatures with livers have hearts," "All fish have gills," etc. But such generalizations tend to be superceded in two ways. First, the terms that they employ come to have theoretical meanings, come to be no longer purely ostensive. Then, though the generalization may remain, it is no longer a simple generalization about ostensively defined terms, but a part of a theoretical structure. Often it comes to be derivable from more powerful theoretical axioms, and thus no longer plays an axiomatic role. Second, exceptions to such generalizations tend to turn up (indeed, a good part of the task of science consists in the search for just such exceptions), so that they can no longer be accepted at all, except in an attentuated, statistical form.

[128]

There are also axiomatic generalizations in formal systems relating theoretical terms and ostensive terms: "Every seed that is homozygous for red flowers will produce a plant that has red flowers." They can go the other way, too: "Every pair of plants with red flowers is such that, if they are crossed they will produce seeds homozygous for red flowers." But of course the most important kind of generalization which is properly included as a material axiom in a formal system is the universal generalization that involves purely theoretical terms: "All triangles have angle sums of 180°," "The gravitational attraction between any two bodies varies inversely with the square of their distance and directly with the product of their masses," and the like.

The statements, "There is a maximum velocity," or "There is a minimum temperature," might be taken as axiomatic in a particular formalization of a part of physics, and should be regarded as theoretical statements, as well as such particular-sounding statements as, "Phosphorus melts at 43°C." We may thus have as axioms purely existential statements, and statements which (in English) sound singular or particular, but which in the strictly formalized system may be seen to have universal form. Thus "Phosphorus melts at 43°C" does not mean that the substance phosphorus is constantly engaged in melting at 43°C, but that for every x, if x is a sample of this substance phosphorus, and x is heated for a suitable length of time under standard conditions, then x will melt at this temperature.

It should be clear from this that there is no clue as to the nature of an axiom—whether it is material or a meaning postulate—in the syntactical form of the axiom. A statement of any syntactical form at all may turn out to be an axiom of either kind. In order to see whether a statement in an actual body of scientific knowledge is an axiom of one or another of these kinds, we must see how it functions in the system; and perhaps even more important, how it would function in the system under various possible hypothetical circumstances. If the statement is an axiom at all, it functions as a premise (characteristically) and not as a conclusion in arguments formulated in the system. If it is a meaning postulate, it will often function as a suppressed or enthymematic premise. Sometimes we can spell out precisely what circumstances would cause us to reject the statement as false, and then it is clear that its function is material; and similarly, if we cannot imagine what it would *mean* to regard it as false, we can be sure that it functions as a meaning postulate. And sometimes we simply won't be able to tell.

VI

Not all scientific laws are so neat and clean as the ones we have considered so far. There are many that might be taken as axioms in certain formalizations which only hold within certain ranges. The ideal gas law is one example, Hooke's law is another. Hooke's law states that stress is proportional to strain—within elastic limits determined by the substance and the state (temperature, pressure) of the substance. Properly speaking, the law is not fully formulated until the limits are stated. But there is a difficulty in stating the limits: the law does not hold perfectly within one range and then break down outside that range. It is only approximate (but so close to accurate as to make no difference) in the best part of its range; and it is still a good enough approximation to be useful, sometimes, pretty far outside its range of highest accuracy. What should be included as a part of such a law in a formal system, is a statement of its range of application, and the magnitudes of discrepancy within various parts of that range. There are two possibilities here: if the law is the central postulate in a small formal system (e.g., a formal system describing elastic behavior), we may make the stipulation of the range of substances to which it applies, and perhaps even the range of errors that may be expected, to be metalinguistic stipulations *about* the formal system, perhaps limiting the domain in which the variables of the system may take their values. On the other hand, if, as is generally the case, Hooke's law is to be a law within a broad framework of physical theory, then the indication of the ranges and errors involved in applications of the law must be stated *within* the theory. Indeed, in a general system of physics, such limitations would be deducible consequences of more abstract axioms characterizing the behavior of matter; and indeed Hooke's law itself would become merely an approximation, applicable to special cases, of such axioms or their implications.

This approximative character of much of what is accepted as scientific theory is something that commentators on science often seem to overlook. They write, for example, as if the fact that Einsteinian physics has replaced Newtonian physics has created a novel situation in that we now use Newtonian principles, even though they are strictly incorrect, to calculate the trajectories of missiles and the rise and fall of the tides. But this, so far from being novel, is precisely what is typical of physical science. So long as there has been physical science, we have used for calculation formulas that we have known with practical certainty to be "incorrect", not because we had no better ones, but because these "incorrect" ones were simpler and perfectly accurate enough for our purposes. The fact that this engineering aspect of scientific calculation has been forgotten about has led people to ignore altogether the fact that many of the formulas that are used in physics and engineering hold good only within a certain degree of approximation and within a certain range of application.

Nevertheless, the fundamental axioms of such a science as physics, are to be understood as holding precisely; and of course that is the goal toward which we strive in any science. We want no "about's" or "approximately's" in our axioms. But the formal system (or at any rate our philosophical view of it) must be such as to take account of the fact that in many, or even most, of the practical applications of the system for making predictions about the world, or constructing explanations, a certain amount of looseness of fit is inevitable. To deal with

[130]

this looseness, to bring it under control, we require a theory of error to be built into the formal system itself. And to make philosophical sense of the formal systems that we actually have—i.e., the sciences that we have developed— and particularly to make sense of the connection between these systems and the messy old world to which we attempt to apply them, we must take very seriously this matter of errors and discrepancies.

The next two chapters are directly concerned with measurement and probability; but they are also essentially both concerned with the concept of error.

BIBLIOGRAPHICAL NOTES TO CHAPTER 5

The ingenious technique by which the axioms of the sociological theory were turned into geometrical truths is due to W. V. O. Quine, "Implicit Definition Sustained," *Journal of Philosophy* **61**, 1964. Quine's more serious Philosophical treatment of the issue of conventionalism is to be found in "Truth by Convention," *Philosophical Essays for A. N. Whitehead*, 1936, and "Two Dogmas of Empiricism," Philosophical Review **60**, 1951. Both of these latter essays are included in *The Philosophy of Mathematics* edited by Hilary Putnam and Paul Benacerraf (Englewood Cliffs, New Jersey: Prentice-Hall, 1964). "Implicit Definition Sustained," and "Truth by Convention," also appear in *The Ways of Paradox*, a collection of Quine's essays (New York: Random House, 1966). Another important contemporary essay on the same subject is Morton White's, "The Analytic and Synthetic: An Untenable Dualism," in *John Dewey* (Sidney Hook, ed.), (New York: Basic Books, 1950).

For the classical background of the suggestion that physical laws might be understood as conventions regarding the use of technical terms (i.e., as meaning postulates) rather than as factual laws (i.e., as empirical axioms), see Pierre Duhem, *La Theorie Physique*, Paris, 1906, translated as *The Aim and Structure of Physical Theory* (Princeton, New Jersey: Princeton University Press, 1954), and Henri Poincaré, *Science and Hypothesis* (New York: Dover Publications, 1952).

The approach followed here of distinguishing between meaning postulates and axioms with empirical content is defended by Rudolf Carnap in *Meaning and Necessity*, Chicago, 1947 and in *Introduction to Semantics*, Cambridge, Mass., 1948. Carnap also discusses these issues in "The Methodological Character of Theoretical Concepts," *Minnesota Studies in the Philosophy of Science*, Vol. I, 1956, and in "Meaning Postulates," *Philosophical Studies* **3**, 1952. This latter paper is reprinted in the most recent edition of *Meaning and Necessity*. For Carnap's treatment of these matters as they bear on natural science, see his *Philosophical Foundations of Physics*, Part V (New York: Basic Books, 1966).

Further discussion of the knotty issues involved may be found in Quine, "Carnap and Logical Truth," and Herbert Bohnert, "Carnap's Theory of

Definition and Analyticity," both of which appear in *The Philosophy of Rudolf Carnap* (Schlipp, ed.).

For a discussion of the various forms that material scientific axioms may have, see Ernest Nagel's *Structure of Science*, Chapters Four and Five and Hempel's *Philosophy of Natural Science*, Chapters Five and Six.

Chapter **6**

PROBABILITY AND ERROR

I

A fundamental concept in understanding science, and in understanding the role which scientific formal systems play in knowledge, belief, and practical action, is that of a rational corpus or body of knowledge. Fundamental to that, in turn, and also dependent on it, is the concept of probability. Interdependent as they are, both concepts must be developed simultaneously.

A rational corpus is a body of knowledge; in keeping with the formalistic approach that I have adopted throughout, I shall consider it a set of statements. The ground on which a statement comes to be included in a rational corpus, is its probability relative to some other rational corpus. I shall suppose that this is always the case, although there are many details concerning this matter that remain to be worked out. They are technical details, however, and need not bother us unduly.

[133]

One immediate question, which deserves to be immediately answered, is this: if probability is defined relative to a rational corpus, and inclusion in a rational corpus is conditioned by probability, how do we avoid circularity? The answer is that we can consider a particular basic rational corpus as a starting point, the statements of which are accepted not because they are probable, but because they are indisputable. "Indisputable" is a better word than "certain", which has overtones of logical or analytic truth. Included in this basic rational corpus, then, will be such statements as the axioms of our logic, the semantic rules governing the relations among the terms we use, etc.—i.e., everything that we may appropriately regard as devoid of empirical content. These statements may quite appropriately be regarded as both indisputable and certain. In addition, we may include a stock of statements which, for the purposes at hand, are regarded as reporting observations: "*a* looks red", "*b* looks like a dog and looks brown", and so on, at one extreme; "*a* is a rat", "*b* is hungry", "*c* is angry", at the other extreme. Such a set of statements is a result of rational reconstruction, to use a descriptive phrase of Carnap's—it does not in any sense need to be historically accurate or even plausible. Indeed it is simply historically false: one can only formulate the distinction between *being* red and *looking* red on the basis of a fairly full fledged and complex scientific structure.

Relative to this rational corpus, which is determined without reference to probabilities, we can define probabilities, and, with their help, other rational corpora. We may distinguish *levels* of rational corpora, according to the degree of probability which is taken to be necessary and sufficient for admission into the rational corpus. We take the rational corpus of indisputable contents as the highest level. The degree of probability that is necessary and sufficient for the admission of a statement into a rational corpus, corresponds to "practical certainty"; we may say in general that a statement that is "practically certain" is one that may be accepted; but the practical certainty, or level of acceptance, that is appropriate in one worldly situation may not be appropriate in another— and that is one reason that we must be prepared to talk of a series of rational corpora.

Before we can define more than one level of rational corpus, we must introduce the concept of probability. Following Carnap, we shall take probability statements to be metalinguistic statements—i.e., statements that have as their subject matter linguistic expressions. In particular, a probability statement, on this view, has direct reference to a body of knowledge (a set of statements), and implicitly has reference to an individual expression (a name, or a definite description) and a pair of class expressions (names or descriptions or abstracts). Finally, it involves reference to a pair of arithmetic terms that represents a probability interval (often idealized as a point). An example will help. One might run across such a statement as: the probability in an experiment involving the exposure of a photographic film to radiation, that four spots will be found on the film is about $\frac{1}{3}$. This may be interpreted as follows: There is an experiment e denoted by the proper name "e"; a class E, denoted by "E", and a class $4S$, consisting of experiments like e (elements of E) which have the outcome described: four spots on the film; this class is denoted by "$4S$". And contained in the rational corpus (reference to which is implicit in the probability statement) is a statistical statement: "The proportion of elements of E that are elements of $4S$ is about $\frac{1}{3}$"—or, better, "The proportion of elements of E that are elements of $4S$ is $\frac{1}{3} \pm \epsilon$." One further condition, yet more difficult to spell out, is that the object e be a *random member* of the set E, with respect to membership in the set $4S$, relative to that rational corpus.

The most important ingredient of the probability statement is the statistical statement. A simple statistical statement is a statement of the form: "The proportion of A's that are B's lies between p and q." Often only perfectly precise statistical statements are considered; but this is an unfortunate simplification when it comes to attempting to make sense out of induction and the way in which past experience makes certain types of future experiences probable. Let us represent such a statistical statement by the expression: "$Ra(A,B,p,q)$", which is to be read, "The ratio of B's among A's (or the proportion of A's that are B's) lies between p and q." This is a complicated locution, but it is one that is central to the whole of science as it is to be reconstructed. One avoids it only at the cost of being forced into utterly false positions. The expression "$Ra(A,B,p,q)$", as directly interpreted, only makes good sense, of course, when A is finite—i.e., when there are only a finite number of A's. But initially there is no cause to deal with infinite classes; and when we do deal with infinitely large classes, we will have enough body of theory with us to give us good reason to assign *measures* to them in terms of which we can make sense of "$Ra(A,B,p,q)$" even when A is infinite. When A is infinite there are often several measures which make good intuitive sense, so it is perhaps going too far to say that "Ra" is simply an idealization and extension of the notion of ratio; but it is very nearly that.

Examples of statements of this form that we have good reason to believe: "The proportion of heads on tosses of a coin, if a great many tosses are made, will fall between 4/10 and 6/10." "The proportion of sweet peas with white flowers that result from a cross of pure red and pure white strains will be between 0.2 and 0.3." Further statements of this type that we might have reason to accept: "The proportion of white salaried males who are healthy in their thirty-ninth year, who survive to their fortieth year, lies between 0.984 and 0.986." "The proportion of electrons in interference experiment I, that pass through the right hand slit of the apparatus, lies between 0.4999 and 0.5001." "In a cross between two strains S_1 and S_2, of drosophila, the characteristic C will occur in approximately 0.375 of the offspring." In general the locution most often employed to express the parameters of the simple statistical statement is "approximately p", where p is the midpoint between the parameters, and "approximately"

[135]

is intended to mean "plus or minus ϵ"; the approximate value of ϵ is determined by the context.

There are statistical statements that are not simple. Although their fundamental role is merely to lead to simple statistical statements that can be used as guides to action, that role is tremendously important in science. These non-simple statistical statements are statements that give the distribution of some quantity over a class, or the distribution of a pair or triple or ... of quantities. For example: the proportion of people less than x inches tall is between $F_1(x)$ and $F_2(x)$, or is about $F(x)$—i.e., $F(x)$ plus or minus ϵ. The proportion of pigeons that weigh less than x grams, and have wingspans of less than z centimeters, is between $G_1(x,z)$ and $G_2(x,z)$, or about $G(x,z)$—i.e., $G(x,z)$ plus or minus δ. The only difference between these statements and the simple statistical ones, is that these contain a free variable "x", or several free variables, "x", "z", etc. They thus give rise to a whole family of simple statistical statements, one for each possible value of x, or for each possible pair of values of x and z, or.... There are other kinds of statements that one runs into in statistics, as some readers may know; but these are merely auxiliary statements whose relation to the statements already mentioned is such that their interesting mathematical properties may be utilized in computations, and in uncovering further relations between the statements of the forms mentioned already: frequency functions, generating functions, etc.

Now of course if we know a statement of the form "$Ra(A,B, 0.2,0.3)$" we will also know a statement of the form "$Ra(A,B,0.1,0.7)$"—it is trivially entailed by the former. But it doesn't interest us; and so in our discussion of statistical statements and probability we shall restrict our attention to *strongest* statistical statements: "$Ra(A,B,p,q)$" is a strongest statistical statement provided that there is no other statement "$Ra(A,B,p',q')$" which belongs to the rational corpus or body knowledge under discussion, and which is such that $p' \geq p$ and $q' \leq q$, with inequality holding in at least one case. This corresponds perfectly to the ordinary and intuitive sense of "strength" that one would attribute to statistical statements.

A statement about probability thus always depends on statements about proportions—either simple statistical statements or nonsimple statistical statements. But in order to make a statement about probability, more conditions must be satisfied than that we know the corresponding statistical statement. In particular, our body knowledge or belief must satisfy criteria concerning randomness: the probability of a statement of the form "$a \in B$" will be the interval (p,q) only if (1) we know (reasonably believe) a strongest statistical statement of the form "$Ra(A,B,p,q)$", and (2) a is a *random* member of A with respect to B, relative to what we know. Again this is a metalinguistic criterion. It is a criterion that is exceedingly difficult to spell out in detail. But the idea is simple enough: a is a random member of A with respect to B, provided we do not know any statement of the form "$a \in A^*$", such that we know that A^* is a subset of A and also know

[136]

the proportion of A^*'s that are B's, and know that it differs from the proportion of A's that are B's. The second criterion, like the first, is a metalinguistic one.

We may attempt to spell out the criterion of randomness formally as follows: we say that a is a random member of A, with respect to B, relative to a given body of knowledge or rational corpus, only if

(1) "$a \in A$" belongs to that rational corpus.
(2) If "$a \in A^*$" belongs to that rational corpus, then either:
   (a) "A is a subset of A^*" does belong to the rational corpus, or
   (b) If "$Ra(A,B,p,q)$" is a strongest statement about A and B, and "$Ra(A^*, B,p^*,q^*)$" is a strongest statement about A^* and B then $p \geq p^*$ and $q \leq q^*$.

Things are not really this simple: it would be found, on investigation, that the second condition does not serve the purpose we want it to serve, for a number of quite different reasons. Nevertheless, the formulation, incorrect though it be, does provide a framework which is sufficient to allow for reasonable discussion of most of the instances that will concern us.

II

For an example of how the definition works, let us consider the question of the probability, for an insurance company, that John Appleby will die next year. The insurance company knows a great deal about John Appleby, besides his name and initials. It knows that he is married; the name of his wife and the number and ages of his children; the name of his employer; that he is white and salaried; that he drives twenty miles a day to work; that he is underweight, and smokes a pack of cigarettes a day, and is subject to no noticeable disease. He is 39 years old.

The insurance company also has a lot of statistics at its disposal. Let us use the code "12" for "dies within specified 12-month period"; in general this will be death rate per year; in the case of people of specified age, it is death within 12 months of their attaining that age. Further let us use "Obs" as an operator on classes that yields the observed part of the class; thus "Obs(A)" denotes the observed part of A.

Ra(Obs(white male racing drivers), 12, 0.076,0.076)
Ra(Obs(males), 12, 0.024,0.024)
Ra(Obs(39-year-old males), 12, 0.011,0.011)
Ra(Obs(smokers), 12, 0,1)
Ra(Obs(39-year-old males, married, 2 children), 12, 0,1)
Ra(Obs(white males) 12, 0.021,0.021)
Ra(Obs(salaried white males), 12, 0.018,0.018)
Ra(Obs(39-year-old, salaried white males), 12, 0.009,0.009)
Ra(Obs(39-year-old, salaried, white male smokers), 12, 0,1).

[137]

There will be other information as well; but let us suppose that this suffices. Notice that the interval in each of these statements is either the whole interval (0,1), or else is a degenerate interval of the form "(p,p)". The reason for this is that the foregoing list simply represents the statistics that the insurance company has collected on the classes involved: either the insurance company has actuarial tables (in which case the interval is degenerate), or they do not have actuarial tables for the classes in question, in which case the interval is (0,1). Now of course we know that John Appleby does not belong to any of the classes for which there are statistics in the tables: for it is data, not conjecture that goes into the tables, and John will not be data for an actuarial table until he has breathed his last. But the tables support general hypotheses that do apply to John Appleby, and to all the other live ones who take out insurance with the company. For if in the past, on the average, 24 males out of a thousand have died during a specified year, it is reasonable to suppose that in the coming year *about* 24 out of a thousand will die; and if on the average, in the past, 18 salaried white males have died during a given year, out of a thousand, it is reasonable to suppose that in the coming year, *about* 18 salaried white males out of a thousand will die. These figures, of course, only apply to very large populations; some of the reasons underlying this are purely mathematical and can be demonstrated in purely mathematical terms. We shall give some indication of the nature of this demonstration later, when we consider induction in science. The interest of these statistical reports just listed, for the insurance company, is that they support general statistical statements that do apply to the living individuals that the insurance company is dealing with.

So in general, the preceding statistical statements serve to support the following (although the latter may never appear in the insurance company records; it may be that the company leaves the inferential step implicit):

Ra(white male racing drivers, 12, $0.076 - \epsilon_1$, $076 + \epsilon_1$)
Ra(males, 12, $0.024 - \epsilon_2$, $0.024 + \epsilon_2$)
Ra(39-year-old males, 12, $0.011 - \epsilon_3$, $0.011 + \epsilon_3$)
Ra(smokers, 12, 0, 1)
Ra(39-year-old males, married, 2 children, 12, 0,1)
Ra(white males, 12, $0.021 - \epsilon_4$, $0.021 + \epsilon_4$)
Ra(salaried white males, 12, $0.018 - \epsilon_5$, $0.018 + \epsilon_5$)
Ra(39-year-old, salaried white males, 12, $0.009 - \epsilon_6$, $0.009 + \epsilon_6$)
Ra(39-year-old, salaried, white male smokers, 12, 0,1).

To be precise and realistic, the descriptive phrases "males", "39-year-old males", etc., should be understood to denote all those objects in the present, the recent past, and the short term future, to which they apply. In philosophical and logical discourse they are often understood to denote all those objects to which the phrases apply at *any* time in the past, present, or future, but living conditions change, and we have good reason to suppose that the ratios mentioned in our statistical generalization will not hold for the indefinite future. Observe that it is a very different thing to have good reason to suppose that certain ratios will not be maintained in the future, and to have *no* reason to suppose that they *will* be maintained. I am referring here not to any uncertainties we may have about induction, but to the extensive knowledge we have concerning human longevity.

To return to John Appleby: the insurance company will attribute the probability $(0.991 - \epsilon, 0.991 + \epsilon)$, to his survival for the coming year; he is a member of the class of 39-year-old, white salaried males, and a random member of that class, so far as the representation of the rational corpus of the insurance company is concerned; and the proportion of that class that dies within a year is, according to the next to last statistical statement in the preceding list, between $0.009 - \epsilon$ and $0.009 + \epsilon$. He is a random member of that class, with respect to the property of dying within a year (or surviving for a year) relative to the body of information in the insurance company archives, because although he is known to belong to a vast number of other classes, none of them violate condition (2): He is a male, but [(2)(a)] the class of 39-year-old, salaried white married males is certainly known to be included in the set of males. He is a 39-year-old, salaried, white married male who smokes, but [(2)(b)], the strongest statistical information the insurance company has about this class (since it has collected no statistics, or not enough to count), is that the proportion of survivors in this class for 12 months is between 0 and 1, and $0 < 0.991 - \epsilon$ and $0.991 + \epsilon < 1$.

Consider Peter Potter, who didn't fill in all the forms on his application to the insurance company. His form tells us that he is salaried, white, male, has two children, flies an airplane, and that his grandfather lived to be 109. In point of fact, the insurance company would ask him how old he was, and what his wife's name was, and so on; but as matters stand they can still give a probability for his survival for the next year: $(0.982 - \epsilon, 0.982 + \epsilon)$. The argument is just the same: for every other class to which he is known to belong, either the class of white salaried males is included in that class (e.g., if the class is that of white males), or else (e.g., he is a smoker) the relevant statistical statement is not so strong as the one we already have.

Finally, consider Albert Allen, who is another salaried white male, but who is also, in season, a racing car driver. For him the insurance company has no probability of survival. This is not because he is a racing car driver, but because he is both a racing car driver and a salaried man. Because of the particular state of the insurance company's body of knowledge (its records), he cannot be a random member of either the class of white male racing car drivers (because he is a salaried white male, and neither is the class of white racing car drivers a subclass of this class, nor do we have $0.825 - \epsilon > 0.982 - \epsilon$ and $0.825 + \epsilon < 0.982 + \epsilon$).

[139]

Similarly, he cannot be a random member of the class of salaried white males. In point of actual fact, the insurance company wouldn't hesitate to insure him—at the racing driver's rate; they have perfectly good grounds for believing that the mortality among people who race cars only a small part of the time cannot be greater than that among those who race cars all the time. (Any difference in skilfulness would be swamped by the difference in exposure.) This is to say that the grounds the insurance company has for accepting the first and seventh statistical statements on page 138, will also be grounds for accepting the further statistical statement:

$$Ra(\text{salaried white male racing drivers, } 12, 0.018 - \epsilon_5, 0.076 + \epsilon_1).$$

The insurance company is not interested in the lower limit of mortality, but I have put in the lower limit for salaried white males on the grounds that just as the mortality for salaried white male racing car drivers cannot exceed the mortality for racing car drivers in general, so the mortality for salaried white male racing car drivers is bound to be at least as great as for salaried white males in general.

One further principle of probability we need is that if a certain statement S is known to be true if and only if a certain statement T is true—and this may depend on facts that we know, as well as on intrinsic logical relationships between S and T—then T will have a given probability, relative to what we know, if and only if S does. To put it in a nutshell: statements that are *known* to be equivalent in truth value must have the same probability.

One of the consequences of the definitions of probability and randomness I have presented is that there will sometimes simply be no probability. Sometimes this will be due to a lack of information (e.g., for a lady who applies to the insurance company whose skimpy records I have given above), and sometimes it will be due to an excess of information, or, better put, to the particular character of the information at hand, as in the case of Albert Allen.

Most of probability theory and mathematical statistics is concerned with statistical statements in which a proportion is said to have a certain value, or the corresponding probability is said to be a certain real number. The reason for this is that far and away the most frequent use of statistics is in a context in which there is a vast background of theory, and theoretical statistical statements very often have the degenerate form. Thus one says that in the case of two pairs of genes that are not linked at all, the proportion of offspring that bear a given possible combination of the genes is exactly the same as the proportion of offspring that bear some other combination. This entails that the relative frequencies in a long run of offspring will be very nearly equal. It is only the latter that we can test—we cannot run an experiment on *possible* offspring, but only on actual ones. But we notice that the larger the number of actual offspring, the closer do the ratios conform to the theoretical proportion. Much the same is true of the most common context of all in which probability statements are used:

gambling talk. One says that the probability of a head on a toss of a coin is a half, not that it is *about* a half, because a coin, in this context, is an apparatus *designed* to yield heads half the time and tails half the time. That the arrangement does do this, we are reasonably well assured by physical theory, which tells us that very small changes in the momenta (particularly angular momentum about an axis lying in the face of the coin) within a wide range of total energies will produce completely different results.

III

Some of the same facts underlie the conventional analysis of error. Although the analysis of error is a chapter of mathematical statistics, or probability theory, all by itself, we shall not need to enter very deeply into it; we are here concerned only to understand measurement, and measurement, on which all of quantitative science depends, (and as we saw, almost all science has quantitative aspects), itself depends for its meaningfulness and interpretation on the concept of error. One could say, indeed, that without error, measurement would be impossible. This means, of course, that if one had no concept of error, one could never reconcile conflicting measurements, conflicts between measurements and predictions made by means of a theory, and so on.

Recall our earlier discussion of quantities. Even there it would have been impossible to construct quantitative measures without introducing the concept of error. Without this concept we have only the brute fact that sometimes transitivity of "longer than" (for example) holds, and sometimes it doesn't hold. With the introduction of error, we can claim that the occasions on which it does not hold are occasions when error plays a role. Error is a delicate concept: for if we can call on it at will, or wilfully, then it no longer explains anything or accounts for anything. And if we can't call on it when we need it, none of our theories (even the theory of transitivity of the quantitative relation "has greater length than") will stand up. If the concept of error makes it too easy to explain discrepancies, our theories will float off into meaninglessness, detached from their empirical roots; if our concept of error is too tough, then it explains too little, and no general theory will avoid obvious refutation.

We noticed, in the earlier discussion, that one of the differences between the preformal ambiguity of terms, and the postformal uncertainty of their application, was that the uncertainty could often be interpreted as error and measured or controlled or both. The beginning of this, in fact, is the observation that certain procedures lead to results that exhibit discrepancies more often than other procedures. Thus to measure a table with a yardstick with inches marked on it will lead to more uniform results, than measuring the same table with an inchstick. We could be more precise (and far more sophisticated) about this: we could measure a given quantity, with a given instrument (by a given technique) over and over again. It is a hypothesis, of course, that the quantity being

[141]

measured remains as given, just as it is a hypothesis of slightly different order, that the measuring instrument remains standardized. Notice here that a footrule is not a foot long "by definition"; it is a foot long, more or less, according as more or less care was used in its manufacture; and the standard object according to which its length was determined in manufacture, was itself manufactured, according to another (presumably superior) standard; and eventually we may work our way back to platinum rods that weigh hundreds of pounds and are kept in glass cases to be taken out once every few years—and perhaps one of these may be regarded as being the length that it is *by definition*. But even this is an open question once we have—as of course we do have—a broad and full body of acceptable statements relating the lengths of things to the lengths of things. If all the platinum bodies in the world suddenly shrank by a factor $1/k$, we would certainly say they did (other things being equal), and accept the fact that they did, rather than saying that every other body, and every other distance increased by a corresponding factor, "because the platinum standard cannot change in length." (In fact, the problem does not arise, because the current standard of length is not a physical object at all but the wavelength of light emitted by a certain kind of atom in a certain state of excitation.)

Now suppose we measure a given quantity over and over again. We get a certain sequence of numbers. The numbers exhibit a certain pattern (noticed in a useful way by Gauss in the eighteenth century). Large discrepancies among measurements are pretty rare, very large ones are much rarer than that; very small ones are pretty common. We can form a clear picture of what the set of numbers will look like by forming a histogram: take all the measurements that are so close as to be regarded as the same (say, in the table example, those that come out to the same eighth of an inch), and call them the same. Thus we might find out of a hundred measurements that 42 are "$54\frac{1}{8}$", 21 are "$54\frac{2}{8}$", 13 are "54", 7 are "$54\frac{3}{8}$", 4 are "$54\frac{5}{8}$", 1 is "$54\frac{6}{8}$", 1 is "55", 6 are "$53\frac{7}{8}$", 2 are "$53\frac{6}{8}$", 2 are "$53\frac{5}{8}$", and 1 is "$53\frac{3}{8}$". The histogram looks like Fig. 1.

This histogram is typical, and the more measurements we take, the more it will look like the standard bell-shaped curve which is represented by the function:

$$y = \frac{1}{\sqrt{2\pi}} \exp\left[\frac{-(x-m)^2}{2\sigma^2}\right].$$

Furthermore, if we measure other objects by the same method, we will get similar curves. And if we measure the same or different objects by another method, we will get another set of curves, different from the first, but still having the same general form.

These are empirical facts. We could have measurement even if the results of measurement did not have this character; we could invent (discover?) quantities, we could think up the concept of error, we could be led to imagine that underlying the various numbers yielded by a group of measurements there was a single

[142]

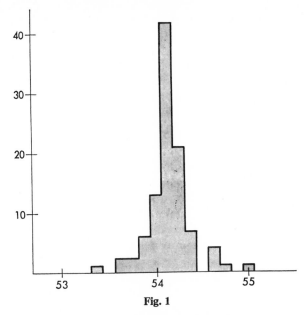

Fig. 1

quantity. It is not the particular form of the distribution of results that is important, but the fact that there is such a distribution.

Notice that these empirical facts do not constitute a condition for having a formal system; we could perfectly well have a biological or psychological formal system without any theory of error; we could even have quantitative predicates in our formal system without having a theory of error: we would have to have error, to account for the failure of our observations to satisfy such requirements as transitivity, but it need not be a concept of error which is amendable to theoretical or quantitative treatment. The situation is merely that if these empirical facts did not obtain, it would be more difficult—perhaps impossible—to develop precise quantitative theories: for it is in virtue of these fact that we can in many instances come arbitrarily close to discovering the "true value" of a quantity. That is, it is possible, for any ϵ and any p, within limits, to specify a number n of measurements such that the probability is at least p that the average of that number of measurements lies within an interval of length 2ϵ about the true value of the quantity. The actual ability to specify the n depends on our knowing, roughly, the form of the distribution of the measurements. It is also our ability to specify such an n, and also to perform a sequence of n measurements, that makes it meaningful and fruitful to talk about the true values of quantities.

IV

Since measurement is so fundamental to the quantitative sciences, and since the theory of error plays such a large part in the specification of rules connecting the formulas of the theory to the measurements that are actually made with people's hands, we shall consider in detail a small amount of the mathematical theory of error.

The curves that one gets from repeated measurements of a given quantity by a given method are not always symmetrical, but it is generally the case that the lack of symmetry, if any, can be reduced by increased carefulness. Similarly, any other deviations from the standard bell-shaped form can be (generally) reduced in magnitude by increased attention to detail. Now the standard bell-shaped form of the distribution of measurements is a well-known form; it is characterized, as above, by a formula with two parameters that determine the particular curve that the measurements fall near: the parameter m, which is the number at which the curve reaches its maximum, is called the *mean*, and corresponds to the notion of "average" for a finite number of values; m indicates the *location* of the curve; and the parameter σ, called the *standard deviation*, indicates its dispersion, or how spread out it is along the line. These are the only two variables there are in the formula: a set of measurements of almost any kind can be described by such a curve and thus can be characterized by the location parameter m, and by the dispersion parameter σ. When we take such a curve as representing a set of measurements, we say that the measurements are distributed *normally*; the bell-shaped curve is called also the normal curve, or the error curve, or the Gaussian curve.

Now we make a theoretical leap. It is one thing to take such a (continuous) curve to characterize in some significant way a finite set of measurements that have actually been made (it is like the statistical statements that represent the actuarial tables of the insurance company); it is something else to take that curve as characterizing a set of measurements that have not been made—potential measurements, we might say. The passage from the known statistical statement in the tables of the insurance company, to the conjectured statistical statement on which the insurance company bases its expectations about the future, is a simple matter of generalization, and thus suffers a certain determinate amount of uncertainty; the passage from the concept of a normal curve characterizing a given set of measurements, to the normal curve as characterizing the *process* of measurement is similar in principle, even though it is quite different in detail. It is different because we consider the two parameters σ and m, to correspond to quite distinct factors in the measurement situation. We take σ to be characteristic of the measuring process and to be the same, whatever magnitude (within limits) we are measuring; and we take m to be characteristic of that magnitude, and to be independent of the process by which we measure it.

In our theory of quantity, we required that the quantity, the magnitude, be something with certain theoretical properties. It was related to observable things only roughly and indirectly: if two quantities were different enough, we were to be able to judge that they were different with little likelihood of error; in assign-

[144]

ing numbers to quantities, it was required that the assignment be fairly uniform, but not that it be infallible. Now we have a theory of error, and also a theory of measurement provided we take the m of the theory of error to be the *quantity*. But then m is no longer characteristic of any particular sequence of actual measurements; rather, m is characteristic of a set of numbers (a population of numbers, if you will) from which each actual measurement is a selection. The population may be thought of, as suggested above, as a set of potential or possible results of measurement. These results exist only in potentiality: we can't ever measure the same object by a given method more than a finite number of times, yet there cannot be a finite number of possible results, for then the Gaussian curve would not define their distribution. Nevertheless, this infinite set of possible results serves to define the relation between the result of measurement and the abstract theoretical quantity. The set of possible results needn't be supposed to exist in some strange extra-material realm: it can be regarded simply as a *theoretical property*—a potentiality—of the measurement process; or it can be considered simply as a mathematical abstraction—a bare mathematical gimmick—that allows us to make computations which lead to results that are in statistical conformity with experience.

The Gaussian or normal curve of error is a statistical distribution, and like any statistical distribution that is of practical interest to us, it serves to provide a basis for probability statements. Let us take σ, characteristic of the measuring process, for granted for a moment. Then, given m, we can calculate from the curve the proportion of measurements that will yield results less than x, for any arbitrary x; or the proportion that will be greater than y; or the proportion that will lie between x and y. Here is a case where the word "proportion" is incorrect, strictly speaking, since the population or set we are considering is strictly infinite (in fact nondenumerably infinite), and the word "proportion" is well defined only for finite populations. But here is a case also where there is a strong theoretical framework in which "proportion" can be interpreted unambiguously as *measure*, and in which a given theoretical proportion can be realized with closer and closer accuracy, according to the theory itself, by taking increasingly larger samples. Notice the difference: it is not that we *define* the "proportion" of the theory as the limit, as we take larger and larger samples, of the ordinary finite population proportion; it is that the theory itself leads to the consequence that this number, that I have called "proportion", is more and more closely approximated in larger and larger samples. And even this connection is strictly only a probabilistic one: we can't be sure that a larger sample will be closer, but we have every reason to believe that it will.

Now this is just to say that, given the true value of a quantity (which we have identified with m, the mean of the distribution of measurements of that quantity), we can calculate proportions and thus figure probabilities about the results of measurements. The process is almost automatic, for the randomness

[145]

requirement we need to meet in order to arrive at probabilities is met almost automatically, or if it is not met, we have no need to introduce probabilities at all. If a magnitude is Q, we can ask for the probability that a given measurement of it, by a process with given σ, will yield a number less than k. There are two possibilities: if the measurement has been performed, then it is a member of a class (e.g., its unit class, the class consisting of it alone) in which the relevant proportion is 0 or 1, according as that measurement is not or is less than k. And if the measurement has not been performed, then its result is generally a random member of the set of numbers whose distribution is given by the error curve, and the probability that it is less than k, is just the proportion (in the extended sense) of those numbers that are less than k.

In general, the probability that a measurement that *has been made* and whose value we know to be less than a given number, or greater than a given number, or to lie in a given interval, is 0 to 1, according as it lacks or possesses the property in question. The probability that a measurement that *has not been made* is greater than a given number, or less than a given number, or lies in an interval, is (since we do not know anything about it at all except that it comes from the general population of possible or potential measurements of the given quantity) just the corresponding proportion, which we can calculate from the tables that evaluate the Gaussian error curve. Now a measurement may perfectly well have been made and we may be in a state of *partial* ignorance concerning it: thus we may have been told that it was less than k, and, conditional on this information, we may be interested in the probability that it is also less than j where $j < k$. These probabilities are perfectly straightforward to calculate, but they are not of any theoretical significance in this context, and I shall say nothing about them.

In a certain sense the content of the foregoing two paragraphs is of primarily academic interest, since we never know a magnitude precisely; but we have often perfectly good and sound reasons for accepting the statement that it lies in a small interval around a certain number—just as the insurance company had perfectly good reasons (if it ran its business of collecting data well) for accepting the hypothesis that the death rate of those people who are to die in the future will be quite close to the death rate of a similar group in the past. Given a range for m, we can go through just the process outlined in those two paragraphs to arrive at a range for the relevant proportions, and thus a range for the probability in question. Here is an example: suppose that we know that a magnitude is in the interval $(18.5, 19.1)$, or as is more often written, 18.8 plus or minus 0.3; we can ask for the probability that the next time we measure it by a method which has a value of 0.5 for σ we will get a result less than 18.4. The proportion of the hypothetical family of possible measurements M that are less than 18.4 (let us denote this subset of M by "$[\leq 18.4]$") varies from 0.11507, in case m is 19.1, up to 0.42074, in case m is 18.5. In any case, then, we know the statistical statement

[146]

" $Ra(M,[\leq 18.4], 0.115, 0.420)$ ", and thus, for the future measurement, we have: the probability that it is less than 18.4 is the range (0.115, 0.420).

V

In measurement, what we are generally more interested in, however, is the inverse problem: we perform some measurements on a quantity Q, and ask, knowing these results, for the probability that Q lies between certain limits. This is also a perfectly straightforward and solvable problem. We need merely consider the fact that if the difference between the measured result and the true value of the quantity is less than ϵ, then the difference between the true value of the quantity and the measured result is less than ϵ. Given knowledge of σ, which is characteristic of the measuring process, we can calculate the one probability as well as we can calculate the other, for the relevant measure is just the same.

It is thus possible, given knowledge of the standard deviation σ characteristic of the method of measurement, to pass from an observed result of measurement, a reading, to a probability statement about the magnitude being measured. Thus we might take a measurement of an object, and read its length as 4.0 centimeters; if we know that the standard deviation characteristic of the method of measurement we employed is 0.2 centimeters, then we can pass to the probability statement about the true value of the length: the probability is (about) 0.683 that the length lies between 3.8 centimeters and 4.2 centimeters. Sometimes when statements are probable enough, relative to what we know, we wish simply to accept them; we take them to be *practically certain*. Obviously the level of probability that corresponds to "practical certainty" varies with the circumstances. In matters that are not of great import, a probability greater than a half will suffice; if the length of the object referred to above is of no great moment, we may accept the fact that, or take it to be the case that, its length is between 3.8 and 4.2 centimeters. On the other hand, if the length is very important—if the object is a vital part in a passenger plane, for example—we will take the credibility of any statement whose probability is not very high indeed to fall short of practical certainty. Under the circumstances described, the probability that the length of the object is between 3.3 and 4.7 centimeters is greater than 0.999—we have less than one chance in a thousand of being wrong if we accept the statement that the length lies between these limits.

The scientist, of course, may not know to what uses his measurements will be put, and therefore he does not presume to tell you what statement (if any) you should be willing to accept. What he does instead is to provide you with the means of calculating your own intervals, by reporting (a) what he reads, what he observes, and (b) the value of σ (the standard deviation, s.d.) characteristic of the measuring process he used. Thus in general (in recent books, at any rate) when you see:

$$145.3 \ (\pm 1.2),$$

[147]

the "145.3" represents the reading, the "1.2" represents a standard deviation, and by consulting tables, you can discover that

> the probability is 0.683 that M lies within 1 s.d.
> $$144.1 < M < 146.5$$
> the probability is 0.955 that M lies within 2 s.d.
> $$142.9 < M < 147.7$$
> the probability is 0.99 that M lies within 2.58 s.d.
> $$142.2 < M < 148.4$$
> the probability is 0.999 that M lies within 3.29 s.d.
> $$141.4 < M < 149.2,$$

and so on. All but the final assertion in each line, indeed, is the same whatever the value of the reading may be, whatever the value of the magnitude may be, and even whatever the value of the standard deviation may be.

A scientist will often take several measurements and combine them, reporting the result as one number. We may regard the whole process as a single complex process of measurement, and the final result—the average of the individual readings—as the single reading which is the result of the whole complex process. The advantage of taking several readings and averaging them is that the standard deviation of the average is less than the standard deviation of the individual measurements. The relation is given by the following theorem from statistics:

THEOREM:

> If the standard deviation of a single measurement
> of a particular kind is S, then the standard deviation
> of the average of n such measurements is $S/\sqrt{n}$.

This theorem is an application of a purely mathematical truth; it depends only on the fact that if there is a set N of numbers which are characterized by a normal distribution with mean m and standard derivation S, then we may consider the set N^n of all sets consisting of n of these numbers; from this set in turn we may obtain a new set by adding the members of each of the sets of n numbers and dividing by n; call this new set $N^{(n)}$. We can show by purely mathematical techniques that the set of numbers $N^{(n)}$ (a) has a normal distribution, (b) has the same mean m as the set N, and (c) has a standard deviation $S/\sqrt{n}$. For reasonably large n, these results hold with little error for initial distributions of a wide variety of forms—it is not even necessary that the original distribution be normal.

In order to apply this theorem, we need to be able to regard the sequence of n measurements as a random member of the set of all such sequences of measurements. While a given measurement is almost automatically assured of being a random member of the set N of measurements, the matter is not so

[148]

simple when we come to consider a member of $N^{(n)}$. In order for a certain number m_n (obtained by averaging n measurements) to be a random member of $N^{(n)}$, with respect to being close to the true value m of the magnitude, relative to what we know, it must not belong to any subset of $N^{(n)}$ in which the property of being close to m is more infrequent than it is in $N^{(n)}$ as a whole. What might such a subset be? One obvious subset of $N^{(n)}$ is the set of numbers obtained by making a single observation, and then writing it down n times, and then taking the average. The frequency with which *these* numbers differ from m by less than ϵ (say) is given by the distribution in N, rather than by the distribution in $N^{(n)}$. Almost as bad would be to perform the measurement once, physically, but to read the result n times. On the other hand, something which will insure randomness in the appropriate sense is to *change* the measuring process in some (presumably) inessential way—e.g., by laying off the yardstick from the south end rather than from the north end. The technique of making inessential alterations in the measuring process has an advantage beyond insuring the randomness of the average: it provides a means of detecting certain systematic errors, if we analyse the results and discover that an allegedly inessential change is not inessential after all.

To give a specific example of how all this works, let us return to the measurement of the table. We measure it with a foot rule, and get the result: $54\frac{3}{8}$ inches. Suppose that the standard deviation of using a foot rule to measure this kind of object of this general magnitude—i.e., the standard deviation associated with this kind of measurement—is 0.3 inches. Then we would report this result as: 54.38 ± 0.3 (rounding off 0.375 to 0.38, since the last figure is meaningless, as the size of the standard deviation shows).

The probability is	that L lies within __s.d's of the reading	i.e., that L lies between
0.683	1	54.08 and 54.68
0.99	2.58	53.61 and 55.06

Suppose we now measure the same table with a steel tape (forgetting about the first measurement). We obtain the reading of 54.21. The standard deviation associated with this kind of measurement is, let us say, 0.05 inches. We would report the result as

$$54.21 \pm 0.05.$$

And that in turn would tell us that

The probability is	that L lies within __s.d's of the reading	i.e., that L lies between
0.683	1	54.16 and 54.26
0.99	2.58	52.92 and 55.50

[149]

If this is still not informative enough for us, let us take several readings and average them. Let us make nine steel tape readings. In order to be sure that the average is a random member of $N^{(9)}$—where N is the hypothetical infinite population of single steel-tape readings and $N^{(9)}$ is the hypothetical infinite population consisting of the averages of each set of nine readings—we measure from one end, and then from the other; we may have someone else make some of the readings; and so on. Suppose that the average is 54.266. The standard deviation of a single measurement is (as mentioned) 0.05; but here we have an average of nine measurements. Applying the theorem mentioned above, we thus have a standard deviation for the average of nine, of $0.05/\sqrt{9} = 0.017$. We report:

$$54.266 \pm 0.017.$$

And this in turn will tell us that

The probability is	that L lies within __s.d.'s of the reading	i.e., that L lies between
0.683	1	54.249 and 54.283
0.99	2.58	54.222 and 54.310

We treat the average as if it were one measurement; but we also mention that it is the result of nine measurements. The reason for this goes back to the criterion of randomness; while a single measurement is almost inevitably a random member of the class of possible measurements, it is quite possible for the average of a sequence of n measurements not to be a random member of $N^{(n)}$. To see how this comes about, let us look at the rare case in which a single measurement is not a random member of the set of all possible measurements with respect to the property of being close to the true value of the thing measured, relative to what we know about the measuring process. Suppose we know, for example, that a certain yardstick is a bit less than a yard long. Clearly, we will not take a reading with such a yardstick to be a random member of the set of possible measurements in the appropriate sense. We know (to recur to the definition given on page 137) that it is a member of a subclass of the class of possible measurements (namely the subclass consisting of measurements made with this particular yardstick) in which the relative frequency or proportion of readings that differ by a given amount from the true value is greater than in the class of possible measurements as a whole. Another way of saying the same thing is to say that that particular measurement was taken by a method which is *systematically biased*, or which is subject to a systematic error. If we do not *know* that the measurement was made with the defective yardstick, then we have no grounds for rejecting the randomness of the measurement. And of course, if we do know that the yardstick is short, we will incorporate a correction factor into the reading which will eliminate the bias, and establish the randomness of the (corrected) reading. But there is also a middle ground: we may know that the yardstick is short, without knowing how short it is; and thus we may reject the randomness of the measurement we have without obtaining at the same time a new, corrected, measurement which is random with respect to deviating from the true value by no more than such and such.

We will never, however, want to reject the randomness of a single measurement on the grounds that it *might* have been made by a method that was biased. It is perfectly possible that a single measurement, made at a certain time, will be random, relative to what we know, when it is made, and will cease to be random at some other time when we know more—when, for example, we discover that the method by which it was made is biased. There is never, under any circumstances, one hundred per cent insurance against the possibility. Nevertheless, lacking knowledge of bias, we must take the measurement to be random.

The circumstances are slightly different when it comes to the question of whether a particular average of n measurements is a random member of $N^{(n)}$ with respect to deviating from the true value by no more than such and such, relative to what we know. A particular sequence of n measurements will often be made by one person, or will employ one instrument. If the person or the instrument is biased, that bias will be the same for each of the n measurements, and will therefore be the same for the average of the n measurements. The randomness of this average is thus just as sensitive to the future discovery of bias in the method as a single measurement. In that respect, taking an average constitutes no improvement. We can reduce this sensitivity, however, by varying the circumstances of each member of the sequence of measurements. The more these circumstances are varied, the less are we likely to come to have reason to classify that sequence in a subclass of the overall set $N^{(n)}$ in which errors are larger or more frequent.

VI

Now let us turn our attention to the mysterious σ. Where did our knowledge of that come from? It comes, of course, from a knowledge of the distribution of measurements of a given quantity made by the method in question. Thus in the case of measuring intermediate distances with a foot rule, we can turn to our whole experience of such types of measurements as a basis for the calculation of σ; and we can calculate σ on the basis of these sets of measurements, just as we calculated the length of the table on the basis of the measurements of the table: we would obtain, if we went through such a process explicitly, a sequence of statements like

the probability is 0.90 that σ lies between 0.279 and 0.295
the probability is 0.95 that σ lies between 0.277 and 0.297
the probability is 0.99 that σ lies between 0.274 and 0.300.

[151]

This table cannot be expressed quite as neatly as the earlier tables because σ is not distributed normally; we need a different table to calculate limits for it. But this is not very important, in any case, because we have a vast amount of information—all of our measurements with a foot rule, for example, are data for the size of the standard deviation appropriate to foot rule measurements. We know the value of σ pretty closely.

One further fact should be mentioned, and that is that even if σ were completely unknown—e.g., if we are using a measuring process for the first time, and have no knowledge at all concerning its standard deviation—there are statistical techniques which will allow us to obtain statements of the form:

The probability is p that L lies between M_1 and M_2,

subject only to the condition that the standard deviation is finite, a condition rather obviously (indeed, *necessarily*) met in any empirical process of measurement. The statements we get this way are weaker than those we would get if we knew σ—that is, for a given level of probability, M_1 and M_2 cover a wider range of possibilities than do the corresponding limits for the case where we know (or have a good idea of) σ.

There is more to be said about measurement which bears on the instruments that are used; but this we shall treat under the heading "experiment," since even the process of laying off a foot rule on the surface of a table can be regarded as a small kind of experiment. Certainly hooking a volt-meter across the terminals of a battery is to be classified as an experiment, though the actual reading of the meter will be measurement in the sense in which we have discussed it here.

Observe that just as we hoped (back in the chapter on quantity) the relation between the theoretical entity—the magnitude measured—and the observations connected directly to that entity—the measurement of the magnitude—is a relation that can be understood, measured, dealt with, improved, even though the relation is merely a statistical one. Observe, what is even more important, that in the typical case of measurement, as in the cases we have been discussing, there is a way to reduce the error of observation: by replication, by making the same measurement several times. So that even for a given method of observation, the relation between the theoretical entity and the observation can be expressed quantitatively and, furthermore, the discrepancy can be controlled and reduced.

BIBLIOGRAPHICAL NOTES TO CHAPTER 6

There are a number of strongly divergent views on the interpretation of the concept of probability. They may be divided into three groups:

(1) those that take probability statements to be purely logical statements, logically true, if true at all, logically false otherwise;

[152]

(2) those that take probability statements to be empirical generalizations, to be at best highly confirmed;
(3) those that take probability statements to be empirical but psychological in content and particular, rather than general, in content.

One version of the first view of probability is that presented (more or less dogmatically) here, and given in detail in my *Probability and the Logic of Rational Belief*, Middletown, Connecticut, 1961. A brief account is also to be found in my article, "Probability and Randomness," *Theoria* **29** (1963). The more common version of the first view of probability is that defended by Rudolf Carnap in numerous publications, the two most important of which are *The Logical Foundations of Probability* (Chicago: University of Chicago Press, 1950) and *The Continuum of Inductive Methods* (Chicago: University of Chicago Press, 1952).

In class (2) there are also two main versions: there are those who take probabilities to be the limits of relative frequencies in infinite sequences of events, and those who merely take probabilities to be abstract characteristics of kinds of entities or events. In the former group the principal books are: Richard von Mises, *Probability, Statistics and Truth* (London: George Allen and Unwin, 1957; first German edition, 1928), and Hans Reichenbach, *Theory of Probability* (California: University of California Press, 1949; first German edition, 1934). Most statisticians may be numbered among those who treat probability as an abstract empirical characteristic of kinds of entities or events. As examples, however, see Jerzy Neyman *First Course in Probability and Statistics* (New York: Henry Holt, 1950), and Harald Cramér, *The Elements of Probability Theory* (New York: John Wiley, 1955). The latter book has also a particularly good treatment of error.

The third class of interpretations of probability does not seem to be divided as are the other two. A selection of fundamental papers presenting the personalistic or subjectivistic view that probability statements are essentially expressions of subjective confidence is presented in Kyburg and Smokler, Eds., *Studies in Subjective Probability* (New York: John Wiley, 1964). These papers include F. P. Ramsey, "Truth and Probability," written in 1926 and first published in *The Foundations of Mathematics* (New York: Humanities Press, 1931), and the paper which started the wholer ecent resurgence of Bayesian techniques in applied statistics, Bruno de Finetti's "Foresight: its logical laws, its subjective sources," which first appeared as "La prévision: ses lois logiques, ses sources subjectives," in *Annales de l'Institut Henri Poincaré* 7 (1937). A complete development of the theory, with its applications in statistics, is to be found in L. J. Savage, *The Foundations of Statistics* (New York: John Wiley, 1954).

[153]

Chapter **7**

INDUCTION AND EXPERIMENT

I

We do not treat all formal systems on a par. We want to use them as guides to the future, and so we select among them. This process of selection may be so trivial as the selection of the formal system that contains the statement "Compound X melts at $56.8° \pm 0.2°C$" over and above the formal system that is otherwise just the same as this one, but which lacks that particular statement. It may be so profound as the rejection of a whole theoretical framework in favor of a different one. Any principle or set of principles for selecting among formal systems may be construed, broadly, as an inductive logic. Ideally, of course, one should adopt a principle of inductive logic that will lead to the acceptance of formal systems that will, in point of fact, never be refuted by future experience. It would be nice to have an inductive logic that was like deductive logic in the sense that it is truth preserving—for if our inductive logic has this characteristic and we base our inferences on true premises, the conclusions (the formal systems we select) will be true, and will therefore never lead us astray. Such a goal is of course impossible. One achieves certainty only by eliminating empirical content.

The next most optimistic idea that presents itself is to take as a principle of selection that we accept the formal systems which do not conflict with experience so far. But this is clearly insufficient: there are many alternative systems with this property. The fact that all the crows we have seen so far are black is consistent with (1) the hypothesis that all crows are black, with (2) the hypothesis that some crows are black, with (3) the hypothesis that some crows are either black or white or red, etc. We can get some mileage out of the further principle that we should select the hypothesis that is strongest, the most testable, the one that contains the most information. But this is also insufficient: for although "all crows are black" does have more content than "some crows are black", it does not have any more content than "exactly half the crows are black and half of them are white." Should we call on a principle of simplicity? Such a principle is hard to formulate, and one might expect to run into or to be able to imagine circumstances in which a given formulation fails. It would be better to start from scratch.

The approach to induction and experiment that is adopted here consists of two parts. One part, which we shall simply regard as informal, consists in principles of selection of a language for a formal system. We have already seen that it is difficult to establish principles which will tell us when a technical term of our formal system is eliminable, and so we shall suppose that we are simply given a language for our formal system, consisting of a set of terms, together with a set of formation rules and meaning postulates appropriate to them. We shall, in particular cases, look at ways in which we are led to change our language; but such changes, never being forced on us by experience, we shall make no effort to formalize. It is possible to develop criteria for such changes; but they are complex and involve such intangible characteristics as beauty, clarity, simplicity (in an aesthetic sense), etc.

The other part, inductive logic proper, will be construed as a set of principles that allows us to make selections among formal systems, expressed in a *given* language, on the basis of a given background of experience and experiment. Inductive logic is more complicated than deductive logic, and we cannot go into its details here. But some of its principles must be presented in order to make clear the nature and role of experiment and inference in the pursuit of scientific knowledge.

II

There is a sense in which all inductive inference is probabilistic, but there is another sense in which very little of it is probabilistic. The simplest and crudest form of inductive inference is probabilistic in any sense. This simplest form of inference is straight inductive generalization; it is sometimes called just "induction" and it is what people have in mind when they say that science has little need of induction. Although there is good point to calling this the crudest form of inductive inference, it would be altogether misguided to call it simple in any intuitive sense; it is simple only in the sense that it requires the minimum amount of background knowledge. The general situation is this: we observe a number of A's; we see that a certain proportion, r, are also B's. In vague intuitive terms, we say that on the basis of this evidence, we infer that about a proportion r of all of the A's are B's. This inference is a probabilistic one—i.e., probability only is conferred on the conclusion, relative to the evidence we have. In more precise terms, we can reconstruct the argument as follows:

(1) For a reasonably large n, almost all subclasses of A that contain exactly n members are *representative* of the proportion of B's among A's as a whole, in the sense that: the proportion of these subclasses such that the difference between the ration of B's in the subclass and in the class of A's as a whole is less than ϵ_p, is at least p;

(This kind of statement is one that can be certified on logical grounds alone.)

(2) We have observed exactly n A's (no more, for to have observed more, and not to take them into account, would be suppressing evidence: the cardinal scientific sin), and m of them have been B's;

(3) This sample of n A's that we have observed is a random member of the class of all n-membered subclasses of A, relative to our body of background knowledge, with respect to the property of representing the proportion of B's in A as a whole, in the sense described in (1).

Now this is a common sort of situation; (1), (2), and (3) clearly imply that for us the probability that the proportion of B's among A's in general lies between $m/n - \epsilon_p$ and $m/n + \epsilon_p$ is at least p—i.e., is the interval $(p, 1)$. Now if p is large, it is in some sense *practically certain* that between $m/n + \epsilon_p$ and $m/n - \epsilon_p$ of the A's are B's, and this statement may be accepted into the rational corpus that corresponds to that sense of *practical certainty*.

What has just been described is a situation in which there is simply no relevant knowledge to modify the circumstances. (1) is analytic; further information can only serve to strengthen it, for if we know something about the proportion of A's that are B's (for example, if we know that the proportion differs from $\frac{1}{2}$) then we can have grounds for accepting a *stronger* statistical statement about the proportion of representative subclasses of A than that it lies between p and 1. (2) is regarded simply as an observation statement. And the randomness criterion (3) is met in case we have no prior empirical knowledge, simply because we don't know any relevant class ratio statements other than the one expressed by (1).

[156]

But now suppose that we do have such empirical knowledge—i.e., suppose our rational corpus is such that we cannot assert that the sample we have is a random member of the class of all possible subclasses containing n members, with respect to exhibiting the property of representativeness. This is just to say that there is some subclass of that class of subclasses of A, in which we know that the proportion of representative classes differs: either (a) because there are more of them, i.e., a higher proportion—such might be the case if our sample of A's was not just one that happened to come to hand, but was one that we went out of our way to arrange to be representative by sampling from different physical or temporal parts of A, and so on—or (b) because there is a lower proportion—for example, if the sample of A's was obtained by a technique that has in the past generally resulted in samples that did not represent their parent populations in such respects as proportion of B's.

If case (a) is true, our background knowledge allows us to make an even stronger inference; relative to this background knowledge, the probability that $m/n \pm \epsilon_p$ of the A's are B's is not merely $(p, 1)$, but $(p^*,1)$, where p^* is greater than p. In case (b), our background knowledge prevents us from assigning such a high probability to the statistical statement about A's and B's. But it should be noted in case (a), and it should be particularly noted in case (b), that the randomness criterion fails to be met only because we *already* have accepted into our rational corpus as practically certain empirical generalizations that are more far-reaching than the original statistical generalizations about A's and B's that is being brought into question. The randomness criterion (3) cannot *always* fail.

There is no branch of science in which we are so ignorant that the requirement of randomness (3) is met automatically. Nevertheless, much of this kind of inference is still performed, even in the most sophisticated branches of science. It is a particularly common sort of inference in sociology, psychology, and biology, where, however, it is hedged about with precautions, for two reasons:

First, in making straightforward use of simple statistical generalizations, the randomness requirement is harder to meet when we know more about the subject matter with which we are concerned than when we are relatively ignorant. That this is so may be easily seen from the definition of randomness in the preceding chapter. When we have a vast body of generalizations and statistical statements in our rational corpora, then we can more easily find reasons to deny that our sample is random because of membership in a special subclass of the class we are considering.

Second, we may not only have, at the time we make the inference, knowledge of special circumstances that impugn the randomness of our sample, but we can also guess the direction in which our knowledge is likely to grow; by guess and analogy we can anticipate the kinds of generalizations that may in the future come to be included in our body of knowledge. When some of these do come to be included, the samples on which we have based knowledge at an earlier time may come to be no longer random, relative to what we now know, and thus no longer support the statistical generalizations that they supported formerly.

By way of illustration, suppose that we are biologists interested in the color of a certain species of bird. We must take our sample of birds, on which to base a straightforward inference as to the relative frequency of different colors, from a variety of geographical locations, from a variety of local environments, in such a way as to include birds of both sexes and of a variety of ages. If we were aborigines, we wouldn't need to take these precautions: any class of birds of that species would be a random member of the class of all such (equinumerous) classes, with respect to belonging to the class representive (within distance ϵ_p) of the proportion (say) of black birds. It would be random because we would not know that coloration in a species was different in different environments, nor (if we were aboriginal enough) would we even know that color depended on sex or age. But we aren't aborigines, and we do know that the coloration of birds depends on things like geographical location, local environment, etc. We know this even more definitely when it comes to diet, so that no one would claim a sample of birds from one area to be representative of the species as a whole with respect to diet.

Now suppose that instead of color or diet, our concern was with resistance to a certain disease. In general, we know that resistance to a particular disease (or better, a particular family of diseases) is a characteristic of a species as a whole. It is generally quite independent of local environment, of geographical location, of diet, etc. Thus a class of birds from one particular place, living in a particular way, is random, with respect to the property of being representative of resistance to a given disease. But as biologists, we know that this general fact does not always hold: there are strains developed in special environments that are resistant to diseases that the species as a whole is not resistant to. Similarly, special strains exist that, through lack of contact with a particular disease-causing organism, have from lack of selective pressure developed a peculiar susceptibility to diseases that other strains are resistant to. Although, as distinct from the first situation, we do not *know* anything that prevents this sample of birds from being random in the required sense, and although we could, relative to all the contents of our biological rational corpora, take this sample as representative, nevertheless we will not, We will look further afield, to get a sample of birds that includes those from other locations and environments, in order to insure ourselves against the possibility that it will turn out in the future to be the case that the birds from our particular location constitute a strain of the species with peculiar characteristics of susceptibility or resistance to the disease in question.

This is the principle behind the advisability of *randomization* and *stratification* in sociological sampling. "Stratification" means that the sample is deliberately constructed so that the various social groups in the society we are sampling from are all represented, perhaps even proportionately. This is done sometimes because we know that there are variations among classes (e.g., the proportion of Republicans among coal miners is different from the proportion of Republicans among stock brokers), and thus we know that a sample from one particular class, or that contains a disproportionate number of members of one particular class, will be very unlikely to be representative. (A sample that contains mostly stock-brokers will not indicate how the nation as a whole will vote.) And sometimes we stratify when we don't *know* that the characteristic under investigation has different frequencies among different groups in society, but because we think it *might* have different frequencies. Thus if we are interested in the proportion of patronyms that begin with the letter *B*, we might very well use a stratified form of sampling, because although we know of no connection between social groups and patronym (in the United States), some day some other sociologist might uncover such a connection, and if our inference was based on a stratified sample it will remain valid, while if it was based on an unstratified sample, his results might require us to reject our results.

Randomization, properly used, constitutes another protection against future rejection of the randomness of the sample. (Sometimes its chief function seems to be to simplify the mathematics of statistical inference by throwing away information!) Randomization is the technique of drawing a sample from a population in such a way that every possible sample from the population has an equal statistical chance of being chosen as the sample. The most common method is to assign each member of the population a number, and then to select a set of numbers from a table of random numbers (the first n, or the first n starting on page 34, or . . .), and to take the sample to be the set of n members of the population who bear those n numbers. Before we analyze such a sample, it is certainly a random member of the set of all possible (equinumerous) samples, and thus the probability that it is representative in a given sense is precisely the proportion of such samples that are representative in that sense. The mathematics is clean and straightforward.

When a sample is selected by some other method, various factors other than the proportions in the set of all possible samples may be relevant. An investigator may deliberately *try* to select a sample that is representative; or he may try to select a sample that is *fair* in some other sense, or he may unconsciously select a sample that will conform to his own prejudices or guesses or conjectures—there is no telling how he happens to choose the sample he does choose, unless he chooses it by a randomizing procedure. And if he happens to choose it by some criterion or set of criteria, which at present are known to be related to the characteristic under investigation, or which in the future come to be known to be related to the characteristic under investigation, then the sample that he has selected will not then (at present or at that future time) be random with respect to representativeness of that characteristic.

[159]

The same is true, of course, of a sample selected by a randomizing device. It may perfectly well be that the sample that is picked in point of fact, is a member of a subclass of the class of possible (equinumerous) samples in which the relative frequency of representative classes is known to be particularly low. (E.g., a randomizing device used to sample a population for political preferences, may just happen to select a sample of 9000 stockbrokers.) Or the sample picked by the randomizing device may, in the future, come to be known to be a member of such a subclass. But it is often easier to deal with these possibilities, than with the possibility of unconscious selective forces at work in the deliberate selection of a sample from a population.

The techniques of stratification and randomization are not confined to the social sciences, of course. They are particularly important there, because it is perhaps in the social sciences that there is the greatest unconscious temptation to choose samples that confirm our own theories or that cater to our own prejudices, and it is also perhaps in the social sciences that we have the greatest ability to do this. But these temptations are not altogether missing in any field of investigation, and it is therefore often appropriate to use randomization and stratification in biology, medicine, agriculture, and indeed, in any field where statistics plays a large role.

Comments similar to the foregoing apply to the general statistical problem, that of establishing the distribution of a certain quantity among the members of a population: the distribution of shoe sizes, weights of oranges, lengths of fish, numbers of wives, diameters of bolts, etc. The distribution is given by a distribution function (as described in the last chapter) which tells us, for every real number x, what proportion of the population has a quantitative property less than x units in magnitude. (Of course the distribution may be given by any number of other functions that allow us to derive this proportion.) In any case, the inference is based on a sample, a subclass of the population, which is random (relative to our body of knowledge) with respect to exhibiting the general form of the distribution, or with respect to revealing the values of parameters that determine the distribution if we already know what the form of the distribution is. And often in order to insure this randomness, not only relative to our present body of knowledge, but also relative to future, enlarged bodies of knowledge, various devices, such as stratification and randomization, are resorted to. The outcome, the conclusion, of such an inference, is that with probability p, a certain parameter lies within a certain interval; or a certain pair of parameters lie within a certain pair of intervals; or, most generally, the actual distribution $F(x)$ lies between two bounding distributions $F_1(x)$ and $F_2(x)$.

An important particular case of this sort of statistical inference is measurement. In discussing measurement, we identified the value of a particular magnitude with the mean of an indefinitely large class of normally distributed quantities—measurements of that magnitude. Thus our object, in measuring the

[160]

length of a table, the voltage output of a battery, the temperature of an oil bath, or the intensity of a magnetic field, is to infer the mean of a normally distributed quantity. The *mean* is the magnitude with which we are concerned; the *quantities* this time, are the results of measurement. Since in the case of measurement, the randomness requirement for inference is usually met almost automatically, not much thought need be given to it. The type of inference involved was discussed in the last chapter.

III

One special case of the general form of statistical inductive inference discussed above is of particular importance both for the beginnings and the foundations of science, and that is when the ratio in the sample is unity—i.e., when all of the objects that we have observed at all, belonging to a given class, have been observed to have a given characteristic. Under such circumstances we sometimes feel free not only to assert that the proportion in the population as a whole is *close* to unity, but that it *is* unity; and if we have a case in which the population is infinitely large, or in which we assert, say on theoretical grounds, that the population is infinitely large, then we may even go so far as to say not only that the proportion of members of the population that have this characteristic is unity, but that further, *all* members of the population have the characteristic.

For example, consider the coldness of snow. Every time snow has fallen and I have felt it, it has felt cold. Let "S" stand for the set of samples of snow, "C" for the set of things that feel cold. My sample consists of a large number of S's, all of which have also been C's. In accordance with the principles outlined above, if this sample of S's is a random one, relative to what I know, with respect to belonging to the class of samples of S's representative of the proportion of C's, then the probability is high (p) that the proportion of all S's that are C's is close (ϵ_p) to that in the sample. Since the proportion in the sample is 1, this amounts to having a high probability for

$$Ra(S,C,1 - \epsilon_p,1),$$

provided the randomness requirement is met.

It has been suggested by some philosophers (for example, C. D. Broad) that the randomness requirement is *never* met, either here or in any other statistical inference. In the case at hand, for example, they would say that the sample is not random because all of the specimens of snow that I have felt have had these properties: (a) they have been felt by me, (b) they have occurred near the surface of the earth, (c) they have occurred roughly in the middle of the twentieth century, and so on. Therefore, so the argument goes, the sample is not random with respect to indicating the proportion of all specimens of snow whatever that are cold; for these include specimens in the stoneage, and at an altitude of 100,000 feet, and even in the atmosphere of Mars. But to see what is wrong with this argument, we need merely recall the definition of randomness: to show that the sample is not random, *two* requirements must be met: (1) it must be shown that we have reason to believe that the sample has a certain property (belongs to a certain subclass of the class of possible samples). This has been done: the sample has, among other properties, the special property of having been composed of specimens from the Earth's atmosphere. But also (2) it must be shown that we have *reason to believe* that the proportion of representative samples in the special subclass to which our particular sample belongs, is less than it is among the general run of samples. And this not only has not been done, but clearly can not be done without introducing principles of inference quite as strong (and probabilistic) as those that these philosophers wish to cast doubt on.

Now suppose that the randomness requirement is met, and that p is high enough, for the context with which we are concerned, to justify the inclusion of "$Ra(S,C,1 - \epsilon_p,1)$" in the rational corpus of a given level of practical certainty. Now suppose simultaneously that $1 - \epsilon_p$ is itself greater that p: it is easy to conjecture that just as the fact that "$Ra(S,C,1 - \epsilon_p,1)$" had a probability greater than p justified the acceptance of this statistical statement into our rational corpus, so in general if a is a random member of S, with respect to membership in C, the probability of "$a \in C$" will be so high (i.e., it will be the interval $(1 - \epsilon_p,1)$, where $1 - \epsilon_p > p$) that "$a \in C$" in turn will belong to our rational corpus. (This is a conjecture; to establish it would require the development of the details of a logic of rational acceptance or rational belief. But it is certainly a reasonable conjecture.) Finally, suppose that of every individual a the following is true:

> (1) If "$a \in S$" belongs to our rational corpus, then either "$a \in C$" belongs to our rational corpus, or else a is a random member of S with respect to C, relative to that rational corpus.

From this it follows that if "$a \in S$" belongs to our rational corpus, so does "$a \in C$". But this amounts, in cash value, so to speak, to no more and no less than the inclusion of the general statement:

$$(x)(x \in S \supset x \in C)$$

in our rational corpus of the given level of practical certainty. It amounts to no more, because if there were any statement of either the form "$(a \in S \& \sim a \in C)$" or "$(\exists x)(x \in S \& \sim x \in C)$" in our rational corpus, it would be on the basis of theoretical considerations, or on the basis of observation, and in either case we would have an object a which violates condition (1): we can then specify an object which is known to belong to S, but which is neither a member of C, nor a random member of S with respect to membership in C.

What I am doing here is rather hard and perhaps not quite straightforward; I am talking as if the whole logic of acceptance were laid out, and were much simpler than in fact it is. Developing this logic is one of the biggest tasks that

[162]

face philosophers of science now; and many of them are working on it. Things are not as simple as I am pretending they are. And yet the considerations that I am offering, complicated and inadequate as they are, are nevertheless just the kinds of considerations that will be central in a careful development of this logic, and they are also the kinds of considerations that practicing scientists must (and do) keep in mind when they speak of accepting generalizations.

IV

The form of argument that leads to the acceptance of general statements which has just been outlined is a rare one; the reason that it is rare is two-fold: first, the randomness requirements are very rarely met, when we have a large body of scientific beliefs, and second (also in consequence of our large body of beliefs), we generally have more direct and more powerful methods of achieving universal generalizations. To take up the second consideration first: a rather small sample of birds from a wide variety of geographical locations and local environments will quickly convince us that all members of the given species have the same coloring. Why? Not on the basis of direct simple enumerative induction—the kind of argument we have been considering—but on the basis of an argument like this: On general theoretical biological grounds, we know that if a species is not uniformly colored, variations in coloring will be found, if not among the individuals of one group—as when males and females are differently colored—at least among individuals belonging to different biological communities. Thus if we look at a wide variety of communities, and don't find any variations, we may with considerable safety conclude that all individuals have the same coloration. Observe, however, that this argument is based on wide and powerful prior biological generalizations concerning heredity, genetics, mating patterns, and so on.

An even simpler example is that of determining the melting point of an organic chemical substance S: On theoretical physical grounds, we know (we have good reason to accept) the generalization that under standard pressure, every chemical substance has exactly one melting point—i.e., that if one sample of a substance melts at $t°C$, then *every* sample of that substance will melt at $t°C$. This may be expressed as

$$(x)(\text{Subst}(x) \supset (y)((\exists z)(\text{Sample}(z,x) \,\&\, \text{Melts}(z,y)) \supset$$
$$(w)(v)((\text{Sample}(v,x) \,\&\, \text{Melts}(v,w)) \supset w = y))).$$

Thus we can on the basis of a *single* instance argue to the reasonable acceptance of a generalization that concerns an arbitrarily large class of specimens

$$(z)(\text{Sample}(z,S) \supset \text{Melts}(z,t \pm \Delta t)).$$

But, of course, as we shall see, the single instance does itself involve a probabilistic inference: all we can find from experiment is that the probability is p that the sample tested melted at between $t_1°C$ and $t_2°C$.

[163]

Finally, let us consider the randomness requirements. They are even harder to meet here than in the general case of statistical inference, because we typically have some reason to be suspicious of a sample that is 100 per cent this or that: either we have good reason to suppose that if even a small sample—perhaps even one individual—exhibits the property in question, then all do (cf. the uniform coloration and the melting point examples); or else we have reason to suppose that the sample was chosen in such a way that we could not expect it to be representative—i.e., it is not a random one, relative to what we know, with respect to being representative. For example, if the sample of birds were all males from one local environment, we would expect them to be uniform in color whether or not the species as a whole was; and thus we could specify that they came from a subclass of the class of all possible samples, in which the relative frequency or proportion of representative samples was unusually low. In the case of universal generalizations, the randomness requirements are often either unnecessary, or not met.

V

How about the acceptance of theories? Are there inductive rules which will tell us how to choose among different (non-equivalent) sets of axioms? This is an exceedingly difficult question; it is very clear that some desiderata of theories—that they be beautiful, simple, aesthetically pleasing, that they have a form which is natural to our way of thinking or similar to the form of other acceptable theories—are hard to spell out in detail. But given the vocabulary, formation rules, and meaning postulates of a formal system, and given its interpretation, when all that is at issue is the truth value of its material axioms, do we want to go so far as to say that the acceptance of a theory is tantamount to the acceptance of the statistical hypothesis that all of its consequences that are tested will be verified? This is a controversial question; to some extent every theory is a proposal to speak a certain language, as well as a conjecture about the state of the world.

Although this is a controversial and perhaps arbitrary matter, it is clear that one thing at least that is involved in the acceptance of a theory is the acceptance of its testable consequences or observable consequences. The point of view that I shall accept here is that this is all that is involved, at least in rationally reconstructed inductive logic. All we can ask as grounds for accepting a theory is that we have reason to believe that all of its observable consequences turn out to be true. "Observable", in this case as in every other, is a vague term. I do not want to suggest that there is a small number of observation-type sentences of the form "red-here-now", which are all that count as observations. An observable consequence is any statement, expressible in the formal system as a whole, which is such that independent of the theory—i.e., independent of those material axioms of the theory that are held to embody its content, as distinct from the rest

[164]

of the content of our rational corpus—we can have grounds for accepting it or rejecting it. Thus independent of quantum theory, we can have perfectly good grounds for accepting the statement: "Electrons are deflected by a magnetic field", and so this counts as a perfectly good observable consequence of the quantum theory, despite the fact that nobody has ever seen a magnetic field or met an electron. An observable or testable consequence of a theory is a statement which is (a) a consequence of the theory, and (b) which is such that, within the formal system as a whole, including a set of observation statements, there can be grounds for accepting or rejecting such a statement which are independent of the theory. Now to say that every observable consequence of a theory is rationally acceptable, is simply to say that a hundred percent of them are, and is simply to make a fairly plain (if metalinguistic) generalization. If we have reason for accepting every such consequence, or the general statement that every observable consequence is true, then we have reason for accepting the theory.

Now it may well happen that there is more than one acceptable theory. There are two types of conflict among theories. One type of conflict is that we can have two (or n) theories with exactly the same observable consequences. The other type of conflict is that in which we have two theories, neither of which has been refuted (for that would settle the issue) which have *different* observable consequences.

The first case is easier to handle: when we have two theories with the same observable consequences, we accept the theory that we like better, the more beautiful theory, the theory that makes the least demands on our credulity, the theory that involves the simplest physical structures, the theory that is most natural, has the greatest similarity to other theories that have worked well in the past, and so on. There are a large number of desiderata—perhaps the chief of which are simplicity and elegance—and the weighing of these desiderata is the kind of thing that it is hard to find precise rules for: it is analogous to the problem of evaluating a work of art—or, I should prefer to say, any other work of art. In point of fact the decision is not generally hard to make. (Indeed, we seldom have so many as two good theories). If a theoretical term can be eliminated, without much altering the structure of the system, and without changing the class of observable consequences, then we regard the resulting briefer theory as superior. If we can replace more complex axioms by simpler ones, we do so. We introduce any new theoretical term with such semantic properties that it simplifies the whole structure of the theory, by making axioms simpler and fewer, by leading to the interdefinability of a number of prior terms, and so on.

The second case, though rarer, is far more interesting; for there the notion of the crucial experiment comes up. Sometimes it is possible to arrange an experiment in which the predicted observable consequence of one theory differs from the predicted observable consequence of the other theory. To perform the experiment and observe the result is to know that one theory has been refuted by experience, and the other not. This is the crucial experiment. Until it is performed, we suspend judgment about the theories; we do not, however, suspend judgment concerning all the consequences of the theories: we suspend judgment only about those consequences in which the theories differ. And in truth, we simply do not know what the facts will be, we don't know whether the prediction of theory T_1 or the (contrary) prediction of theory T_2 will be substantiated. Therefore, we suspend judgment with respect to these predictions, and hence defer our choice between the competing theories. Now if the difference between the two theories is not testable (observable) at all, we are in the first case; if the difference is observable, but we don't happen at the moment to be able to perform the test, to make the relevant observations, then we suspend judgment until we can. But either theory may still be used in that region where their consequences agree. Indeed, often a theory will be refuted by an observation that contradicts a consequence of the theory, and yet the theory will continue to be used (and even taught) in areas of application where it has not been refuted. It is a perfectly good and acceptable theory, in these areas, because (we are supposing) we have good reason to believe that its consequences will be verified there. And we can square its acceptance with the rest of what we know by incorporating the proviso: "except under such and such circumstances." But of course we hope to find a better theory that will either lead to verified consequences in the difficult area or will at least explain why that area is difficult.

VI

In a certain sense sampling a population to discover the relative frequency of some characteristic is performing an experiment; so is sampling a population to discover the distribution of some quantity among its members. In a somewhat more real sense, measuring something is an experiment in itself. But we do not come to experiments that are really worthy of the name until something more is at stake: properly speaking we perform an experiment to confirm or refute a hypothesis, to test a theory, to determine the magnitude of a constant in a general law. These are vague characterizations—and yet they rightly suggest that what is crucial in experiment is not only the actual value of something measured or counted or the actual characteristics of something observed, but the context in which that value or those characteristics take on significance for our body of knowledge. The significance may be fairly small and particular, as when we perform an experiment to determine the melting point of a new, hitherto untested, substance. Or it may be fairly overwhelming, when the theory up for test constitutes the framework of a whole system of knowledge, as in the experiment that provided grounds for preferring Einstein's theory of relativity to the Newtonian framework by determining that light rays that pass close to the sun are bent.

In the discussion of the melting point problem, we have already begun to deal with genuine experiments: to determine the melting point of a new chemical substance is to perform an experiment. We set up an oil bath and change its temperature very slowly, until a small sample of the substance immersed in a thin glass container in the oil bath suddenly melts. The temperature of the oil bath at the time that the substance melts ("melts" being a purely visual predicate here) is taken to be the *observed melting point* of the substance. If we do the experiment several times, we get a number of different observed melting points; but if we take the whole apparatus (including the thermometer) to be simply an instrument for measuring the melting point, and thus to have its own characteristic standard deviation, we can combine these observations to yield a single assertion of the form: the melting point is $t°C \pm \Delta t°$, where $\Delta t°$ is the standard deviation of the set of measurements made. Since, as already mentioned, we have the general statement that every chemical substance has one and only one melting point in our body of chemical beliefs, the acceptance of the statement that the melting point in one instance (or two or three) was $t° \pm \Delta t°$, entails the acceptance of the statement that the melting point in every instance is (will be) $t° \pm \Delta t°$.

We can express this somewhat more abstractly, by saying that in the formal chemical framework that constitutes the background of this experiment, we have a statement that there exists exactly one melting point for any given substance; in particular, for the substance in question. An experiment—i.e., a set of circumstances—is described, in the language of that formal system, such that a measurement of a quantity (e.g., the temperature of the oil bath, here, but for higher temperatures, it might be the voltage generated in a bimetallic strip) leads to an assertion (indeed, in this case, a whole distribution) concerning the value of the melting point of the substance in question. For every level of practical certainty there exists a *just acceptable* statement of the limits of the melting point. Put more conventionally, but far less accurately: we perform an experiment to determine the value of a constant.

While it is quite possible to discuss the concept of a formal system in the abstract, and the same is true of measurement, and the terms, the axioms, the meaning postulates of formal systems, and even their connection to the world of experience, it is somewhat more difficult to discuss experiments in the abstract. Partly this is because an experiment is, in its very nature, something concrete— apparatus of steel and glass and plastic, bottles of reagents, covered glass dishes of cultures, bottles of copulating flies, furnaces and stoves, refrigerators and freezers, telescopes and rockets. But it is also partly because the types of experiment appropriate to one science are quite out of place in another: the ideas of experiment formed by the astronomer, the biologist, the geneticist, and the microphysicist, may be utterly different.

Having said this, we will now proceed to describe experimentation abstractly. In a simple minded sense, it is easy to say what an experiment is: it is setting up circumstances, or taking advantages of circumstances that are already set up accidentally in nature or on purpose by other agents, in such a way that one particular observable aspect of the circumstances—the *outcome*, if we understand the word "outcome" in a nontemporal sense—can be regarded as throwing light on a particular theoretical entity (mass of an electron) or a particular theoretical assertion or set of assertions.

Let us begin with the description of the circumstances. An experiment is a set of observable circumstances, describable in the language of the formal system. The description is a description of the experiment. The description is essentially incomplete, in one of two ways. Either there is a statement S containing no free variables which is deducible from the theory together with the description of the experimental circumstances—the experiment then consists in seeing whether, under the experimental circumstances, S is indeed true; or the description of the experimental circumstances contains one or more statements of the form:

$$t_1 < (\imath x)\phi_1(x) < t_1'$$
$$t_2 < (\imath x)\phi_2(x) < t_2'$$

where the definite descriptions "$(\imath x)\phi_1(x)$", "$(\imath x)\phi_2(x)$", etc., are of magnitudes, and the t's are free variables; the experiment then consists of replacing these free variables by quantitative terms. In the first case we say that the experiment is a test of some hypothesis or hypotheses; in the second we say that the experiment is one determining the value of a magnitude. These two sorts of experiments, tests of hypotheses and determinations of magnitudes, seem to be quite distinct, and perhaps also exhaustive.

We may describe the testing situation in formal terms this way: we have a formal system, consisting of vocabulary, formation rules, axioms, meaning postulates, rules of inference, and an interpretation. One of the axioms is singled out as being doubtful: call it D. (Alternatively, a group of axioms can together be singled out as jointly doubtful; but I doubt that it is often the case that a whole set of axioms is singled out this way.) To this we conjoin the (incomplete) statement of the experimental situation. In the formal system, thus supplemented, a further (experimental) statement is derivable. This is the predicted result. It may perfectly well have the form of assigning a certain magnitude to a certain entity (this does not make the experiment one of determining a magnitude); or it may have any of a number of forms. Now when the experiment is performed (or the final observation made) which yields the experimental result, we regard the doubtful axiom as either confirmed or disconfirmed. If it is confirmed, we sit back and feel pleased with ourselves; that the axiom is confirmed may or may not, in the context of the rest of the formal system, and the rest of the contents of our rational corpus, constitute a definitive settling of the doubt about D, but it goes some direction toward settling that doubt. On the other hand, if the experimental result does not match the predicted result, then, in the context of the formal system, doubt is removed positively; that is, we must reject D.

[168]

This is an oversimplification—for of course to know that the circumstances described in the experimental description actually obtain, is a matter of probability: at the very least, some kind of measurement is involved, and no measurement can ever yield certainty. The same is true, of course, of the experimental result. And furthermore, the rest of the formal system, though we have not chosen to doubt it at the moment, may be questioned.

The experiment for determining a magnitude may be similarly described; but the result is never the rejection of a part of the formal system. It is rather the inclusion in the formal system of a statement about the particular magnitude determined by the experiment (e.g., that it lies within a certain range), together with all the consequences of that statement. If the experiment is worth doing the statement will have consequences. Thus we could have a theory of the behavior of a gas, and it could be a consequence of the theory that there is a number, called a Universal Constant, that appears in all the equations; but it need not be a part of the theory that the constant has such and such a value. Therefore, we set up an experiment to determine that value. That value (or rather, a range for it) will be the deductive consequence of a statement about magnitudes justified by the experiment. Similarly, we may know (i.e., that it may be a part of the relevant formal system that constitutes part of our rational corpus) that a certain chemical compound will have just one definite melting point under standard conditions. To determine what it is, we have to perform an experiment; the result of which is the determination of a magnitude, say the temperature of the oil bath in which the substance just melted.

Many of the sentences describing the experiment, sentences from the formal system, are sentences that are vague with the systematic vagueness of measurement. Thus in an experiment one of the factors may be the volume of a certain container. We cannot know this volume, of course; but we can know, in a perfectly good probabilistic sense—i.e., we can accept into our rational corpus of some high level—the statement that the volume is $V \pm k \Delta V$, where ΔV is the standard deviation of the volume calculation—determined by whatever procedure we use in that calculation—and k is a constant such that the statement: "The volume is $V \pm k \Delta V$", is so probable that it can be accepted into the rational corpus in question as practically certain.

The sentence describing the outcome of the experiment is also of this form, whether the experiment is the kind of experiment where a magnitude is determined or the kind of experiment where a doubtful sentence D is being tested. D, together with the experimental description, will generally entail an outcome like, "The x such that $\phi(x)$ is $Q \pm k\Delta Q$", (in our earlier notation: "$Q - k\Delta Q < (\imath x)\phi(x) < Q + k\Delta Q$"), and this must be regarded as being confirmed or disconfirmed by an acceptable sentence like "The x such that $\phi(x)$ is (actually) $m \pm k\Delta m$." The same "k" generally appears throughout; for a given level of rational corpus demands a given level of probability for acceptance, and in the

[169]

case of any quantity distributed normally, if Q is the mean and ΔQ is the standard deviation, "$(Q - k\Delta Q < (\imath x)\phi(x) < Q + k\Delta Q$" will have the same probability, for given k, regardless of the values of Q and ΔQ. To take $k = 1$, as scientists sometimes do, is simply to take .683 as an adequate probability for acceptance, and this, sometimes, seems a rather weak requirement.

VII

From all of this it should be abundantly clear that the observations that represent the description of the experimental setup, as well as the observation that represents the result of the experiment, are not necessarily *observations* in any deep epistemological sense, and far less in any phenomenalistic sense. Sometimes the observation is an observed value: the observation is that the substance S melts at $t \pm \Delta t$ degrees. Sometimes the observation corresponds to something that could once have been immediate, before a change in language: thus we *observe* that there is a dog in the corral, though we are using the word "dog" in a biological sense—as we generally do, notice—such that after having observed a dog in the corral, further observations could lead us to reject that statement: we could find it was an unusual fox or an African wild dog. Nevertheless, the observation of the object in the corral provides perfectly sound grounds for accepting the slightly theoretical statement that there is a dog in the corral, just as the observation of the coincidence of a column of mercury with a certain mark on a glass tube provides perfectly sound grounds for accepting the (somewhat more theoretical) statement that the melting point of the chemical compound S is $t \pm \Delta t°$C.

There are other experimental observations that are even further removed from ordinary day by day observation: thus we can observe electrons in a cloud chamber, viruses through the agency of an electron microscope, particle annihilation and creation in certain physical experiments, nova formation in astronomy (though there are no manipulations involved, in the formation of a nova, so that it may be stretching things a bit to call the formation of a nova an experimental result). In certain parts of psychology, we may even correctly speak of observing anger and of observing aggression. It would be a mistake, and one that was very misleading, to claim that we do not observe these things—that we only observe dog-shaped patches in our field of vision, that we merely observe certain forms of overt behavior, and that we just observe certain bright spots in our telescopes. It would be misleading, because it suggests that we need an *argument* to justify the passage from such an observation to the assertion that we need for our scientific system; it suggests that we need an argument that will lead from dog-shaped patches in our field of vision to an assertion about furry animals of a certain species, from the bright spots in our telescopes to an assertion about celestial bodies, from statements about overt behavior (door-slamming and the like) to statements about internal psychic states (anger). Since the connection between the

[170]

pairs of statements seems often to be a material connection, we can be led (misled) to look for justification for connections which cannot be justified.

Let us look at the dog story in detail. "Dog" comes into our language as a relatively ostensively defined predicate, though there may be certain theoretical connections also supposed to hold between this predicate and others; long before we begin biology, we learn that dogs do not run by clockwork. But in biology the word "dog" is clearly a theoretical term; it has theoretical connections of meaning with a vast number of other theoretical terms. It also, however, retains a simple semantic connection to the new predicate: "looks like a dog". Namely, practically everything that *looks like a dog* is a *dog*. Thus although we have modified the language (in setting up a biological formal system) so that "is a dog" and "looks like a dog" are no longer even roughly synonymous (indeed this is the whole point of introducing the phrase "looks like" into the language), it makes perfectly good sense to claim to observe a dog in the corral. The claim is not irrefutable (while the claim that there is something doglike in the corral may be irrefutable) but is, *in itself*, highly probable. It is not that we learn that most doglike appearances are in point of fact dogs (by conducting experiments on them: seeing if they bark, have ears, gnaw bones, and so on), but that we introduce the distinction only because in terms of the theory or in actual fact we see that it is possible for us to be fooled. What we learn is not that most of our observations of dogs are veridical, but that some of them are erroneous. The difference is real: if the former were the case, we would need an *argument* to justify the passage from "looks like a dog" to "is a dog"; as matters are, we need an argument only to explain "looks like . . . but is not. . . ."

Precisely the same kinds of considerations apply to the observation of a temperature (how on earth could one observe a temperature, other than perhaps "very hot", and "very cold"?) and to the observation of a length, and to the observation of an amoeba, and to the observation of a ruby-throated warbler, and to the observation of an electron in a cloud chamber, and to the observation of anger, and so on. . . . We are led to draw a fine distinction between what we irrefutably do observe and what we can legitimately claim to observe, only when something goes wrong with our legitimate claim—when the dog purrs, or the amoeba spreads out over the whole slide, or we discover that the most plausible explanation of the white mark on the photographic print is that there was a hair on the negative, or the angry man smiles and tell us that the door was grabbed out of his hand by the wind, and that he isn't angry at all, and so on.

All of this is difficult to deal with in the abstract, and in the following chapters we will consider particular kinds of observations appropriate to particular formal systems. We will consider experiments of the types encountered in the sciences corresponding to these formal systems, and we will examine the uses of the observation terms in describing both these experiments and their outcomes.

[171]

BIBLIOGRAPHICAL NOTES TO CHAPTER 7

The classical work on induction and experiment is John Stuart Mill's *System of Logic*, Books III and IV. Morris Cohen and Ernest Nagel, in *An Introduction to Logic and Scientific Method* (New York: Harcourt, Brace and Co., 1934) provide an excellent introduction to modern scientific methology.

Two somewhat technical works oriented toward the statistical basis of scientific inference, are R. A. Fisher, *The Design of Experiments* (Edinburgh, Scotland: Oliver and Boyd, Ltd., 1935) and Harold Jeffreys (Cambridge, England: *Scientific Inference*, Cambridge University Press, 1931).

C. D. Broad's argument that we must simply *postulate* that our samples are representative appears in "The Principles of Problematic Induction," *Proceedings of the Aristotelian Society* 28 (1938). Similar worries appear in Chapter 22 of John Maynard Keynes' *Treatise on Probability* (New York: Macmillan, 1921).

A survey of developments in inductive logic over the past 15 years is to be found in my article "Recent Work in Inductive Logic," *American Philosophical Quarterly* 1, 1966. Among the relevant works mentioned there are these: Stephen Barker, *Induction and Hypothesis* (Ithaca, New York: Cornell University Press, 1957), examines the whole problem of the relations between *confirmation, acceptability*, and *simplicity*. An approach concerned more with the psychology of induction than the forms of its logical justification may be found in N. R. Hanson, *Patterns of Discovery* (Cambridge, England: Cambridge University Press, 1958). Karl Popper denies categorically that there is any such thing as induction, but he nevertheless has much that is interesting and worthwhile to say on the subject. His views may be found in *Conjectures and Refutations* (New York: Basic Books, 1963). Stephen Toulmin, in *The Uses of Argument* (Cambridge, England: Cambridge University Press, 1958), argues that all interesting argument is essentially inductive, and attempts to delineate its principles.

Two further works may be mentioned which have appeared since the publication of the review article. One is a general down-to-earth introduction to inductive logic: Robert Ackermann's *Nondeductive Inference* (New York: Dover Publications, 1966); the other is Isaac Levi's thorough and original treatment of scientific induction viewed as the process of choosing among hypotheses: *Gambling with the Truth* (New York: Knopf, 1967).

Chapter **8**

MATHEMATICS

I

The pattern of this and of each of the following chapters will be the same: we will take a particular subject matter—a fragment of some body of scientific knowledge—and show how it may be regarded as a formal system. We shall choose to examine some of the technical terms that might be regarded as primitive in the formal system, and some of those that might be taken as defined. Formation rules and rules of inference will be essentially the same for all of the systems we shall consider. In each formal system there will be axioms that embody the content of the system, and axioms that function as meaning postulates. This classification of the *initial statements* of the calculus, even though it is not a sharp one, constitutes a partial interpretation: given this classification, we no longer have as much freedom as we did before in interpreting the system. We are

[173]

not free to interpret the system in such a way that the meaning postulates turn out to be merely contingently true. But we shall also consider the most down-to-earth aspect of the interpretation of the system. The network of meaning postulates leads down to terms which are relatively ostensive—terms, that is, which the users of the language can apply dependably (with a high degree of interpersonal uniformity) on an observational basis. Some of the formal systems we consider will admit more than one interpretation in this sense. Finally, we shall consider for each of these fragments of formal systems, the kinds of experiments appropriate to that kind of formal system, and the role that that system plays in our general body of beliefs.

Every science presupposes a system of logic. Most require the services of mathematics as well. Even biology, psychology, and the social sciences require mathematics, if not for the formulation of their basic axioms, at least for the construction of tests of their theories. Most such tests will be statistical, and statistics already makes use of a good measure of mathematical structure. We have already (in Chapter 1) presented a standard segment of quantification theory; we shall always suppose, here and in what follows, that this is part of our formal system. In addition to this logic, we need, not only in mathematics, but in other frameworks as well, some set theory. This set theory may be regarded as also a part of logic; for example, the first order logic with which we are familiar may be generalized as a logic of higher orders, and within this generalized logic we may be able to establish a set theory. Or set theory may be regarded as autonomous, distinct from logic, and yet as having the same general analytic character as logic. In either case, we would then speak of reducing mathematics to logic. An alternative point of view takes set theory to be distinct from logic, and to be simply a particularly pervasive and useful part of mathematics. On this latter view, mathematics is not properly reducible to anything else at all. We shall discuss these matters later on in this chapter, where they more properly belong; they are in large part questions of the interpretation of mathematical calculi, about which there is relatively little dispute.

On almost any point of view, set theory is important. In the next section of this chapter, we shall consider informally such elementary set theory as will make the remainder of our discussion of mathematics simple and efficient. In the third section I shall present an axiomatic formulation of the real number system which forms the basis of much of the ordinary mathematics encountered in the sciences; it provides a basis for calculus, applied algebra, analytic geometry, etc. In the subsequent section I shall consider the *reduction* of this real number system to the arithmetic of natural numbers. This will provide an illustration of the process of reduction, not only as it occurs in mathematics, but also as it occurs in other sciences, when, for example, it is said that chemistry can be reduced to physics, or when it is hoped that in time psychology can be reduced to biology, or when it is denied by vitalists and asserted by mechanists

[174]

that biology can ultimately be reduced to physics. The significance of this reducibility in mathematics will be discussed in the last section, which will be concerned with the interpretation of the mathematical structures that have been described in earlier sections. We shall also, at that point, reexamine the question of whether or in what sense mathematics as a whole may simply be regarded as a part of logic.

II

In this section, our approach will be informal. Our object is to gain a modicum of familiarity with the language of set theory, in order to use it, later, in our discussion of the more familiar parts of mathematics. The fundamental relation with which set theory is concerned is the relation of membership, symbolized by "$\in$". "$A \in B$" means that A is a member of B, A belongs to B, A is an element of B. B is a set or class or collection (these terms are all used here synonymously), and A is an element of that set. A itself may be a set, and thus in turn have members; the members of A may or may not be members of B. Some examples will help to make this clear. One way of forming names of sets is to list their members, and then to enclose the list in curly brackets. The set of positive odd numbers less than ten is thus named by the expression: "$\{1,3,5,7,9\}$". The order in which the list is written is irrelevant; all that counts is the membership roster. The just-mentioned set is also denoted by "$\{1,5,9,7,3\}$". The crucial question is whether it is well determined whether or not a particular entity belongs to the set. Two sets are the same if they contain the same members. The following are instances of true set-theoretical statements:

$$1 \in \{1,3,5,7,9\}$$
$$7 \in \{1,3,5,7,9\}$$
$$\{1,3\} \in \{\{1,2\},\{1,3\},\{2,3\}\}$$
$$\sim 2 \in \{1,3,5,7,9\}$$
$$\sim 11 \in \{1,3,5,7,9\}$$
$$\{1,3,5,7,9\} = \{3,9,7,1,5\}.$$

It is obvious that we shall often (particularly in mathematics) be concerned with sets that have an unlimited number of members; for example, the set of all odd numbers. Such a set, of course, cannot be named by writing down a list of all its members. We therefore adopt another way of forming the name of a set, corresponding to the locution (which I have already used above): "the set of all entities such that...". Our symbolic rendering is: "$(x \mid \ldots x \ldots)$", which is the symbolic name for the set of all entities x such that ... x.... The symbolic name for the set of odd numbers is: "$(x \mid x$ is an odd number)". Another name for the same set is: "$(x \mid (\exists y)(y \in I \ \& \ x = 2y - 1))$", where I is the set of positive whole numbers. Some facts about this set are:

$$3 \in (x \mid (\exists y)(y \in I \ \& \ x = 2y - 1))$$
$$\sim 4 \in (x \mid (\exists y)(y \in I \ \& \ x = 2y - 1))$$
$$(z)(x \in (x \mid (\exists y)(y \in I \ \& \ x = 2y - 1)) \supset (\exists y)(y \in I \ \& \ z = 2y - 1)).$$

[175]

There is only one serious disadvantage to describing sets in this way, and that is that we cannot let the context "... x ..." be completely arbitrary. It is not the case that every possible condition on entities has, corresponding to it, a set. It is easy to show that this is the case. Russell's paradox provides the first and simplest illustration: Consider the set of entities satisfying the condition that they are not members of themselves—i.e., the set of entities:

$$(x \mid \sim x \in x).$$

There is nothing *prima facie* wrong with this set; the set $\{1,2\}$ does belong to it, since $\{1,2\}$ has only two members, 1 and 2, and neither of them is $\{1,2\}$ itself; and the set $(x \mid x$ is a set) or the set $(x \mid x$ is an abstract entity) seem to be members of themselves, and therefore not to belong to the set in question. But we ask whether this set $(x \mid \sim x \in x)$ (let us abbreviate it by "R" in honor of Russell) belongs to itself or not. Is this statement true?

$$(1) \qquad R \in (x \mid \sim x \in x).$$

Or is this one true?

$$(2) \qquad \sim R \in (x \mid \sim x \in x).$$

Though they contradict each other, we can prove them both true! To prove (2) true, we proceed by reductio ad absurdum. We suppose, on the contrary, that (2) is false—i.e., that $\sim(\sim R \in (x \mid \sim x \in x))$. This implies that $R \in (x \mid \sim x \in x)$, which implies that R satisfies the condition expressed by the matrix to the right of the vertical bar—i.e., that $\sim R \in R$. So if we suppose that $R \in R$, we are led to the conclusion that $\sim R \in R$, contrary to our supposition. By *reductio ad absurdum*, then, we conclude that our supposition was false, that is, that $\sim R \in R$. But this is just (2), so we have proved that (2) is true. We can prove that (1) is true in a similar way: we suppose (1) false—i.e., that R does not belong to $(x \mid \sim x \in x)$. But this implies that R fails to satisfy the matrix to the right of the vertical line, or that "$\sim R \in R$" is false—i.e., that "$R \in R$" is true. This contradicts our assumption that (1) was false; therefore by *reductio ad absurdum* we conclude that (1) is true. Thus if we suppose that R is a set and that R is capable of being a member of a set, we are led to an explicit contradiction: that both (1) and (2) are true.

There are various ways of avoiding problems of this sort; they are exploited in various systems of formal set theory. None of these is our concern here. For our purposes it suffices that all of the particular conditions we will employ in the sequel are in fact perfectly all right; they are conditions which are acceptable in any ordinary formalization of set theory.

As mentioned before, there is no reason why a set should not have other sets as members. Thus

$$\{\{2,3\},\{3,4\},\{4,5\},\{5,6\}\}$$

[176]

is a perfectly good set. It has four members, each of which in turn is a set consisting of two members. Observe that the numbers 2, 3, etc., are not themselves members of the set; they are members of *members* of the original set:

$$\sim 2 \in \{\{2,3\},\{3,4\},\{4,5\},\{5,6\}\}.$$

But

$$2 \in \{2,3\}$$

and

$$\{2,3\} \in \{\{2,3\},\{3,4\},\{4,5\},\{5,6\}\}.$$

Another example of a set which has sets as members is the ordered pair (as it is usually defined) consisting of item one (*a*, say), followed by item two (*b*, say); we denote this ordered pair by "(*a*,*b*)". This is not the same as the set consisting of *a* and *b*, because $\{a,b\} = \{b,a\}$, while the ordered pair (*a*,*b*) is clearly distinct from the ordered pair (*b*,*a*). But we can still define the ordered pair as a set consisting of two members, each of which is a set; one member is the set whose *sole* member is the *first* member of the ordered pair, the other member is the set having as members the two objects constituting the ordered pair. We thus define the ordered pair (*a*,*b*):

D1
$$(a,b) =_{Df} \{\{a\},\{a,b\}\}$$

As we wanted, (*a*,*b*) and (*b*,*a*) are distinct under this definition, because $\{a\}$ is a member of the former but not of the latter, and $\{b\}$ is a member of the latter, but not of the former. In what follows, we shall have much occasion to refer to ordered pairs.

There are three important operations on sets that we can define with the help of ordinary logical notation. One of these is *intersection*. The intersection of two sets *A* and *B* (denoted by "$A \cap B$") is the set of just those things that are members of both *A* and *B*. Formally:

D2
$$A \cap B =_{Df} (x \mid x \in A \ \& \ x \in B).$$

Similarly, we define the *union* of two sets, *A* and *B* (denoted by "$A \cup B$"), as the set of just those things that are members of *A* or are members of *B*.

D3
$$A \cup B =_{Df} (x \mid x \in A \ \lor \ x \in B).$$

Finally, we have the operation of forming the *difference* of two sets *A* and *B* (denoted by "$A - B$"). This is the set constituted by just those things that belong to *A*, but not to *B*.

D4
$$A - B =_{Df} (x \mid x \in A \ \& \ \sim x \in B).$$

Two relations that hold between sets will be of particular interest to us. One is *inclusion*: we say that one set, *A*, is included in another set *B* (symbolically, "$A \subset B$") when every object that belongs to the first set *A* also belongs to the second set *B*.

D5
$$A \subset B =_{Df} (x)(x \in A \supset x \in B).$$

[177]

Observe that this is not an operation: "$A \subset B$" does not denote a set, but expresses the fact that a relation holds between sets. "$A \subset B$" is a statement, while "$A \cap B$", "$A - B$", and "$A \cup B$" are names of certain sets. Finally, we can define the relation of identity for sets in a way that corresponds to our informal characterization above:

D6 $$A = B =_{Df} (x)(x \in A \equiv x \in B).$$

It should be noticed that identity is also taken to be a relation between individuals who are not sets; thus if a and b are not sets, we shall take "$a = b$" to mean that a and b are just the same thing, and the sign "$=$" that occurs in that statement to be a primitive sign in our underlying logic. Furthermore, the sign "$=_{Df}$", which we have been using to express definitions, represents still another notion of identity, which we might call *stipulative* identity. "$A =_{Df} B$" is to be taken to mean that the name or sentence A is *to be taken to mean* the same as the name or sentence B; A is being introduced as an abbreviation for B.

There is one rule of inference concerning sets that we shall make use of which has no counterpart in quantificational logic. We have used it above in inferring "$\sim R \in R$" from "$R \in (x \mid \sim x \in x)$"; it amounts to the self evident principle that an object belongs to the set of objects satisfying a certain condition, if and only if it satisfies that condition. In view of the paradox adduced above, we must hedge this rule with a proviso that the condition be an acceptable one which *does* define a set.

Rule S: If $(x \mid \ldots x \ldots)$ is a set, then "$y \in (x \mid \ldots x \ldots)$" may replace and be replaced by "$\ldots y \ldots$"

If we were presenting a formal set theory, there would now be a number of theorems we could prove. I shall state some of them because they represent important facts. The proofs are not at all difficult and will be left for the student.

$$(3) \quad A = B \equiv ((A \subset B) \,\&\, (B \subset A))$$
$$(4) \quad A \cap (B \cap C) = (A \cap B) \cap C$$
$$(5) \quad A \cap B = B \cap A$$
$$(6) \quad A \cup (B \cup C) = (A \cup B) \cup C$$
$$(7) \quad A \cup B = B \cup A$$
$$(8) \quad A \cup (B \cap C) = (A \cup B) \cap (A \cup C)$$
$$(9) \quad A \cap (B \cup C) = (A \cap B) \cup (A \cap C)$$
$$(10) \quad A - (B \cap C) = (A - B) \cup (A - C)$$
$$(11) \quad A - (B \cup C) = (A - B) \cap (A - C).$$

The alert reader will notice that, with the help of the definitions and the rule S, the argument for each of these statements will boil down ultimately to a fact about the sentential calculus. Thus (4) and (6) depend only on the associativity of the sentential operations of conjunction and disjunction and (5) and (7) depend primarily on the commutativity of those operations.

[178]

III

The real number system is the framework for the kind of mathematics most of us are familiar with from high school algebra, calculus, etc., and these are just the parts of mathematics that have the most important and most pervasive applications in the sciences. The object of this section is to provide a formalization of this familiar framework, i.e., to construct a formal system that will embody this bit of mathematical knowledge. We shall consider in turn the vocabulary, the formation rules, the rules of inference, and the axioms; finally we shall very briefly consider the interpretation of the resulting calculus.

A. Vocabulary:
  1. Logical and set theoretical constants:

$$=, \in, \subset, \sim, \vee, \&, \cap, \cup, -, \supset, \equiv$$

  2. Variables: individual variables: $x, y, z, \ldots$
      set variables: $X, Y, Z, \ldots$.
  3. Constants: individual constants corresponding to real numbers:

$$4, 0, \sqrt{2}, -1, e, \sin 10°, \text{ etc.}$$

      set constant: R
      operators: $+$ (plus), $\otimes$ (times)

B. Formation Rules:
  1. Individual terms:
      a. An individual variable is an individual term.
      b. An individual constant is an individual term.
      c. If t_1 and t_2 are individual terms, then $(t_1 + t_2)$ and $(t_1 \otimes t_2)$ are individual terms.
      d. These are the only individual terms.
  2. Set terms:
      a. A set variable is a set term.
      b. R is a set term.
      c. If T_1 and T_2 are set terms, then $(T_1 - T_2), (T_1 \cap T_2)$, and $(T_1 \cup T_2)$ are set terms.
      d. These are the only set terms.
  3. Well-formed formulas:
      a. If t_1 and t_2 are individual terms, $t_1 = t_2$ is a wff.
      b. If T_1 and T_2 are set terms, $T_1 = T_2$, $T_1 \subset T_2$ and $T_1 \in T_2$ are wff.
      c. If t_1 is an individual term and T_2 is a set term, then $t_1 \in T_2$ is a wff.
      d. If S_1 and S_2 are well-formed formulas, and V is an individual variable or a set variable, then $\sim S_1, (S_1 \& S_2), (S_1 \vee S_2), (S_1 \equiv S_2), (S_1 \supset S_2), (V)S_1$ and $(\exists V)S_1$ are all well-formed formulas.
      e. Only these are well-formed formulas.

[179]

C. Rules of Inference:

1. If $(S_1 \& S_2 \& \cdots \& S_n) \supset S$ is a theorem of the logical calculus described in Chapter One, then S may be inferred from premise $S_1, S_2, \cdots, S_n$.

2. Identity rules: If t is an individual or set term, $t = t$ may be inferred from no premises; $t_2 = t_1$ may be inferred from $t_1 = t_2$; $t_1 = t_3$ may be inferred from $t_1 = t_2$ and $t_2 = t_3$. If S_2 is like S_1, except for containing t_2 at one or more places where S_1 contains t_1, then $S_1 \equiv S_2$ may be inferred from $t_1 = t_2$, and S_2 may be inferred from $t_1 = t_2$ and S_1.

3. If t is a term, and V is an individual variable, then $t \in (V \mid \cdots V \cdots)$ may replace and be replaced by $(\cdots t \cdots)$, provided $\cdots V \cdots$ is an acceptable condition for a set.

4. If $\cdots V \cdots$ represents an acceptable condition for a set (and all of the conditions we shall encounter do) then from $\cdots V \cdots, (\exists V)(\cdots V \cdots)$ may be inferred.

D. Axioms:

1. Addition:

$$(x)(y)(z)((x \in R \& y \in R \& z \in R) \supset ((x + y) \in R \&$$
$$(x + y) = (y + x) \& ((x + y) + z) = (x + (y + z)))).$$

2. Multiplication:

$$(x)(y)(z)((x \in R \& y \in R \& z \in R) \supset ((x \otimes y) \in R \&$$
$$(x \otimes y) = (y \otimes x) \& (x \otimes (y \otimes z)) = ((x \otimes y) \otimes z))).$$

3. Additive identity, zero:

$$(\exists x)(x \in R \& (y)(y \in R \supset x + y = y)).$$

4. Multiplicative identity, unit:

$$(\exists x)(x \in R \& (y)(y \in R \supset x \otimes y = y)).$$

5. Additive inverse:

$$(x)(x \in R \supset (\exists y)(y \in R \& x + y = 0)).$$

Strictly speaking, we have not yet defined the additive identity as 0; before we do that we must prove a theorem to the effect that there is only *one* additive identity. Similar remarks apply to the constant "1"; before we can define "1" as *the* multiplicative identity, we must prove its uniqueness. And the same is true of the "$-x$" that occurs in Axiom 8.

6. Multiplicative inverse:

$$(x)((x \in R \& \sim x = 0) \supset (\exists y)(y \in R \& x \otimes y = 1)).$$

7. Distributive law:

$$(x)(y)(z)((x \in R \& y \in R \& z \in R) \supset x \otimes (y + z) = (x \otimes y) + (x \otimes z)).$$

[180]

8. Ordering:

$$(\exists X)(X \subset R \;\&\; X \neq R \;\&\; (x)(x \in R \supset (x \in X \lor -x \in X)) \;\&\; (x)(y)((x \in X \;\&\;$$
$$y \in X) \supset ((x \otimes y) \in X \;\&\; (x + y) \in X))).$$

9. Least upper bound axiom:

$$(X)(X \subset R \supset ((\exists y)(UB(y,X)) \supset (\exists y)(LUB(y,X)))).$$

A number of theorems and definitions are required to make good sense out of these axioms. The idea behind Axiom 5, for example, is that for every number there exists another number such that the sum of the two numbers turns out to be the additive identity 0. But this presupposes, of course, that there is only one additive identity 0. In the same way the notation "$-x$" in Axiom 8 presupposes that for a given number there can be only one additive inverse. We could state the axioms in such a way as not to make these presuppositions, but the statements would be far more complicated than those above. Axiom 5, for example, becomes

$$(x)(x \in R \supset (\exists y)(y \in R \;\&\; (z)(z \in R \supset z + (x + y) = z))),$$

and the clause "$x \in X \lor -x \in X$" in Axiom 8 becomes

$$x \in X \lor (y)((y \in R \;\&\; (z)(z \in R \supset z + (x + y) = z)) \supset y \in X).$$

We first prove the uniqueness of the additive identity:

THEOREM 1.

$$(x)(x')((x \in R \;\&\; x' \in R \;\&\; (y)(y \in R \supset (y + x = y \;\&\; y + x' = y)) \supset x = x')$$

Proof:

1. $y \in R \supset (\exists z)(z \in R \;\&\; y + z = 0^*)$ Axiom 5. Prior to the proof of Theorem 1, Axiom 5 merely assures us that there *is* a z such that $y + z$ is some additive identity; hence I have written "0^*" rather than "0"

2. $y \in R$ hypothesis
3. $(\exists z)(z \in R \;\&\; y + z = 0^*)$ 1,2, MP
4. $z' \in R \;\&\; y + z' = 0^*$ 3, EI
5. $x \in R \;\&\; x' \in R \;\&\; (y)(y \in R \supset (y + x = y \;\&\; y + x' = y)$ hypothesis
6. $y \in R \supset (y + x = y \;\&\; y + x' = y)$ 5, simplification, UI
7. $y + x = y + x'$ 2,6, MP
8. $z' + (y + x) = z' + (y + x)$ Identity

[181]

9. $z' + (y + x) = z' + (y + x')$ — Identity, 7,8
10. $x + (y + z') = x' + (y + z')$ — Axiom 1, 9
11. $x + 0^* = x$ — 0^* is an additive identity
12. $x' + 0^* = x'$ — 0^* is an additive identity
13. $x' = x$ — 11,12,10,4, identity
14. $y \in R \supset$ (Theorem 1) — conditionalizing on 2 and 5
15. $(\exists y)(y \in R) \supset$ (Theorem 1) — 14
16. [Theorem 1] — the antecedent of 15 may be obtained e.g., from Axiom 3

Having shown that there is only one additive identity, we may define 0 to be *the* additive identity. We use the notation "$(\imath x)(\cdots x \cdots)$" to stand for the one and only x such that $\cdots x \cdots$. For those to whom it is unfamiliar notation, let it suffice to mention that in well-formed formulas it is eliminable in favor of the notation of quantification theory and identity.

D7 $\qquad\qquad 0 =_{Df} (\imath x)(x \in R \ \& \ (y)(y \in R \supset x + y = y)).$

In just the same way, we prove there is just one multiplicative identity, and then christen it "1".

THEOREM 2.

$$(x)(x')((x \in R \ \& \ x' \in R \ \& \ (y)(y \in R \supset x \otimes y = y) \ \&$$
$$(y)(y \in R \supset x' \otimes y = y)) \supset x = x')$$

The proof is in principle just the same as the proof of Theorem 1. The theorem justifies the following definition:

D8 $\qquad\qquad 1 =_{Df} (\imath x)(x \in R \ \& \ (y)(y \in R \supset x \otimes y = y)$

These two definitions justify the occurrences of "0" and "1" in the postulates. To justify the notation "$-x$" for the additive inverse of x, and the notation "x^{-1}" for the multiplicative inverse of x, we must prove two more uniqueness theorems. All that the postulates guarantee directly is that there is some additive inverse for every x, and some multiplicative inverse. If, for a given x, there were more than one additive inverse, we could not introduce the notation "$-x$" on pain of contradiction. If, for example, x had two distinct additive inverses both denoted by "$-x$", we would have "$\sim -x = -x$" in direct contradiction to the logical theorem, "$(x)(x = x)$".

THEOREM 3.

$$(x)(y)(z)((x \in R \ \& \ y \in R \ \& \ z \in R \ \& \ x + y = 0 \ \& \ x + z = 0) \supset y = z)$$

Proof:

1. $x \in R \ \& \ y \in R \ \& \ z \in R \ \& \ x + y = 0 \ \& \ x + z = 0$ — hypothesis
2. $x \in R \supset (\exists y)(y \in R \ \& \ x + y = 0)$ — Axiom 5; UI
3. $(\exists y)(y \in R \ \& \ x + y = 0)$ — 1,2, MP

[182]

4. $y' \in R$ & $x + y' = 0$ 3, EI
5. $y' + 0 = y' + 0$ identity
6. $y' + (x + y) = y' + (x + z)$ 1,5; substitutivity of identity

7. $(x + y') + y = (x + y') + z$ Axiom 1,6
8. $0 + y = 0 + z$ 4,7; substitutivity of identity

9. $y = z$ 8, definition of 0
10. [Theorem 3]   conditionalization, generalization

D9 $-x =_{Df} (\imath y)(y \in R$ & $x + y = 0)$.

In the same way, we have a theorem and a definition to account for the notation "x^{-1}".

THEOREM 4.

$$(x)(y)(z)((x \in R$ & $y \in R$ & $z \in R$ & $\sim x = 0$ & $x \otimes y = 1$ & $x \otimes z = 1) \supset$$
$$y = z)$$

D10 $x^{-1} =_{Df} (\imath y)(y \in R$ & $x \otimes y = 1)$

The subset of real numbers mentioned in Axiom 8 is the set of positive real numbers; in order to have a definition to this effect, we must show that this set is unique.

THEOREM 5.

$(X)(Y)((X \subset R$ & $Y \subset R$ & $(x)(x \in R \supset (x \in X \lor -x \in X))$ &
     $(x)(x \in R \supset (x \in Y \lor -x \in Y))$ & $(x)(y)((x \in X$ & $y \in X) \supset$
     $(x + y \in X$ & $x \otimes y \in X))$ & $(x)(y)((x \in Y$ & $y \in Y) \supset (x + y \in Y$
     & $x \otimes y \in Y))) \supset X = Y)$

The proof of this theorem is tedious but straightforward. The consequent, "$X = Y$", is a set theoretic statement. On the basis of our informal discussion of set theory, we can see that it amounts to

$$(z)(z \in X \equiv z \in Y).$$

The technique of proof for Theorem 5 is to assume the antecedent of the theorem as a hypothesis, to assume "$z \in X$" as an additional hypothesis, and to derive from these hypotheses (and the axioms!) "$z \in Y$"; by a perfectly parallel argument, from the antecedent of the theorem and the additional hypothesis "$z \in Y$", we derive "$z \in X$". It is then merely an argument in the sentential calculus to derive the conditional statement whose antecedent is the antecedent of the theorem, and whose consequent is "$z \in X \equiv z \in Y$". But since "z" does not occur free (or at all) in the antecedent of the theorem, we may generalize directly on the

[183]

consequent, and obtain the desired result. The theorem justifies the following definition:

D11 $\quad P =_{Df} (\imath X)(X \subset R \ \& \ (x)(y)((x \in X \ \& \ y \in X) \supset (x + y \in X \ \&$
$$x \otimes y \in X)) \ \& \ (x)(x \in R \supset (x \in X \ \lor \ -x \in X))).$$

We are now in a position to define the terms that appear mysteriously in the final axiom. We first define the relation of being greater than:

D12 $$x > y =_{Df} x + -y \in P.$$

With this notion available, it is simple to define the relation between a number and a set of numbers that holds when the number is an *upper bound* of the set of numbers. Intuitively, to say that x is an upper bound of X is to say that it is a real number, that X is a non-empty set of real numbers, and that x is at least as big as any number in X. Formally,

D13 $\quad UB(x,X) =_{Df} (y)(y \in X \supset x > y \ \lor \ x = y) \ \& \ (\exists y)(y \in X) \ \& \ X \subset R.$

As an illustration, consider the set $\{3,4,6,8,13,-4,-7\}$. The numbers 15, 17, and 13 are all upper bounds of this set. The numbers 3, 1.5, and 1.42 are all upper bounds of the set $(x \mid x \in R \ \& \ 2 > x \otimes x)$.

A *least* upper bound of a set X is just what it sounds like: it is an upper bound of X which is smaller than any other upper bound of X.

D14 $\quad LUB(x,X) =_{Df} UB(x,X) \ \& \ (y)(UB(y,X) \supset (y > x \ \lor \ y = x)).$

In the two preceding illustrations, 13 is the least upper bound in the first case, and $\sqrt{2}$ is the least upper bound in the second case.

The foregoing system is all we need to do polynomial algebra, to solve equations, to develop the calculus and analytic geometry, and indeed to do analysis generally. There remains the question, however, of the *interpretation* of the structure which is built up on the basis of our nine axioms. One interpretation would be to take the elements of R to be distances in a given direction, negative elements of R corresponding to distances in the opposite direction. One could interpret the positive elements of R as lengths or masses. The operations $+$ and $\otimes$ become interpreted then as the physical operations of juxtaposition (in a straight line), combining into one lump, multiplication of quantities, and so on. The interpreted calculus is then a formal system of real-valued quantities.

But there is also a purely logical or purely abstract interpretation. We can regard the things about which the theory is concerned as pure numbers, and then we do not have to take the theory as a theory about the world; it is a theory about certain abstract objects. One may take these abstract objects to be definable in logical terms alone—one may take then to be be purely logical constructs, having no intrinsic connection with the empirical world at all. Nonetheless, the abstract system will be useful, and applicable to the world, in virtue of the *similarity of*

[184]

structure between the abstract system (or parts of it) and the quantities that we take our scientific theories to relate.

In the final section of this chapter, we shall see that there is an intermediate program. In order to prepare the way for this, however, we must see how (and in what sense) the formal system we have just presented for the real number system can be reduced to a formal system that involves only the arithmetic of positive whole numbers (the natural numbers).

IV

We now turn to an alternative formal system for the real-number framework of ordinary mathematics. This approach takes its variables to range over classes and natural (nonnegative whole) numbers, rather than over classes and the set of all real numbers. It thus shows that the set of real numbers may be *reduced to* classes of natural numbers, in the sense that there is an interpretation of a real number calculus which does not require the existence of any objects but those corresponding to natural numbers, together with sets. We shall return to the questions of interpretation and of reduction in the next section; here we are concerned primarily to present the calculus of this alternative formal system.

A. Vocabulary:
1. Logical and set theoretical constants:

$$=, \in, \subset, \sim, \vee, \&, \cap, \cup, -, \supset, \equiv$$

2. Variables: individual variables: $x, y, z, \ldots$
set variables: $X, Y, Z, \ldots$

3. Constants: individual constant: 0_N
successor function: S
set constant: N

B. Formation Rules:
1. Individual terms:
a. An individual variable is an individual term.
b. 0_N is an individual term.
c. If t is an individual term, $S(t)$ is an individual term.
d. These are the only individual terms.
2. Set terms:
a. A set variable is a set term.
b. N is a set term.
c. If T_1 and T_2 are set terms, then $(T_1 - T_2)$, $(T_1 \cap T_2)$, and $(T_1 \cup T_2)$ are set terms, and if V is a set variable and ϕ a well-formed formula, $(V \mid V \subset T_1 \& \phi)$ is also a set term.
d. These are the only set terms.

[185]

3. Well-formed formulas:
   a. If t_1 and t_2 are individual terms, $t_1 = t_2$ is a well-formed formula.
   b. If T_1 and T_2 are set terms, $T_1 = T_2$ and $T_1 \subset T_2$ are well-formed formulas, and $T_1 \in T_2$ is a well-formed formula.
   c. If t is an individual term and T is a set term, then $t \in T$ is a well-formed formula.
   d. If S_1 and S_2 are well-formed formulas, so are $\sim S_1, (S_1 \,\&\, S_2), (S_1 \lor S_2)$, etc., and if V is either an individual or a set variable, then $(V)S_1$ and $(\exists V)S_2$ are wffs.
   e. These are the only well-formed formulas.

C. Axioms:
   1. $0_N \in N$
   2. $(x)(x \in N \supset (\exists y)(y \in N \,\&\, Sx = y \,\&\, (z)(Sx = z \supset z = y)))$
   3. $(x)(x \in N \supset \,\sim Sx = 0_N)$
   4. $(x)(y)(Sx = Sy \supset x = y)$
   5. $(0_N \in X \,\&\, (x)(x \in X \supset Sx \in X)) \supset X = N$

D. Rules of Inference:
   1. If $(S_1 \,\&\, S_2 \,\&\, \cdots \,\&\, S_n) \supset S$ is a theorem of the logical calculus described in Chapter One, then S may be inferred from premises $S_1, S_2, \cdots, S_n$.
   2. Identity rules: if t is an individual term or a set term, $t = t$ may be inferred from no premises; $t_2 = t_1$ may be inferred from $t_1 = t_2$; $t_1 = t_3$ may be inferred from $t_1 = t_2$ and $t_2 = t_3$. If S_2 is like S_1, except for containing t_2 at one or more places where S_1 contains t_1, then $(S_1 \equiv S_2)$ may be inferred from $t_1 = t_2$, and S_2 may be inferred from S_1 and $t_1 = t_2$.
   3. If t is a term of either sort, and V is the corresponding sort of variable, then $t \in (V \mid \cdots V \cdots)$ may replace and be replaced by $(\cdots t \cdots)$, provided $\cdots V \cdots$ represents an acceptable condition for a set.

The derivation of the axioms of the preceding system for the real numbers and the definition of the operations (together with the justifying theorems) can be rather drawn out and tedious, and is not necessary here. It is important and interesting, however, to see *how* the operations are defined, and to indicate the general strategy involved in the proofs of the required theorems.

Let us begin with the operation of addition. We want to define the operation of addition as *the* operation A that satisfies these two conditions for every x and every y:

$$\text{(a)} \quad A(x,0_N) = x$$
$$\text{(b)} \quad A(x,Sy) = S(A(x,y)).$$

In order to use these conditions to define addition, we must prove that there *exists* such an operation A, and further that there is only *one* such operation as A. (In the preceding calculus we had to establish uniqueness theorems; existence theorems were provided for directly by the axioms.) We shall not give formal proofs of these theorems, but merely indicate how the two theorems could be proved.

THEOREM I (EXISTENCE).

$$(\exists A)(x)(y)(A(x,0_N) = x \ \& \ A(x,Sy) = S(A(x,y))).$$

The proof proceeds by induction—i.e., through the use of Axiom 5. Consider X, the set of x for which there is an operation A satisfying (a) and (b) above. Let $A(0_N,y) = y$, for all y. Then $0_N \in X$, since both $A(0_N,0_N) = 0_N$, and $A(0_N,Sy) = Sy = S(A(0_N,y)) = Sy$. Furthermore, let $A(Sx,y) = S(A(x,y))$ whenever $x \in X$. Under this definition of A, it is easy to see that (a) and (b) hold of Sx whenever they hold of x. Suppose $x \in X$. Then (by (a)) $A(x,0_N) = x$, and by our definition of A, $A(Sx,0_N) = S(A(x,0_N)) = Sx$, so that (a) is satisfied for Sx. And by (b), $A(x,Sy) = S(A(x,y))$, so that $A(Sx,Sy) = S(S(A(x,y)))$, by our definition, and thus $A(Sx,Sy) = S(A(x,Sy))$, and (b) holds of Sx. The set of x such that A can be defined in such a way that (a) and (b) hold is therefore N itself.

THEOREM II (UNIQUENESS).

$$(A)(A^*)(x)(y)((A(x,0_N) = x \ \& \ A(x,Sy) = S(A(x,y)) \ \& \ A^*(x,0_N) = x \ \&$$
$$A^*(x,Sy) = S(A^*x,y))) \supset A(x,y) = A^*(x,y))$$

Again we have a theorem that can be proved by induction, this time on the set Y of y such that for every x, $A(x,y) = A^*(x,y)$. Since $A(x,0_N) = 0_N = A^*(x,0_N)$, $0_N \in Y$. And if $y \in Y$, then $A(x,Sy) = S(A(x,y)) = S(A^*(x,y)) = A^*(x,Sy)$, so that $Sy \in Y$. Thus $Y = N$.

In view of the facts embodied in Theorems I and II, we may define addition to be *the* operation satisfying (a) and (b) above. More precisely, we give an *inductive* definition of the operation $+$; such a definition consists of two parts, a part which provides an explicit definition for contexts of the form "$(x + 0_N)$" and a part which allows us to reduce a context of the form "$(x + Sy)$" toward the former context by reducing it to "$S(x + y)$", in which the problematic context is only "$(x + y)$". Each such step reduces the right hand component of the sum one unit closer to the natural number zero, and thus the sum itself closer to the form "$(x + 0_N)$" for which we have an explicit definition.

D15
$$(x + 0_N) =_{Df} x$$
$$(x + Sy) =_{Df} S(x + y)$$

This definition clearly amounts to the proposal to regard the sum of two natural numbers x and y as the number that is obtained from x by adding 1 to it y times.

In a perfectly analogous manner, we may show that there exists exactly one operation M satisfying

(c) $M(x,0_N) = 0_N$
(d) $M(x,Sy) = M(x,y) + x.$

[187]

THEOREM III (EXISTENCE).

$$(\exists M)(x)(y)(M(x,0_N) = 0_N \& M(x,Sy) = M(x,y) + x)$$

The proof of this theorem proceeds like the proof of Theorem I. We let X be the set of x, such that (c) and (d) hold for every y, when we let $M(0_N,y) = 0_N$ and $M(Sx,y) = M(x,y) + y$ for every y. It is possible to show that $0_N \in X$, and that if $x \in X$, then $Sx \in X$, and thus that $X = N$.

THEOREM IV (UNIQUENESS).

$$(M)(M^*)(x)(y)((M(x,0_N) = 0_N \& M(x,Sy) = M(x,Sy) + x \&$$
$$M^*(x,0_N) = 0_N \& M^*(x,Sy) = M^*(x,y) + x) \supset M(x,y) = M^*(x,y))$$

Let Y be the set of y such that $M(x,y) = M^*(x,y)$ for every x. We can prove that $0_N \in Y$, and that if $y \in Y$, then $Sy \in Y$, and thus that $Y = N$.

We are thus free to define the operation of multiplication for natural numbers as follows:

D16
$$(x \otimes 0_N) =_{Df} 0_N$$
$$(x \otimes Sy) =_{Df} (x \otimes y) + x.$$

The usual notation for the natural numbers themselves is introduced simply enough:

D17
$$1_N =_{Df} S0_N$$
$$2_N =_{Df} S1_N$$
$$3_N =_{Df} S2_N$$
$$\cdots$$

We can now prove the usual theorems for natural numbers. (Indeed, had we wanted to produce proofs of Theorems 3 and 4, it would have been advantageous to have established some of these Theorems before now!)

THEOREM V.

$$(x)(y)((x \in N \& y \in N) \supset (x + y \in N \& x + y = y + x \& (z)(z \in N \supset$$
$$z + (x + y) = (z + x) + y))).$$

THEOREM VI.

$$(x)(y)(z)((x \in N \& y \in N \& z \in N) \supset (x \otimes y \in N \& x \otimes y = y \otimes x \&$$
$$z \otimes (x \otimes y) = (z \otimes x) \otimes y)).$$

THEOREM VII.

$$(x)(y)(z)((x \in N \& y \in N \& z \in N) \supset x \otimes (y + z) = (x \otimes y) + (x \otimes z)).$$

We can define an ordering relation for the natural numbers as follows:

D18
$$x >_N y =_{Df} (\exists z)(\sim z = 0_N \& x = y + z).$$

[188]

And we can then prove:

THEOREM VIII.

$$(x)(y)(z)((x \in N \ \& \ y \in N \ \& \ z \in N) \supset ((x >_N y \lor y >_N x \lor y = x) \ \&$$
$$((x >_N y \ \& \ y >_N z) \supset x >_N z))).$$

It is evident that the foregoing axioms and theorems embody the usual content of the arithmetic of natural numbers. The next step is to proceed to construct rational numbers on the basis provided by the natural numbers. We may begin by considering the set of all ordered pairs of natural numbers of which the second member is not 0_N:

$$(X \mid (\exists y)(\exists z)(y \in N \ \& \ z \in N \ \& \ {\sim}z = 0_N \ \& \ X = (y,z))).$$

Among the members of this set, we define a relation of equivalence, abbreviated "equiv":

D19 $\qquad\qquad (x,y) \text{ equiv } (x',y') =_{Df} x \otimes y' = x' \otimes y.$

The next theorem shows that it is proper to call this an "equivalence relation" i.e., that it has the appropriate properties of an equivalence relation: it is reflexive, symmetrical, and transitive.

THEOREM IX.

$$(x)(y)(x')(y')(x'')(y'')((x \in N \ \& \ x' \in N \ \& \ x'' \in N \ \& \ y \in N \ \& \ y' \in N \ \& \ y'' \in N) \supset$$
$$((x,y) \text{ equiv } (x,y) \ \& \ ((x,y) \text{ equiv } (x',y') \supset (x',y') \text{ equiv } (x,y)) \ \&$$
$$(((x,y) \text{ equiv } (x',y') \ \& \ (x',y') \text{ equiv } (x'',y'')) \supset (x,y) \text{ equiv } (x'',y'')))).$$

It will be readily seen that the pairs of natural numbers correspond to *fractions*, and that the relation of equivalence divides the set of all pairs of natural numbers up into exclusive classes, called equivalence classes, corresponding to *ratios*. The ratios—the nonnegative rational numbers—can indeed be identified with these equivalence classes of ordered pairs of natural numbers:

D20 $\qquad\qquad x/y =_{Df} (X \mid X \text{ equiv } (x,y) \ \& \ {\sim}y = 0_N).$

"x/y" denotes a *class* of pairs of natural numbers, it should be observed, and not the fraction (x,y), which is a member of that class. We may define the whole set of nonnegative rational numbers:

D21 $\qquad\qquad F =_{Df} (Y \mid (\exists y)(\exists x)(Y = y/x)).$

Ratios are thus identified with sets; in particular they are identified with sets of ordered pairs of natural numbers. Since an ordered pair of natural numbers is a set of sets of natural numbers, this makes a ratio set of sets of sets of natural numbers.

For these new entities, defined in terms of the natural numbers, we can define

[189]

a new ordering relation on the basis of the old one. The definition depends on the following theorem:

THEOREM X.

$$(x)(y)(z)(w)(x')(y')(z')(w')((x/y = x'/y' \& z/w = z'/w' \& \\ x \otimes y' >_N x' \otimes y) \supset z \otimes w' >_N z' \otimes w).$$

Thus if the relation mentioned in Theorem X holds between an ordered pair of natural numbers belonging to Y and an ordered pair of natural numbers belonging to Y', where Y and Y' are ratios, then that relation holds between any ordered pair belonging to Y and any ordered pair belonging to Y'. This fact justifies the following definition:

D22 $Y >_r X =_{Df} (\exists x)(\exists y)(\exists z)(\exists w)((x,y) \in Y \& (z,w) \in X \& x \otimes w >_N y \otimes z).$

The trichotomy law for rational numbers is expressed by Theorem XI:

THEOREM XI.

$$(X)(Y)((X \in F \& Y \in F) \supset (X >_r Y \lor Y >_r X \lor Y = X)).$$

I have written "$>_r$" here, rather than "$>_N$", because the two relations should be kept distinct. One applies to natural numbers, and the other applies to ratios. Since our individual variables and individual terms are distinct from our set variables and set terms, we could tell from the context which relation is intended; nevertheless it is advantageous to use distinctive notation for the two relations simply as a reminder that they are two. I shall similarly use a subscript "r" for the operations of addition and multiplication for ratios, which will be defined immediately below.

D23 $X +_r Y =_{Df} (Z \mid (\exists x)(\exists y)(\exists z)(\exists w)(x,y) \in X \& (z,w) \in Y \& \\ Z \text{ equiv } (((x \otimes w) + (z \otimes y)),y \otimes w)))$

D24 $x \otimes_r Y =_{Df} (Z \mid (\exists x)(\exists y)(\exists z)(\exists w)((x,y) \in X \& (z,w) \in Y \& \\ Z \text{ equiv } (x \otimes y,z \otimes w))).$

Properly speaking, supporting theorems, corresponding to Theorem X, should have been provided for these two definitions.

On the basis of these definitions, we can prove the usual things about the arithmetic of ratios:

THEOREM XII.

$$(X)(Y)(Z)((X \in F \& Y \in F \& Z \in F) \supset (X +_r Y = Y +_r X \& X +_r (Y +_r Z) = \\ (X +_r Y) +_r Z \& X \otimes_r Y = Y \otimes_r X \& X \otimes_r (Y \otimes_r Z) = (X \otimes_r Y) \otimes_r Z \& \\ X \otimes_r (Y +_r Z) = (X \otimes_r Y) +_r (X \otimes_r Z)).$$

We could also prove the existence of an additive identity and a multiplicative identity, and of a multiplicative inverse.

[190]

The next step is to obtain the nonnegative real numbers as classes or sets of nonnegative rational numbers. (They will thus be sets of sets of sets of sets of natural numbers.) These classes are to be called *cuts*, and are defined as follows:

D25   cut $X =_{Df} (Y)(Y \in X \supset Y \in F) \ \& \ (\exists Y)(Y \in X \ \& \ Y \in F) \ \& \ (Y)(Z)$
$$((Y \in X \ \& \ \sim Z \in X) \supset Y <_r Z) \ \& \ \sim(\exists Z)(Z \in X \ \&$$
$$(Y)((Y \in X \ \& \ \sim Y = Z) \supset Y <_r Z)).$$

A cut thus consists of a nonempty set of rational numbers such that every number belonging to the set is smaller than every number not belonging to the set, and which does not contain a greatest number. Examples of cuts are:

$$(Y \mid Y \in F \ \& \ Y <_r (1_N/2_N))$$
$$(Y \mid Y \in F \ \& \ Y <_r (5_N/1_N)$$
$$(Y \mid Y \in F \ \& \ Y \otimes Y <_r (2_N/1_N).$$

The order relation is defined for cuts in the obvious way:

D26 $X <_c Y =_{Df}$ cut $X \ \&$ cut $Y \ \& \ (\exists Z)(Z \in Y \ \& \ \sim Z \in X).$

The trichotomy law follows easily from D25 and D26:

THEOREM XIII.

$$(X)(Y)((\text{cut } X \ \& \ \text{cut } Y) \supset (X <_c Y \vee Y <_c X \vee Y = X)).$$

The next problem is to define the operation of addition for cuts, or, as we could also call them, the nonnegative real numbers. We must begin by formulating a theorem:

THEOREM XIV.

$$(X)(Y)((\text{cut } X \ \& \ \text{cut } Y) \supset \text{cut } (Z \mid (\exists X')(\exists Y')(X' \in X \ \& \ Y' \in Y \ \&$$
$$Z = X' +_r Y'))).$$

The cut described on the right hand side of Theorem XIV we shall take to be the *sum* of the cuts X and Y, and we shall denote it by "$X +_c Y$".

D27 $X +_c Y =_{Df} (Z \mid (\exists X')(\exists Y')(X' \in X \ \& \ Y' \in Y \ \& Z = X' +_r Y')).$

We have already proved, preparatory to stating D27, that the sum of two cuts is a cut. We can now prove that the usual commutative and associative properties of addition hold for $+_c$ as it has been defined.

THEOREM XV.

$$(X)(Y)(X +_c Y = Y +_c X).$$

THEOREM XVI.

$$(X)(Y)(Z)(X +_c (Y +_c Z) = (X +_c Y) +_c Z).$$

[191]

Multiplication we may deal with in the same way. We justify the coming definition by the theorem:

THEOREM XVII.

$$(X)(Y)((\text{cut } X \,\&\, \text{cut } Y) \supset \text{cut } (Z \mid (\exists X')(\exists Y')(X' \in X \,\&\, Y' \in Y \,\&\,$$
$$Z = X' \otimes_r Y')))).$$

The definition is the obvious one, identifying the product of two cuts with the set mentioned in the consequent of Theorem XVII.

D28 $\quad X \otimes_c Y =_{Df} (Z \mid (\exists X')(\exists Y')(X' \in X \,\&\, Y' \in Y \,\&\, Z = X' \otimes_r Y')).$

Multiplication, thus defined, has the appropriate properties:

THEOREM XVIII.

$$(X)(Y)(X \otimes_c Y = Y \otimes_c X).$$

THEOREM XIX.

$$(X)(Y)(Z)(X \otimes_c (Y \otimes_c Z) = (X \otimes_c Y) \otimes_c Z).$$

And there is a distributive law:

THEOREM XX.

$$(X)(Y)(Z)(X \otimes_c (Y +_c Z) = (X \otimes_c Y) + C (X \otimes_c Z)).$$

Observe that there is, as yet, no zero cut, and thus no additive identity; the set of rational numbers consisting of $0_N/1_N$ alone is not a cut, since it has a greatest member (viz., $0_N/1_N$). But the real number 0 will reappear when we take our last step, that of defining the signed real numbers.

Consider the set of all pairs of cuts:

$$(X \mid (\exists Y)(\exists Z)(\text{cut } Y \,\&\, \text{cut } Z \,\&\, X = (Y,Z))).$$

Just as we took the rational numbers to be subsets of the set of all pairs of natural numbers, so we shall take the real numbers to be subsets of this set. We may think of the ordered pair, (Y,Z), as representing the real number we should ordinarily think of as $(Y - Z)$. This suggests that we think of two ordered pairs of cuts as equivalent if the first member of the first pair plus the second member of the second pair, is equal to the second member of the first pair plus the first member of the second pair. More simply, (X,Y) is to be equivalent to (W,Z) when $X +_c Z = Y +_c W$. Formally:

D29 $\qquad\qquad (X,Y) \text{ equiv}_c (W,Z) =_{Df} X +_c Z = Y +_c W.$

It is easy to prove that "equiv$_c$" stands for an equivalence relation:

THEOREM XXI.

$(X)(Y)(Z)(W)(X')(Y')((X,Y) \text{ equiv}_c (X,Y) \,\&\, ((X,Y) \text{ equiv}_c (Z,W) \supset$
$(Z,W) \text{ equiv}_c (X,Y)) \,\&\, (((X,Y) \text{ equiv}_c (Z,W) \,\&\, (Z,W) \text{ equiv}_c (X',Y')) \supset$
$(X,Y) \text{ equiv}_c (X'\,Y'))).$

[192]

Real numbers may now be introduced as equivalence classes of pairs of cuts under this equivalence relation:

D30 $\quad R =_{Df} (X \mid (Y)(Y')((Y \in X \ \& \ Y' \in X) \supset ((\exists Z)(\exists W)(\text{cut } Z \ \& \ \text{cut } W \ \&$
$$Y = (Z,W)) \ \& \ Y \text{ equiv}_c Y'))).$$

That subset of the real numbers that we represented by P earlier, the positive real numbers, can be easily defined:

D31 $\quad P =_{Df} (X \mid X \in R \ \& \ (\exists Y)(\exists Z)((Y,Z) \in X \ \& \ Z <_c Y)).$

The theorem which justifies this definition, as well as the one to follow, is

THEOREM XXII.

$(X)(Y)(Z)(X')(Y')(((X,Y) \in Z \ \& \ Z \in R \ \& \ (X',Y') \in Z) \supset ((X <_c Y \supset X' <_c Y')$
$$\& \ (X = Y \supset X' = Y'))).$$

D32 $\qquad\qquad\qquad 0 =_{Df} (X \mid X \text{ equiv}_c(1_c,1_c)).$
$$\qquad \cdot \ 1 =_{Df} (X \mid X \text{ equiv}_c(4_c,3_c)).$$

The subscript "c" indicates that the numeral to which it is affixed is to be understood as denoting a cut. No subscripts are affixed to "0" and "1", since these are the entities toward which we have been working our way; they are the "0" and "1" of ordinary algebra, analytic geometry, etc.

The ordering relation for the real numbers is easy enough to define, but requires a justifying theorem. For clarity, I have dropped the initial quantifiers.

THEOREM XXIII.

$((X,Y) \in Z \ \& \ (X',Y') \in Z \ \& \ (X'',Y'') \in W \ \& \ (X''',Y''') \in W \ \&$
$$X +_c Y'' <_c X'' +_c Y) \supset X' +_c Y''' <_c X''' +_c Y'.$$

D33 $\quad X < Y =_{Df} (\exists X')(\exists X'')(\exists Y')(\exists Y'')((X',Y') \in X \ \& \ (X'',Y'') \in Y \ \&$
$$X' +_c Y'' <_c X'' +_c Y').$$

A similar theorem–definition pair will do for addition:

THEOREM XXIV.

$((X,Y) \in Z \ \& \ (X',Y') \in Z \ \& \ (X'',Y'') \in W \ \& \ (X''',Y''') \in W \ \&$
$$(X +_c X'', Y +_c Y'') \in Z') \supset (X' +_c X''', Y' +_c Y''') \in Z'.$$

D34 $\quad X + Y =_{Df} (X \mid (\exists Y)(\exists Z)(\exists Y')(\exists Z')((Y,Z) \in X \ \& \ (Y',Z') \in Y \ \&$
$$X \text{ equiv}_c(Y +_c Y', Z +_c Z'))).$$

And now we may state the final set of facts about addition, corresponding to the first axiom of the original system:

THEOREM XXV.

$$X + Y = Y + X$$
$$(X \in R \ \& \ Y \in R) \supset X + Y \in R$$
$$X + (Y + Z) = (X + Y) + Z$$

[193]

Our original system contained an axiom to the effect that for every member of R, there was another member of R such that the sum of the two was 0. We can define this entity easily enough:

D35 $-X =_{Df} (Y \mid (\exists W)(\exists Z)(\text{cut } W \& \text{cut } Z \& (W,Z) \in X \& Y \text{equiv}_c(Z,W)))$.

Multiplication follows the pattern of division; the definition will be given here without the justifying theorem.

D36 $X \times Y =_{Df} (Z \mid (\exists X')(\exists Y')(\exists X'')(\exists Y'')((X',X'') \in X \& (Y',Y'') \in Y \&$
$$Z \text{ equiv}_c(X' \otimes_c Y') +_c (X'' \otimes_c Y''),$$
$$(X' \otimes_c Y'') +_c (X'' \otimes_c Y'))))$$.

The theorem corresponding to Axiom 2 of the earlier system is:

THEOREM XXVI.

$$(X \in R \& Y \in R) \supset X \times Y \in R$$
$$X \times Y = Y \times X$$
$$X \times (Y \times Z) = (X \times Y) \times Z.$$

Corresponding to Axioms 3 and 4 of the earlier system, we have

THEOREM XXVII.

$$(X)(X \in R \supset X + 0 = X).$$

THEOREM XXVIII.

$$(X)(X \in R \supset X \times 1 = X).$$

Axiom 5 of the old system is represented by

THEOREM XXIX.

$$(X)(X \in R \supset X + -X = 0).$$

Before we can define the multiplicative inverse for real numbers in general, we need two new definitions involving cuts. We must define the *reciprocal* of a cut, and the *difference* between a larger cut and a smaller one. To define the reciprocal of a cut we simply make use of the fact that if a positive fraction x / y is less than a number M, then the positive fraction y / x is greater than the number $1 / M$. The only thing we have to worry about is that the set we obtain in this way might turn out to have a greatest member, and thus not be a cut; we therefore add a clause to exclude this number from the reciprocal cut. We have

D37 $X^{-1c} =_{Df} (Y \mid (\exists w)(\exists z)(\exists x)(\exists y)(Y \equiv x/y \&$
$$w/z \in F - X \& w \otimes x <_N z \otimes y))$$

D38 $X -_c Y =_{Df} (Z \mid (\exists Y')(\exists X')(Y' \in Y \& X' \in X \& X' = Y' +_r Z)).$

[194]

In view of the fact that there is no 0 cut, we must use a little trivial trickery in framing our definition of the reciprocal of a real number.

D39 $X^{-1} =_{Df} (Y \mid (\exists Z)(X \text{ equiv}_c (Z,1) \& Z >_c 1 \& Y \text{ equiv}_c ((Z -_c 1)^{-1c} +_c 1,1))$
$\vee (\exists Z)(X \text{ equiv}_c (1,Z) \& 1 >_c Z \& Y \text{ equiv}_c ((1 -_c Z)^{-1c} +_c 1,1))$
$\vee (\exists Z)(X \text{ equiv}_c (1,Z) \& Z >_c 1 \& Y \text{ equiv}_c (1 -_c (Z -_c 1)^{-1c},1))$
$\vee (\exists Z)(X \text{ equiv}_c (Z,1) \& 1 >_c Z \& Y \text{ equiv}_c (1 -_c (1 -_c Z)^{-1c},1))$
$\vee X = -1 \& Y \text{ equiv}_c X).$

Note that we have defined the reciprocal of a negative number as the negative of the reciprocal of the corresponding positive number. Observe also that if $X = 0$ X^{-1} isn't a number at all. The theorem corresponding to Axiom 6 can now be stated:

THEOREM XXX.

$$(X)(\sim X = 0 \supset (X \times X^{-1}) = 1).$$

The distributive law, Axiom 7, is perfectly straightforward:

THEOREM XXXI.

$$(X)(Y)(Z)(X \times (Y + Z) = (X \times Y) + (X \times Z)).$$

The set of positive reals asserted to exist by the old Axiom 8 was easy to define (D31); we must still prove that it satisfies the conditions laid down in Axiom 8.

THEOREM XXXII.

$$P \subset R \& (X)(X \in R \supset (X \in P \vee -X \in P) \& (X)(Y)((X \in P \& Y \in P) \supset (X + Y \in P \& X \times Y \in P)).$$

Finally, we have the last axiom of the original set, the least upper bound axiom, which asserts that any nonempty set of real numbers that has an upper bound at all has a least upper bound. We first need a definition of upper bound and a definition of least upper bound:

D40 $\quad UB(X,Y) =_{Df} X \in R \& (Z)(Z \in Y \supset (Z \in R \& (Z < X \wedge Z = X)))$

D41 $\quad LUB(X,Y) =_{Df} UB(X,Y) \& (Z)(UB(Z,Y) \supset (X < Z \vee X = Z))$

THEOREM XXXIII.

$$(Y)((Y \subset R \& (\exists X)(X \in Y) \& (\exists Z)(UB(Z,Y))) \supset (\exists Z)(LUB(Z,Y))).$$

The technique of proving this theorem consists of first proving the corresponding theorem for cuts, and then extending the result to the real numbers. For cuts, we consider the set of all ratios less than any ratio which is not in a cut which is an upper bound of the set of cuts in question. This set of ratios turns out to be a

[195]

cut, and thus the least-upper-bound-cut of the set of cuts in question. Since cuts correspond to positive real numbers, this takes care of the case in which Y contains positive numbers. Where Y contains only negative real numbers, the argument is more complicated but not essentially different.

And thus we have reduced the system of real numbers to a system of natural numbers that contains five axioms, only the number 0_N, and the successor function. Everything else, we have been able to define away—even the basic operations of addition and multiplication. But what is reduction?

V

What have we accomplished when we have reduced the real number system to the arithmetic of zero and successor? We have accomplished a reduction in the number of kinds of things we must suppose our universe to contain. In the first version of the real number calculus, we must suppose we have on hand the whole continuum of real numbers; we must suppose we have on hand two primitive operations, addition and multiplication, as well as entities corresponding to additive inverses and multiplicative inverses. In the second version, the real number calculus is merely a superstructure on the natural number system, or indeed on a system which contains only one constant and one operation (successor of). All of the assertions of the real number arithmetic, of calculus and analytic geometry, for that matter, are merely disguised assertions about 0_N and the successor function. For example, the assertion that $\frac{3}{2}(1 - \sqrt{5})$ is a root of the equation $x^2 + 3x - 9$, and the assertion that if $f(x)$ is a continuous real valued function defined on the open interval (a,b) and the first derivative of $f(x)$ is positive somewhere in that interval and negative somewhere in that interval then there is a point y in that interval at which the first derivative of $f(x)$ has the value 0, are both assertions that, when the abbreviating definitions are swept away, are simply about 0_N and S (and of course classes). By reducing analysis to the arithmetic of zero and successor, we have also simplified the problem of interpretation. In zero and successor we have a model of the counting operation; counting, a physical process with which we are all perfectly familiar, provides an interpretation of the arithmetical calculus, and thus indirectly, through our reduction of the real number system to the arithmetic of natural numbers, provides an interpretation of the real number system itself. We cannot provide an interpretation of the real number system directly; that is, we can find no objects of experience which can be construed as real numbers or as corresponding to real numbers. Distances, weights, etc., quantities, that is, can be supposed to correspond to real numbers in a certain partial sense; but they must be understood theoretically, and not merely as results of measurements. No measurement, of course, can give any infinitely long, nonrepeating decimal as its result. But measurements can, as we say in the chapter on quantity, be given a direct interpretation in terms of counting.

[196]

The background of set theory and mathematics, like the background of the formal system of logic, lies in ordinary language. It is in ordinary language that we may look initially for the interpretation of the formal system. But, as in the case of logic, the intuitions embodied in ordinary language are not honored without exception. We speak of one hen, five golden rings, etc., in ordinary language. But a hundred does not have the properties in ordinary language that it has in mathematics—we cannot count a hundred objects, for example, without *counting* them; and to count requires establishing a one to one correlation between natural numbers or numerals or some set of known cardinality, and the set in question. "One hundred" is not an ordinary language term in the sense that "two" is. In ordinary language we speak of classes and members and pairs, and (as we just did) of the relation is-a-member-of; but many classes in set theory seem strange to our intuitions. Even the common "ordered pair" as it is often represented in set theory, bears a barely recognizable relation to the "ordered pair" of ordinary language.

We have a situation here that we will encounter again and again, in which we not only have an official interpretation for the primitive terms of the formal system, but in which the defined terms too have their own interpretation; and making the formal system square with the total interpretation involves doing some violence to the system of terms that are taken from ordinary language to be the interpretation of the terms of the formal system. Whereas, for example, an ordered pair in ordinary language is just a couple of things of which one "comes first", in set theory it is often a class composed of two members, one member being the class whose only member is the thing that we think of as coming first, the other member being the class whose two members are the object that comes first and the object that comes second. Quite a difference!

What about the connection between ordinary language quantitative notions and arithmetic, and the arithmetic of our formal system? In the first place the numbers of our formal system far outrun the numbers of our intuitions. A dozen is about as large a number as we can deal with without using a helpful structure of some sort. People with no set theory can use bigger numbers; but they do so by taking advantage of formal structures like the formal structure of our system —i.e., they count by correlating objects and numerals or fingers or the entities that belong to some standard class of objects. Wordsworth's 10,000 ("...saw I at a glance") is simply not available to unaided ordinary language. Ostension boggles at a dozen. Or perhaps (it is a thought experiment hard to perform) at two or three or four.

Most of the theorems that are of interest to us involve operations: addition, multiplication, etc. The operations defined in the formal system for the formal objects—the numbers—of the system, are quite different from the corresponding operations of ordinary language. Thus when someone says "add five drops of water to seven drops of whiskey" the word "add" is being used in a

[197]

very different sense from that used in "add the number five to the number seven". In the first case one may get one spoonful, twelve drops, or any number of drops in between; in the second, there is only one thing one can get: the number 12. Most of the discussions of that famous theorem "$5 + 7 = 12$," have hinged on the relation between the "plus" of the theory and the ordinary language "add" or "plus" used in the sense of "combine", or "juxtapose."

One argument for the empirical content of arithmetic might be that arithmetical laws would be false in a universe in which, whenever five things and seven things were juxtaposed, the result was eleven things. What is at issue here is whether the arithmetic "plus" (defined in terms of "$\in$" and logical machinery) can plausibly be interpreted (among other things) as juxtaposition. The answer is that, in our universe, it can; this is a fact about the world, which helps to explain the utility of arithmetic. But even in our world it doesn't always work: if you don't juxtapose five drops of water and seven drops carefully, you are very likely to end up with eleven drops; if you don't do your counting quickly and carefully in juxtaposing groups of rabbits or micro-organisms, you are very likely to have more after the juxtaposition than the sum of the numbers of rabbits or micro-organisms you had before.

What this kind of argument suggests is not that arithmetic is a body of contingent truths, but that one connection between arithmetic and the empirical world can be found in the counting operation. And here one can see that the relation between arithmetic and the real world is not so very different from the relationship between a physical theory and the real world. We do not reject arithmetic, if we count five objects alone; seven other objects alone, and then count both groups together and get eleven: what we say is that either one object ran away, or that we miscounted—made an error. But this is just what we say when an ordinary experiment in physics turns out to have not the predicted result, but some other. Of course we demand, in physics, that the error be predictable and controllable. (Cf. the discussion of measurement.) The same is true here. We can always save our arithmetic, by recourse to *ad hoc* causes or to error. But unless we can, at least usually, make sense out of the *ad hoc* happenings (the amoeba divided; one of the cats ran away while we weren't looking; two of the drops coalesced...), and control and reduce error (let's both count them; let us use one of those counting gadgets to keep track; let us hire five graduate students...) we would simply forget about the project of taking arithmetic—considered as a certain part of set theory—to represent our countings of ordinary objects. But, of course, if the world were so ill suited to counting, we would never have learned to count in the first place. Consider again the perceptual world of the dog's nose: surely countings in that world are pretty pointless. But that is no reason why a very smart dog could not learn set theory.

The same kind of connection holds between the rest of mathematics and the real world. Just as counting is the fundamental operation that gives meaning to

[198]

arithmetic, so measurement is the fundamental operation that gives meaning to much of analysis. If formal systems that made use of mathematics were not successful in predicting and explaining the world, other sorts of formal systems would be used. In view of the fact that arithmetic and analysis are never considered by themselves, it is reasonable and appropriate to say that they are not subject to test; that they will be held on to no matter what; that they are not tested in any real sense by confrontation with experience. But it is reasonable and appropriate only if it is also kept in mind that in another, indirect sense, set theory, and therefore arithmetic and the rest of mathematics, like language and logic themselves are put to a pragmatic test whenever any theory that uses them is tested. Reluctant as we may justifiably be to change the structure of our language or to the character of our mathematics, to do so is always a (barely) live option.

Just as we interpret the symbols " $\supset$ ", " $\sim$ ", " $\vee$ ", etc., in such a way that the resulting sentential logic turns out to perform the function we want it to —i.e., to embody truth preserving inferences, to be free from contradiction, to reflect, insofar as that reflection does not conflict with these desiderata, the ordinary English usage of "if...then...", "and", "or", "not", "neither... nor...", and so on, just so do the axioms of set theory determine the interpretation of the set theoretic primitive " $\in$ ". But things are not quite so simple in the case of " $\in$ " as they are in the case of " $\vee$ " or " $\&$ ", for we have a much clearer idea of what constitutes simple truth-functional conjunction (as opposed to temporal conjunction) than we have of what constitutes a class or an element. The interpretation is still in ordinary English, and such that the axioms come out to be true, and if we wish to say so "analytically" true. It is certainly the case that we will never interpret our set theory in such a way that we need to perform experiments in a laboratory to find out if we have one that we can accept.

Whether or not one wishes for this reason to call set theory "logic" seems to be a rather trivial terminological question. There seem to be fairly good reasons (among them the controversiality of the axioms of set theory and the relative universality of the principles of logic) to regard set theory as a theory which is not empirical, nor yet quite logical. Set theory and mathematics may be regarded as saying (asserting) nothing about the particular world of the logician's hatful of worlds that we actually live in; but it is clear that the usefulness of the particular set theory and mathematics we use does depend, to some extent, on the character of the world we live in. It could be maintained, with some plausibility, that the usefulness of the sentential calculus and quantification theory— i.e., basic logic—depends not so much on the character of the world, as on the character of the language we have chosen to talk, or that we simply happen to talk. Since the language we talk seems to be a more arbitrary thing—less influenced by the character of the world—than the mathematics we use, it is easier for us to choose a logic and stick to it in the face of everything than to choose a

[199]

mathematics and stick to it in the face of everything. Our logic is even less likely to fail its pragmatic test than our mathematics.

Incidentally, we shall find in physics, and perhaps in some other fields, that the higher level axioms can be regarded as irrefutable in much the same way as the axioms of set theory: the question may be taken to be that of usefulness, rather than truth; and usefulness is a matter that is open to question in the case of mathematics and set theory, and, though to a much smaller extent, in the case of pure logic. But there is no way of performing tests or experiments to find out how useful our set theory is; to find out how useful it is, we must use a very indirect procedure: we must see if the physical, nonlogical theories that use the mathematics based in turn on that set theory, turn out to perform the work of prediction and explanation that we demand of them. Nevertheless, we can consider the circumstances which would militate against the usefulness of the theory: we can look at particular theorems and try to see what role they play in formal systems into which they enter.

In set theory we already run into the problem of formulating a distinction between logical and empirical theories, and making the distinction stick. Most writers, with good justification, regard logic and mathematics and set theory as all sharing the character of analyticity, as being true by virtue of the meanings of the terms they employ, rather than by virtue of external circumstances. It is impossible to conceive of circumstances under which we would want to regard, say, "2 + 3 = 5" as false. Some ardent empiricists have tried to describe such circumstances: for example, suppose that the universe was not composed of simple, durable, discrete objects, like stones and people and dogs, but was altogether fluid, everything constantly flowing into everything else. But then we would not have a falsification of "2 + 3 = 5", so much as a set of circumstances under which natural numbers had no very useful application, and were therefore of little interest.

But actually the impossibility of finding circumstances under which we would want to reject arithmetical laws doesn't cut much ice. The indescribability of such circumstances may simply be an accident of our language (there are many perfectly good languages in which certain things cannot be said) and the inconceivability of such circumstances may simply be an accident of our psychic makeup. We cannot conceive of the world that the dog perceives through his nose. Indeed, that world is a world in which arithmetic would be quite irrelevant: for smells do not come in discrete, durable chunks, but flow into each other, divide and combine in unimaginable ways.

What we can do in the case of sentential logic, is to show that if we accept the denial of any of the statements of the logic, we have a system that is inconsistent, and therefore (though in one sense compatible with every state of affairs, and in another sense incompatible with every state of affairs) quite useless. Somewhat the same can be proved of quantification theory: within the general framework, there is a certain set of statements that we want to accept, and to accept the denial of any of these statements is in this system to accept every statement. There are also statements (e.g., "$(\exists x)\ Fx \supset (x)Fx$") which do not lead directly to contradiction, but which hold only in very special universes (this one only holds in universes in which there is exactly one thing, or in which every mentionable property which is possessed by anything is possessed by everything).

The situation in set theory (and hence in mathematics) is somewhat different, and this provides us with a motivation for making a distinction between the status of set theory and the status of general sentential and quantificational logic. There are alternatives in set theory that are simply alternatives of formulation, that lead to just the same mathematical theorems, though they may, on the way, involve different sets, different objects. But there are also alternatives that are genuinely substantive. There are statements S, expressible in a number of theories, such that in some of these theories S is a theorem, and in other theories, the denial of S is a theorem. Here is a situation precisely parallel to that which in physics or any other science would cry out for an *experimentum crucis*. Yet such a proposal would seem strikingly inappropriate as applied to set theory.

VI

There are three general approaches to the foundations of mathematics which are distinctive enough to have been given names. They are *formalism*, *logicism*, and *intuitionism*. Formalism maintains that mathematics is purely a calculus: that we do not have and do not need any interpretation for the symbols with which we work in mathematics. Thus when we are doing mathematics, we need no interpretation for the "$\in$" of membership: it is simply an uninterpreted two-place predicate, which is postulated to have just those properties that it is postulated (e.g., by Quine's or von Neuman's axioms of membership) to have. In a different system it would be postulated to have quite different properties, perhaps. When we come then to apply the mathematics, that's a different story; but for the formalist, it is a story of no interest: anyone can do anything with any formal system—there are no rules and regulations for that, he says. If a particular way of manipulating the symbols, or of interpreting them—i.e., associating other things with them—turns out to have useful consequences, why, that's fine. If deep breathing helps you pick the winners of horse races, that's fine too. From this point of view the fact that mathematics is as useful and pervasive as it is, is something of a mystery.

The implausibility of this story is just that in every formal system the "$\in$" is given almost the same interpretation—it is always taken to be a membership relation. And the axioms that it is expected to obey are not just arbitrary axioms, but axioms of membership—axioms that we may expect to be *true* of "$\in$" interpreted as a membership relation, insofar as any membership relation is understood to have some definite properties. As usual, our axioms outrun our

[201]

intuitions, so we cannot demand that they simply embody our intuitions and nothing more. Consider the defined terms: the symbol "4", or rather the complex expression of which it is an abbreviation, is not just an uninterpreted symbol; it always has essentially the same interpretation wherever we encounter it, in whatever system. When arithmetic (and the rest of mathematics) is taken to be a part of the formal system of other sciences, a great many of the symbols that it uses are taken to have perfectly standard interpretations. And it is in order to keep those interpretations intact that we choose the particular axioms for the primitive two-place predicate "$\in$" that we do choose, and also in order to keep those interpretations intact that we choose the particular definitions of "4", "5", etc., that we do.

It is this insight, that we do not have complete freedom either in formulating our axioms or in laying down our definitions, that inspires the logicist. For him the mathematics is not an uninterpreted calculus, but an interpreted one: a formal system. On his interpretation, the "$\in$" of membership comes to denote the membership relation. This interpretation determines its properties, just as the interpretation of "(x)" determines its properties. "0_N" and "S" are defined as pure set-theoretical entities, and all of mathematics comes to be a long development of logic. The axioms of membership just spell out the logical properties of the membership relation, precisely as the axioms of quantification spell out the logical properties of quantification.

The difficulty here, of course, is that we have various choices open to us when it comes to deciding what the logical properties of the membership relation are— or, put another way, when it comes to deciding just what membership *is*. By this I do not mean merely that we have a choice in what we regard as axioms governing the membership relation, as we have a choice of axioms for quantification theory; there is just one specific set of quantificational truths that we want our axioms for quantification theory to lead us to, and any set of axioms and rules of inference that leads us to all and only those truths is perfectly adequate. There is no doubt about what they are. One can propose an alternative logic (e.g., an intuitionistic logic, a modal logic) but one cannot plausibly propose to strengthen or weaken standard quantification theory. But this is precisely what is not the situation in the case of general set theory: given that our set theory is consistent, whatever axioms we add to it that preserve this consistency, there will remain set-theoretical (arithmetical) truths that are not entailed by these axioms. Furthermore, there are even particular statements that are needed for large parts of mathematics, whose truth is compatible with the rest of the axioms of set theory, and whose denial also is compatible with the rest of the axioms of set theory.

The intuitionist employs a different logic, and obtains a different mathematics. For him what is fundamental is not set theory at all, but the intuitively given sequence of natural numbers. Everything else is constructed on this basis, and only by constructions that can actually be performed. A considerable portion of what ordinarily passes for mathematics must be done without, from this point of view. But what remains is quite clearly and naturally related to our ordinary countings and measurings (measuring being fundamentally a matter of counting). It is perhaps questionable whether the intuitionist regards the mathematical statements that he proves as truths about the world; in any event, he is quite sure that they will not be belied by experience. If they are synthetic, they are still known to hold *a priori*. If they are analytic, they are analytic of the counting process. The trouble here is that intuition provides a notoriously unreliable basis for any theory; and that the other sciences are not prepared to get along without the parts of analysis (for example) that would have to be sacrificed on the intuitionist altar. The former difficulty has been somewhat reduced by the formalization of parts of intuitionistic mathematics; but the latter remains formidable.

We cannot here provide any kind of careful study of these points of view concerning the foundations of mathematics. Indeed, the study of the foundations of mathematics is a deep and difficult field of philosophy (or of mathematics) all by itself; and I have lightly touched on these three points of view here more for the sake of alerting the reader to their existence than for the sake of anything educational I had to say about them.

The point of view I have adopted here that with respect to the connection of mathematics with experience falls somewhat between the formalist and logicist view of the matter. I do not regard mathematics as purely empty (or emptily pure) as the thorough formalist does; but neither do I regard it as embodying a special kind of truth, logical truth, as the logicist does. Mathematics (set theory) is not empirically testable, either as a whole or part by part, and therefore by itself does not have any empirical content. It plays a central role in many scientific theories which definitely do have empirical content. Although we could never be forced to abandon our set theory, it might turn out that we were forced to abandon many of the theories which used it—i.e., that we could not construct pretty and useful empirical theories within the framework that it provides. This is not at all to say that it has empirical content itself; but it does suggest that it is not purely formal. The fact that there are alternative contents (i.e., we can make our set theory stronger or weaker) also suggests that it is not a matter of pure logical fact.

Mathematics can be regarded as a generalized logic which includes a primitive term "∈", and some axioms or axiom schemata that concern that term. The rules of inference are the standard rules of inference of logic. For example, in Quine's *Mathematical Logic*, there are three axiom schemata introduced to govern "∈", and the only rule of inference remains the standard *modus ponens*.

[203]

Theorems of the system thus generated include the truths of arithmetic and analysis and the other branches of pure mathematics. The interpretation that I have offered for these systems is overrich, as seems to be generally the case in formal systems: thus not only is "∈", the new primitive, given an interpretation (as membership), but many of the defined signs, like "0", "9", etc., "plus", "times", etc., are also intended to have a certain ordinary interpretation. Under this interpretation, the theory comes out to be true, and even irrefutable; but in view of the flexibility of the axioms characterizing the primitive "∈", it does not seem quite right to call it logically true. Counting and measuring are operations that are involved in the tests of many formal systems in which mathematics plays a role; although they do not constitute tests of mathematics itself in any sense, the fact that they are useful ingredients in the interpretation of these other formal systems exhibits mathematics in turn as a useful part of these systems.

Mathematics plays a central role in many empirical formal systems. The fact that it does, says something about the world we live in. This is not a part of the content of mathematics, but a fact about the methodology in which mathematics plays a role.

BIBLIOGRAPHICAL NOTES TO CHAPTER 8.

There are two splendid little books that contain the details of the development of the real number system on the basis of the five postulates I have used in the text: H. A. Thurston, *The Number System* (London: Blackie and Son, 1956); and Edmund Landau, *Foundations of Analysis* (New York: Chelsea Publishing Co., 1957). The best source of information at present on the interpretations of logical and mathematical systems, and on the major varieties of views concerning the foundations of mathematics is a book of readings edited by Hilary Putnam and Paul Benacerraf, *Philosophy of Mathematics*, Prentice-Hall (N.J.: Englewood Cliffs, 1946).

The classic attempt to demonstrate that all of mathematics can be reduced to logic is Bertrand Russell's and Alfred North Whitehead's monumental three volume *Principia Mathematica* (Cambridge, England: Cambridge University Press, 2nd ed., 1950).

A streamlined universal system that carries out the development of the real number system from its beginnings in logic and set theory is W. V. O. Quine's *Mathematical Logic* (Cambridge, Mass.: Harvard University Press, revised ed., 1958). This is one of the systems most often referred to. The viewpoint is midway between logicism and formalism.

A good technical introduction to the various philosophical aspects of different approaches to the foundations of set theory—and a good introduction to those approaches themselves—may be found in Quine's *Set Theory and its Logic* (Cambridge, Mass.: Harvard University Press, 1963).

A general and readable introduction to the logical view of mathematics may be found in Rudolf Carnap's *Foundations of Logic and Mathematics*, Vol. 1, No. 3, *International Encyclopedia of Unified Science* (Chicago: University of Chicago Press, 1939).

Chapter 9

GEOMETRY

I

Geometry was the first branch of human knowledge that came to be presented in the fashion of a formal system, around 300 B.C., and it has stood as the ideal of human knowledge ever since. Geometry is particularly useful for our purposes here; it illustrates many of the facts about formal systems that we need to understand in order to understand modern science. It can be regarded purely abstractly, as a calculus consisting of undefined terms (vocabulary), arbitrary statements (axioms), a list of permissible moves (rules of inference), and a grammar (formation rules). Its primitive terms can be given interpretations which make the axioms unfalsifiable mathematical truths. They can be given interpretations which are perfectly natural and closely related to the corresponding terms of ordinary language, but only at the cost of a loose fit between the formal

[206]

structure of the theory and the structure of the corresponding entities of experience. The terms can be given quite precise physical meanings, but at the cost of rendering the verification or falsification of the theory tedious and indirect. We may, faced with a falsification of the formal system (as historically we have been), take any one of several options. We may take the technical interpretation that we had given the terms of the theory to have been over-hasty, and propose another interpretation; we may, instead of proposing another interpretation, merely state that physical entities do exist which provide a valid interpretation; or we may, finally, keep the well established technical interpretation, and alter the axioms in such a way that there is no longer a conflict between our body of scientific knowledge and the consequences of the theory.

Let us begin by looking at the calculus of two dimensional Euclidean geometry. This calculus as presented by Euclid (or his students) was imperfect by modern standards; nevertheless, it was the first time a successful attempt had been made to construct a formal system. No doubt the idea of a formal system— that is, an organization of knowledge in terms of first principles or axioms, together with a set of principles of deduction which would lead from the axioms to all the truths of the theory—no doubt such an idea had been around for a long time before Euclid. But even if other attempts were made, Euclid's was the first system to survive to modern times. Furthermore, and more remarkable, it was the only successful formal system to be presented for two thousand years. Aristotle, like philosophers of science today, greatly admired the formal scheme, and proposed that all sound human knowledge should be organized in this axiomatic way; and yet he himself (again like modern philosophers of science) never bothered to try to fill in any of the details.

There are of course any number of ways of axiomatizing Euclidean geometry: there are a number of different terms and relations that one could take as primitive, and similarly, there is considerable latitude in the choice of axioms. The choice that I make is dictated by the requirement of making the exposition of later points as easy as possible; I have chosen to present fragments of Hilbert's system.

II

A. Primitive Terms:
    1. Logical terms: we suppose the geometrical formal system embedded in a first order logic, with identity.
    2. Nonlogical terms: *point, line, between, congruent, lies on*. Other terms and relations may be defined by reference to these terms, together with logical material: thus to say that two lines intersect is to say that there is a point that lies on both.
B. Formation Rules:
    1. "Point" is a one place predicate, like "line".

2. "Lies on" is a two place predicate. "Congruent" applies to pairs of pairs of points, initially; it is extended by definition to apply to figures.

C. Axioms:

Quite a number of axioms are needed. We need axioms for the underlying logic, of course; but we also need a number of geometrical axioms other than those with which Euclid provided us. In particular, we need axioms, not provided by Euclid, that will establish the necessary properties of continuity for lines and figures. For example we want figures to be "closed" in the sense that they divide all points into two kinds, such that any line joining points of the two kinds has a point that lies on the figure. These continuity axioms, or postulates of connection, are the same for all the kinds of geometry we shall consider.

Hilbert's Postulates fall into five groups; I shall not present the full system, but only give examples from each group.

I. Postulates of Connection

Examples: I-1. There is one and only one line passing through any two given distinct points.

I-2. Every line contains at least two distinct points, and for any given line there is at least one point not on the line.

II. Postulates of Order

Example: II-1. If A, B, and C are three distinct points on the same line, then one of the points is between the other two.

III. Postulates of Congruence

Example: III-1. If two pairs of points are congruent to the same pair of points, then they are congruent to each other.

IV. Postulate of Parallels

There is only one postulate in this group: it is Playfair's form of Euclid's famous Fifth postulate. It is the replacement of this postulate by others that leads to alternate geometries, as we shall see.

Example: IV-1. Through a given point A not on a given line m there passes at most one line which does not intersect m.

V. Postulates of Continuity

Example: V-1. Archimedes' postulate: if A B, C, and D are four distinct points, then there is on the ray AB a finite set of distinct points $A_1, A_2 \ldots, A_n$ such that (1) each of the pairs A, A_1; A_1, A_2; $\ldots$; A_{n-1}, A_n is congruent to the pair CD and (2) B is between A and A_n.

D. Rules of Inference:

The ordinary rules of first-order logic with identity.

Theorems:

As theorems there are forthcoming the usual theorems of plane Euclidean Geometry. For example (we shall refer to this theorem later), we have: "The sum of the angles of a triangle is equal to two right angles."

One thing that interests us about formal systems is their consistency and the independence and completeness of their axioms. A way of establishing results about these matters, is through the notion of a model; a model is essentially an *interpretation*, in the sense in which I have been using the term, although I have been using it primarily to refer to ordinary semantic models that relate the calculus of a formal system to something that has ordinary meaning, and might be regarded as the conventional or ordinary interpretation or model of the calculus. Nevertheless, there are special cases in which we want to invent artificial models for the sake of proving things about the formal system.

The thing that is of most concern to us is consistency. All of the calculi with which we are concerned are embedded in ordinary logic, and make use of the ordinary logical rules of inference. It is a simple consequence of those rules of inference that from a contradiction any statement whatsoever can be derived, so that if our axioms for any formal system are inconsistent, or hide or contain an inconsistency, that calculus contains all statements whatever that can be formulated in that system. For certain special systems, such as sentential logic and the first order predicate calculus, it is possible to construct an explicit proof that the system is free of contradiction (by showing that not every statement is a theorem). But in general, all we have are *relative* consistency proofs (for the most interesting formal systems). A relative consistency proof consists in showing that if a given system is inconsistent, then some other system (about which we generally have less doubt) is also inconsistent. The method of showing this kind of fact, is to find an interpretation of the first system, which makes it a part of the second system;—that is, to exhibit a model of the first system in the second system. Then if an inconsistency exists in the first system, it (the inconsistency) will also occur in that part of the second system which is serving as a model of the first system. "Model" is most properly applied to the objects and properties that are referred to in the second system; "interpretation" to the act that associates these objects and properties with the terms of the first system.

There are many alternative presentations of the Euclidean geometry calculus. When we say that they are different sets of postulates for the same system, we need a criterion for *sameness* of formal systems. We do not want to have that criterion depend on the interpretation we give to the primitive terms of the system, for we want to be able to talk about alternative formulations of the same calculus, without regard to whether the interpretation of that calculus makes it part of the same or a different formal system. We can do this as follows:

In general, calculus A is *the same as* calculus B when there is a one-to-one

[209]

correlation between the terms of calculus A and terms of calculus B (primitive terms need not be mapped onto primitive terms: what is taken as a primitive term in one system may perfectly well be regarded as a defined term in the other system) such that the axioms of calculus B are theorems or axioms of calculus A, under that correlation, and also the axioms of calculus A are theorems or axioms of calculus B. (It is supposed here that definitions, if they appear, function only to introduce abbreviations for more cumbersome expressions; if there are definitions that are *creative* in the sense that they enlarge the class of theorems of a system, then the definitions of that system must also appear as theorems in the other system.)

For example, E. V. Huntington has offered a calculus for three dimensional Euclidean geometry which takes as its primitive terms "sphere" and "is included in" (a relation between spheres). This is the same calculus as Hilbert's, in the sense that "line", "point", etc., can be defined in the Huntington system, and "sphere" and "is included in" can be defined in Hilbert's system, in such a way that to every theorem in the one system a theorem in the other corresponds.

Now when we talk of alternatives to (rather than alternative formulations *of*) Euclidean geometry, we do not mean alternatives in this sense; we do not mean merely that there are alternative formulations of the calculus. This is true in a trivial sense of every formal system. What we mean is that there are geometrical calculi that are substantively different from the Euclidean calculus. Before passing on to the interpretation of the Euclidean calculus, it would be well to consider the two major alternative calculi.

One alternative is the Bolyoi–Lobachevsky geometry. We obtain the calculus of this geometry, by replacing Hilbert's postulate IV-1 by

> IV-1.L. Through a given point A not on a given line m there
> pass at least two lines which do not intersect line m.

To arrive at the Riemannian calculus of geometry, we must make several changes; we must modify I-1:

> I-1.R. There is at least one line passing through any two points.

II-1 must also be modified, for in Riemannian geometry, every point on a line is between every other pair of points on the line. This merely involves deleting a clause from the first postulate of group II. And finally we replace the parallel postulate by

> IV-1.R. Through a given point A not on a given line m, there
> pass no lines which do not intersect line m.

For future reference, I list here also one theorem from each of these geometries, which corresponds in an obvious way to the triangle theorem cited for Euclidean geometry.

[210]

T.E.   The sum of the angles in a triangle is 180°.

T.R.   The sum of the angles in a triangle exceeds 180°, and the excess is proportional to the area of the triangle.

T.L.   The sum of the angles in a triangle is less than 180°, and the deficiency is proportional to the area of the triangle.

These three theorems will be particularly useful later on in deciding which of these three geometries is true and in what sense. Here it is important to be clear, however, that we have, so far, three calculi, and nothing more. We have displayed three statements from three calculi. They are all theorems. There is nothing more to be said about them.

III

To suggest drawing three triangles to see which of the three statements is really true is misguided, for *qua* statements in a formal calculus, these statements have nothing to do with physical or quasi-physical triangles. When it is claimed that a certain figure drawn with a pencil on a piece of paper is a triangle, an *interpretation* of all three calculi is being offered. That is, by adding an interpretation— a paper and pencil interpretation—to the calculus, it is transformed into a formal system. But it should be immediately apparent that none of the three formal systems that you arrive at by the proposed interpretation is true: it is not the case, for example, that one and only one pencil line can be drawn through two pencil points—particularly if the pencil is blunt; it is not at all the case that on a given piece of paper, only one line can be drawn through a point not on a given line which does not intersect that given line; and so on. Indeed it is immediately obvious, as soon as you stop to think about it, that the geometry of pencil lines and pencil points on finite pieces of paper will be quite complex, like the geometry of points on a blackboard. It is not pencil points or chalk points that one is concerned with when one draws figures; one draws the figures, in doing geometry, merely to aid the imagination; the points and lines that we draw merely stand for the points and lines of our geometry, and we are not surprised that they do not have just the properties that our geometrical points and lines are postulated to have. Roughly speaking we can offer the pencil point, pencil line interpretation for the calculus; but roughly speaking, all three calculi are equivalent: that is, if the area of a triangle is small enough, there will be no noticeable difference between them. I shall return to this later.

Let us begin with a number of purely formal interpretations of the geometrical calculi, designed to exhibit their relative consistency. To choose the most familiar first:

Consider the calculus E, with the following interpretations for its primitives:

A is a point: A is an ordered pair of real numbers (x_A, y_A).

[211]

m is a line: m is the set of all the ordered pairs of real numbers (x,y) satisfying a given linear equation $ax + by = c$.

A lies on m: The ordered pair (x_A, y_A) satisfies an equation $ax + by = c$ corresponding to m. (Note that several equations correspond to a given line m.)

A lies between B and C: The ordered pair of real numbers (x_A, y_A) corresponding to A, the ordered pair of real numbers (x_B, y_B) corresponding to B, and the ordered pair of real numbers (x_C, y_C) corresponding to C, all satisfy the same linear equation $ax + by = c$, and either $x_B < x_A < x_C$ or $x_B > x_A > x_C$ or $y_B < y_A < y_C$ or $y_B > y_A > y_C$.

(A,B) is congruent to (C,D):

$$(x_A - x_B)^2 + (y_A - y_B)^2 = (x_C - x_D)^2 + (y_C - y_D)^2.$$

The fact that the axioms are satisfied under this interpretation, or, said another way, the fact that there is a *model* of Euclidean geometry in ordinary number theory, shows that our geometrical axioms are at least as consistent as the set theory that gives us number theory. Not the other way about: it might be that geometry was consistent and that there was an inconsistency in number theory. But it does establish that *if* number theory is consistent, so is our Euclidean geometry.

Now how about the other geometries? We can show that if E is consistent so is R, and so is L; and further that if L is consistent, so is E, and that if R is consistent so is E. The latter two proofs are fairly trivial in principle: they involve the notion of curvature, which can be thought of as representing the *degree* to which the geometry (R or L) deviates from the *flat* Euclidean geometry: then Euclidean geometry may simply be taken to be the special case of Riemannian or Lobachevskian geometry, in which the curvature is 0. Put another way, we find a model of Euclidean geometry in Riemannian geometry (Lobachevskian geometry) by taking the special case of curvature 0, and interpreting the Lobachevskian point as the Euclidean point, the Lobachevskian line as the Euclidean line, etc.

The former proofs are more interesting, both intrinsically and because we are far more likely to have real doubts as to the consistency of Riemannian geometry and Lobachevskian geometry, than we have about Euclidean geometry. Thus if we can find models of these two geometries *within* Euclidean geometry we will have satisfied what is possibly a genuine worry.

Interpretation of (plane) Riemannian geometry in (solid) Euclidean geometry:

A is a point: A is a (Euclidean) point on the surface of a (Euclidean) sphere S.

m is a line: m is a great circle on S.

A is on m: A is (Euclidean) on m.

[212]

A is between B and C: A,B, and *C* all lie on the same great circle in *S.* (Remember that one of the order postulates had to be changed to produce Riemannian geometry.)

(A,B) is congruent to (C,D): *(A,B)* is (Euclidean) congruent to *(C,D).* (Congruence of pairs of points in Riemannian geometry thus merely becomes congruence of the corresponding pairs of Euclidean points on *S.*)

Now under this interpretation, the axioms of *R* are all truths of Euclidean geometry. Thus we have constructed a system of objects (points, lines, etc.) which satisfy the axioms of *R,* and thence we have shown that *R* is as consistent as Euclidean geometry. Of course, not every system of objects that satisfies the *R* postulates will correspond to the system of points and great circles on the surface of a Euclidean sphere; by using a suitably distorted metric, we could substitute a football for the basketball. All we need to show in order to show the relative consistency of *R* to *E* (that if *E* is consistent so is *R*) is that there is (in Euclidean geometry) *some* system of objects that satisfies the axioms of *R.*

The interpretation of Lobachevskian geometry within Euclidean geometry is not quite so natural and simple. For this we use a *Poincaré model,* developed specifically for this purpose by Henri Poincaré in the nineteenth century. Consider a fixed plane Euclidean circle, *C.* We offer the following interpretations of the primitive terms of the Lobachevskian calculus:

A is a point: A is a (Euclidean) point in the interior of *C.*

m is a line: m is a circular arc, orthogonal to *C,* in the interior of *C.*

A is on m: A is (Euclidean) on *m.*

A is between B and C: A, B, and *C* lie on the same arc, and *A* is between *B* and *C* on that arc in the obvious Euclidean sense.

(A,B) is congruent to (C,D): the line segment *AB* has the same *P*-length as the line segment *CD,* where *P*-length is defined as follows: Let the (Euclidean) length of the arc *AB* be denoted by $\overset{\frown}{AB}$ and the points at which the line determined by *A,B* intersects the circle *C* be A_c and B_c. Then we take the *P*-length of the segment *AB* to be log $[(\overset{\frown}{AB_c} / \overset{\frown}{BB_c})(\overset{\frown}{BA_c} / \overset{\frown}{AA_c})]$.

With these interpretations the Lobachevskian calculus is true in this Euclidean model, which establishes that the Lobachevskian calculus is consistent, at least so long as the Euclidean calculus is (see Fig. 1).

So much for formal interpretations and models—that is, interpretations of the terms of one system through terms of the other, or the modeling of the entities of one calculus in the entities of another. None of this brings us any closer to the empirical world. It is of interest only in establishing such characteristics as consistency, independence, and so on, of the axioms of a calculus. Thus

[213]

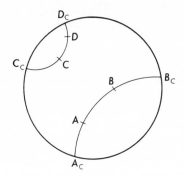

Fig. 1

the fact that Lobachevskian geometry, which differs from Euclidean geometry only in Axiom IV, can be modelled in Euclidean geometry, shows that Axiom IV is independent of the other axioms of Euclidean geometry. It may be false, while the remaining axioms are true. This kind of interpretation is interesting and important, but it does not take us outside the realm of the purely formal, or, better, beyond the calculi whose mutual interpretations we are concerned with.

IV

We are also interested in the question of an empirical interpretation for geometry—what used to be called "the geometry of physical space." We have already given very brief consideration to one such interpretation: that which takes pencil points as points, and pencil lines as lines. Under this interpretation, considered strictly, the axioms of geometry (any geometry) are false. But we can make the geometry a bit more flexible by taking the possibility of error into account; or, put the other way about, by taking the possibility of idealization into account. We have already discussed this in connection with the abstract treatment of formal systems. If we don't demand a high degree of accuracy, then a spot made with a pencil, and a line drawn with a ruler, will serve indifferently as Euclidean points and lines, Lobachevskian points and lines (for spaces of small curvature) or Riemannian points and lines (again for spaces of small curvature). Although this is a possible interpretation of each of these geometries, there is not very much intrinsic interest in it: we are not interested particularly and specifically in spots made with pencils and lines drawn with rulers. In fact, our interest leads in the other direction: pencil spots and ruled lines can help us in our derivations in the calculus of the formal system by suggesting approaches to proofs and lines of attack; most important, they can suggest things to prove; but the calculus doesn't help us much in drawing.

What do we use geometry for? We use it as an ingredient of physics, we use it in astronomy, in surveying, in calculating distances and positions on the basis of sights and observations. Each of these uses of geometry involves light. There is another class of uses in geometry, to which we shall return later: these uses are involved in the design of machinery, and involved the physical fit of one surface to another.

Let us begin with the optical uses. What we need here, as soon as we have the concepts available, is an interpretation of geometry in which "line" is interpreted as the path of a light ray in a homogeneous medium; "point" is interpreted as the intersection of two such light rays; "between" and "congruent" are interpreted in terms of measurement. Thus two light ray segments are congruent if they have the same length; one point on a light ray is between two other points, if the distance between it and each of the other points is less than the distance between the other points; and we measure angles by the length of arc of a standard circle (as on a protractor). This method of measuring angles already presupposes a bit of theory of angles, just as a method of measuring lengths presupposes a bit of the theory of length. Thus we must divide angles into equivalence classes, we must have a way of adding angles, and so on. But given such a theory, we can then replace the direct measurement of angles by a measurement of arc length on a standard circle.

Measurement is a physical process; it involves error, but it also carries with it a theory that allows us to estimate errors, and to reduce them by various devices. Therefore, given the optical interpretation just outlined, and given a method of measurement, which we do in fact have, it would seem to be quite straightforward to decide whether or not one of the three geometries whose calculi were presented above is in point of fact the geometry of light rays. One of the inconvenient things about light rays is that they are invisible—i.e., you can't see a light ray unless it hits you in the eye. To identify lines with light rays, and points with their intersections, and to adopt standard measuring techniques for lengths and angles, does not at all settle the question of comparing our geometrical system to the world. We have interpreted our geometrical entities as physical entities (and their metrical properties as physical properties) but we have not yet established any way of catching any of these entities.

In a smoke-filled room we can easily identify a beam of light, because light from the beam is scattered at every point along it. This suggests that we can take a source of light to be producing light rays and scattering them in every direction. If we cut down on the directions by placing a screen with a small hole in it in front of the source, we can think of the result as a bundle of light rays that can be made smaller and smaller by making the hole smaller and smaller. We can observe such a bundle of light rays, not as it is passing through the homogeneous medium (for if it is homogeneous, there isn't anything in it to scatter the light rays) but at any point we want to, by interposing a surface from which the light will be scattered. Thus, given a light source, and a movable surface, we can trace the path of a bundle of light rays. And we can imagine making the bundle

[215]

arbitrarily small. Although we can never isolate a single light ray, yet we can come as close to it as we wish.

Now how about intersections of light rays? Well, we can find the intersection of two bundles of light rays with the help of our movable screen: when both light rays are scattered from the same place in the screen, they (roughly) intersect. Again, by making the bundles of light rays smaller and smaller, their intersection will be a smaller and smaller volume; and in the ideal limit that we can never actually attain, their intersection will be a point.

One thing about this description which might be a source of uneasiness, is that we use the idea of moving a screen through *space*, and we talk about *same place* on a screen; but these are not technical notions: a spot on a screen is something that is ostensively understandable; two spots on a screen being close together is something that is ostensively understandable. In other words, these things themselves are not taken to be official geometrical entities, but the source of our contact with the official geometrical entities.

Now of course there are practical limits as to how small a bundle of light rays can be and still be detected. (Indeed there are theoretical limits imposed by Quantum Theory.) What the practical limits are depends on a number of things: what intensity we can create for our source; what kinds of optical equipment—lenses and the like—we can develop. Note that for small regions all three geometries are essentially the same, so that we can design optical equipment on the Euclidean basis to be used to test whether the theory of light rays in the large in homogeneous media is Euclidean, Riemannian, or Lobachevskian. There is nothing beyond Euclidean geometry applied to very small regions behind the physical optics required for developing optical instruments.

V

Now, given these interpretations of "points", "lines", etc., how can we go about testing the three formal systems?—for, given these interpretations of the primitive notions, the three calculi that were discussed earlier in the chapter become formal systems. Any trio of statements that represent three exclusive possible outcomes of an experiment may be used. We might consider, for example, Axiom IV-1E, IV-1R, and IV-1L themselves. But it is difficult to see how to construct an experiment which will determine whether through a point not on a given line in a plane, there can be drawn one, more than one, or no lines parallel to the given line. If space were curved sharply enough (to use picturesque language) we might be able to confirm experimentally that no light rays through a given intersection of light rays, can exist that do not intersect a given light ray; but we would have to be able to project light rays indefinitely far to be able to confirm or disconfirm either of the other two versions of Axiom IV-1.

A better test case is suggested by the theorem about the sum of the angles of a

[216]

triangle: for this can be examined in a finite region. We can construct a finite triangle of light rays, and measure the three angles. According to the Euclidean formal system their sum will be 180°, according to the Riemannian formal system, it will be more than 180°, and according to the Lobachevskian formal system it will be less than 180°. Furthermore, according to both the Riemannian and the Lobachevskian formal systems, the difference between the actual sum of the interior angles and 180° will be proportional to the area of the triangle: so we know that we can get more definite results by using a larger triangle. Thus we will construct as large a triangle as we can out of bundles of light rays that are as small as possible, and measure the angles at the three vertices as accurately as possible.

This experiment was allegedly performed once, using three mountain tops as the three vertices of the triangle. The result: within the limits of experimental error, 180°. The experimental result was that the sum of the angles was $m° \pm k°$, where $k°$ represented standard deviation of the method of measurement employed, and $m - k \leq 180° \leq m + k$; i.e., 180° was a perfectly reasonable value for the sum to have.

Let us suppose, for illustrative purposes, that the experiment had not turned out this way; let us suppose that the sum of the angles had turned out to be about 210°. Would this have established Riemannian geometry as the geometry of physical space? At least, among three formal systems in question, it would have established the Riemannian formal system as the one that conformed to experiment. But remember that a formal system consists of a calculus and an interpretation. If we didn't like the calculus to which we were led, we could always reject the interpretation. Indeed, this was precisely Poincaré's conjecture: that no set of circumstances would ever cause us to abandon Euclidean geometry, because (a) Euclidean geometry is simpler than the other two (e.g., in that the sum of the angles of a triangle doesn't depend on how big the triangle is), and (b) any interpretation of the primitive terms of geometry which, combined with the Euclidean calculus, led to conflicts with experience, could be rejected as an interpretation. In the case in point, rather than sticking to the interpretation as the path of a light ray in a homogeneous medium for "line", intersections of them for "points", and so on (which forces us to reject the Euclidean calculus), we could stick to the Euclidean calculus, and conclude that our interpretation was "wrong"—that light rays do not travel in straight lines. If we stick to the Euclidean calculus, we may have no ostensive interpretation for the primitive terms "point", "line", etc., and no way of identifying the corresponding entities directly. We can get at them through light rays as before; but we have to take account of the curvature of the light rays. Thus if ABC is the path of a light ray, we can, by reference to this path, and knowing the curvature of the light ray, calculate the *place* of the straight line from A to C (see Fig. 2).

On the original interpretation, such as assertion would be meaningless: a

[217]

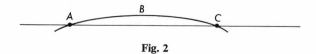

Fig. 2

"straight line" just *is* the path of a light ray. And then it is a factual matter, whether or not lines, thus interpretated, satisfy Euclidean, or Riemannian, or Lobachevskian postulates. Alternatively, we are perfectly free to decide that *points* and *lines*, whatever else may be true of them, obey the Euclidean postulates; if we do so it is meaningless to ask whether or not *space* is Euclidean. Space becomes just the Euclidean system of points and lines and planes. But then it is a factual matter, whether the path of a light ray in a homogeneous medium is a line. Since it seems quite obviously wrong-headed to decide in advance which of these two possible stands we are going to take before we begin to find out about the nature of the world and light rays, the point of view that seems most plausible is that it is the formal system as a whole—the calculus together with its interpretation—that is being tested.

In point of fact, despite the outcome of the three mountain experiment, Poincaré was wrong: physicists have come to reject the Euclidean framework. It is not a matter of finding that the sum of the angles in a triangle of light rays is defective or excessive, however, but of the way that the rest of physics fits into the framework of geometry. There are many things in physics besides the paths of light rays; there are the movements of bodies, the directions of forces, accelerations and velocities. In fact the very necessity of postulating the existence of certain forces may depend upon the geometry we adopt. Hans Reichenbach argues that we may always choose our geometry in such a way that there is no need to postulate the existence of any universal forces that affect all objects equally—as, for example, the force of gravitation does. And indeed this is the most important feature of Einstein's theory of relativity: that there exist no gravitational forces, and all bodies (not under the influence of differential forces) travel always in straight lines. "Straight" is here a term applicable to certain paths in the non-Euclidean, four-dimensional geometry that Einstein developed for this purpose. Although the physical theory developed by Einstein is far more direct and simple than any Euclidean theory that would fit the same facts, it is far more complicated than any of the theories we have considered above. On this theory, for example, the space inside a solid body is Riemannian, with a constant positive curvature, and shades off smoothly into a Lobachevskian space with variable curvature that gets more and more Euclidean (flatter) the farther you get from the body.

VI

It was mentioned earlier that we are interested in geometry not only because we are interested in optical phenomena, but also because we are interested in the

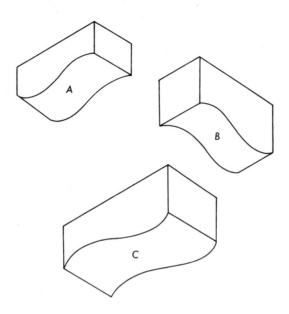

Fig. 3

ways in which physical objects fit together. This leads to another physical interpretation of the primitive terms of geometry.

Let us take three blocks of steel, with surfaces, *A*, *B*, and *C* (see Fig. 3). If
these three surfaces are such that *A* can slide around on *B*, maintaining contact
with it at all points, and also such that *A* can slide around on *C*, maintaining
contact with it at all points, and also such that *B* can slide around on *C*, maintaining contact with it at all points, then all three surfaces have zero curvature, and
are Euclidean planes (see Fig. 3). The intersection of two such planes is a Euclidean straight line, and the (noncolinear) intersection of three such planes is a
Euclidean straight line, and the (noncolinear) intersection of three such planes
is a Euclidean point. It can be proved that these points and lines and planes,
as ideally described, will satisfy the Euclidean postulates. Furthermore, it is
just these lines and points and planes that the machinist and tool and die maker
are concerned with. Thus the mechanical engineer does not (as some philosophers
have suggested) use Euclidean geometry because it is a good *approximation* to
the true geometry of space for things of the size that he is concerned with, but
because Euclidean points and lines and planes have precisely those properties
that are required of the surfaces and edges that are to occur in machines. We
want the surface of a lathe bed to match *any* "flat" surface. We want all flat
surfaces to fit against each other—i.e., to have zero curvature. This applies to

[219]

the machinery we use to test physical theories, too: it is not designed by Euclidean geometry because that's a good approximation, but because only Euclidean planes have the physical interchangeability properties that are needed in machinery.

In scientific activity, then, we really have two formal systems of physical geometry that are of real relevance, as well as geometrical calculuses that have as yet received no empirical interpretation that will raise them to the level of useful formal systems. They are nonetheless interesting as calculuses, and do admit of interesting formal interpretations. The two formal systems of geometry that are of current use are: (1) Einstein's physical geometry, consisting of a non-Euclidean calculus, with a physical (optical) interpretation; and (2) Euclidean geometry, with the steel block interpretation. The Euclidean geometry is useful not only for designing machinery, as mentioned above, but also as a close approximation to physical geometry when the distances involved are small. Thus even though we do our surveying by optical means, we take the optical line of sight of the surveyor as being so close as never-mind to the Euclidean straight line of the steel block. Indeed, the fundamental unit of surveying is just the 180° triangle, so that all of our map making is done in the Euclidean framework. That is the point in saying that the underlying geometry is the Euclidean steel block geometry, and that the optical techniques the surveyer uses are permissible because they are very close approximation (in terrestrial orders of magnitude) to the steel block truth. Again, I think many philosophers of science have gotten things backwards, saying that although true geometry is non-Euclidean, surveyers can get away with using Euclidean geometry because the distances involved are small. The point is just the opposite: their geometry is Euclidean, and they can get away with using optical techniques because the distances are small.

BIBLIOGRAPHICAL NOTES TO CHAPTER 9

For a careful statement of the various geometries of constant curvature, which is also a relatively elementary statement, see H. Eves and C. V. Newsom, *An Introduction to the Foundations and Fundamental Concepts of Mathematics* (New York: Rinehart and Co., 1958). This contains the complete statement of David Hilbert's axioms, which first appeared in 1899 in Hilbert's classic *Grundlagen der Geometrie*, a work that is as responsible as any other for the extraordinary development of abstract mathematics in this century. E. V. Huntington's axioms may be found in his article, "A Set of Postulates for Abstract Geometry, Expressed in Terms of the Simple Relation of Inclusion," *Math. Ann.* **73**, 522–559 (1913). John Playfair (1748–1819) was a Scottish physicist and mathematician; he is remembered for his statement of an equivalent of Euclid's Fifth postulate; it is his version that is most often encountered in geometry textbooks today.

Non-Euclidean Geometry has an interesting history; see, for example, H. Eves, *An Introduction to the History of Mathematics* (New York: 1958), or E. T. Bell, *The Development of Mathematics* (New York, 1945). The great German mathematician Carl Friedrich Gauss was the first to dabble in non-Euclidian geometry, but he never published any of his results. Johann Bolyai and Nicholai Lobachevsky were the first to publish (around 1830) works in which the possibility of non-Euclidian geometry was taken seriously. Twenty-five years later, Bernhard Riemann developed the other major system of non-Euclidean geometry.

A careful discussion of the distinction between a geometrical calculus (formal geometry) and a geometrical formal system (physical geometry) will be found in Carl Hempel, "Geometry and Empirical Science", *American Mathematical Monthly* **52** (1945) [reprinted in Feigl and Sellars, *Readings in Philosophical Analysis* (New York: Appleton-Century Crofts, 1949)]. More complete discussions of physical geometry, as it is actually developed in the theory of relativity, may be found in R. Carnap, *Philosophical Foundations of Physics* (New York: Basic Books, 1966), and Hans Reichenbach, *The Philosophy of Space and Time* (New York: Dover Publications, 1958). The most painstaking and detailed examination available of the physical concepts of space and time is to be found in Adolf Grünbaum's, *Philosophical Problems of Space and Time* (New York: Alfred Knopf, 1963).

Chapter **10**

PHYSICS

I

The first formalized subsystem of physics that we shall consider is a system of linear statics (the formal theory of see-saws). This is not an especially interesting part of physics, but its very familiarity and homeliness will enable us to concentrate effectively on its formal characteristics. Furthermore, despite the fact that the theory is a very simple one, in the sense that its axioms are few and familiar, it is a rich one in the sense that the basic concepts of the theory include most of those concepts that enter into full-blooded physical theories of statics, dynamics, kinematics, etc. Thus we need a vocabulary for the discussion of the measurement of distances and the measurement of forces, and so on, and large parts of this vocabulary will be just the same as the corresponding parts of the vocabularies of the more complex theories. For this reason, in the subsequent

[222]

paragraphs that deal with the theory of see-saws, I shall devote more care and space to the basic terms involved than the intrinsic interest of the subject matter might otherwise warrant.

For the sake of clarity, I shall depart from my usual pattern of presenting first the calculus of the formal system, and then the interpretation of that calculus. The bare calculus would be overwhelming and unintelligible, presented all at once. Furthermore, there is nothing to be gained here by repeating the treatment of quantities already displayed in Chapter 3; so I shall offer no more than indications of how the quantitative predicates are developed out of the primitive predicates. The formal system that follows will be presented in three parts: a part that concerns lengths and distances; a part that concerns forces (pushes and pulls); and a part that embodies a theory proper. It is only the last part that will contain nonlogical axioms.

Part I
Primitive terms: "L", "J", "one-foot-standard", "D", and "R".
Interpretation, formation rules, and *meaning postulates.*

"L" and "J" are the primitive terms we encountered in our theory of lengths of Chapter 3. "L" is a relational predicate, "Lxy" being interpreted to mean that x is longer than y. It is understood to satisfy the three meaning postulates:

MP1 $\quad Lxy \supset \sim Lyx$
MP2 $\quad (Lxy \,\&\, Lyz) \supset Lxz$
MP3 $\quad (\sim Lxy \,\&\, \sim Lyz) \supset \sim Lxz.$

"L" is a typically quasi-ostensive term. It is one whose interpretation is given mainly by ostension, and yet which is subject also to the foregoing axiomatic restraints. We can, with a very high degree of confidence, observe that x is longer than y; but such observations are not infallible. So far from indicating a confusion here between theoretical terms (governed by axioms) and observation terms (whose application is infallible) this highly typical circumstance indicates that just this distinction is implausible. It is surely absurd to say that we can never accept a statement like "A is longer than B" on the basis of a simple observation; and it is also surely absurd to say that we do not know for certain that if A is longer than B, then B is not longer than A.

An alternative (but less attractive because more complex) way of looking at the matter is to take the observation predicate corresponding to the ordinary language "longer than" to be "looks longer than". Judgments of the form "A looks longer than B" are, of course (?), infallible. And "A looks longer than B" provides very good evidence indeed for the physical-language statement, "A is longer than B." The only inconvenience is that the connection between these statements, in virtue of which the first provides good grounds for accepting the second, lies in a third statement that we might call psycho–physical: namely,

[223]

"Practically all the time, when Z looks longer than W, Z *is* longer than W." We certainly have grounds enough for accepting this statement (if we have grounds enough to accept any inductively established statement); and if we were concerned to construct the whole of human scientific knowledge, we might very well adopt this approach. But when we are concerned only to formalize a bit of physics, it seems out of place to include a fragment of psychology—even such an innocuous fragment as the psycho-physical hypothesis in question.

"J", as in Chapter 3, will be taken to express the physical operation of colinear juxtaposition. Like the relation term "L" it is quasi-ostensive. We learn what colinear juxtaposition is by seeing it done. But as in the case of "L", "J" exhibits important theoretical characteristics. It shares commutativity and associativity with the mathematical operation of addition, in the sense embodied in the following axioms:

(For the sake of intuitive perspicuity, I write "xJy" for "Jxy".)

MP4 $\sim L(xJ(yJz))((xJy)Jz) \cdot \sim L((xJy)Jz)(xJ(yJz))$
MP5 $\sim L(xJy)(yJx)$.

The formation rule is the obvious one: if t_1 and t_2 are terms, "(t_1Jt_2)" is also a term.

"One-foot-standard" is a term denoting a particular body, namely the body we take (in this study) as a unit of length. Its meaning is given purely ostensively: "*This* is our standard length."

Using only these three primitive terms, together with a good supply of logical terms, it is possible to define our quantitative predicates of length, "$_rL$". This has been done in Chapter 3, and will not be repeated here. We shall suppose that these predicates are now available:

$$_rL(x) =_{Df} (\cdots x \cdots).$$

These predicates are applicable to rigid bodies; we also require to be able to speak of the distances between points lying on rigid bodies, and it is no more trouble to speak of distances between points in general. For this purpose we must make use of terms "RB", "En", which will be discussed and interpreted only in Part III. In a preliminary way, "RBx" will be interpreted to mean that x is a rigid body, and "$Enxy$" will be interpreted to mean that x is an end of the rigid body y.

"D" is interpreted as a three-termed relation that holds of an ordered triple rxy when x and y are points, and the distance between them is r feet. We take "D" to satisfy the following meaning postulates, which also serve to connect it to the quantitative length predicates. Observe that we cannot provide an explicit definition of distance in terms of length: neither MP6 nor MP7 can be strength-

[224]

ened into a biconditional, if the terms that occur in them are to have anything like their usual meaning.

MP6 $\quad\quad\quad (\exists z)(RBz \,\&\, Enxz \,\&\, Enyz \,\&\, x \neq y \,\&\, {}_rL(x)) \supset Drxy$

MP7 $\quad\quad\quad Drxy \supset (z)((RBz \,\&\, Enxz \,\&\, Enyz \,\&\, x \neq y) \supset rL(z))$

Two further meaning postulates that hold for "D" are

MP8 $\quad\quad\quad\quad\quad\quad\quad Drxy \supset Dryx$

MP9 $\quad\quad\quad\quad\quad\quad\quad Drxy \supset D0xx.$

What we are really interested in here is the concept of directed distance. This can be introduced by definition, once we have introduced a preferential direction. This latter, we will take to be purely ostensive: "R" will be a relational predicate, which will hold of two things x and y, only if they are points and x is to the right of y. "Rxy" means that x is to the right of y, looking in the direction we are now looking—i.e., x is to *that* side of y. Just as "R" applies to points and "L" (and thus "$_rL$") applies to rigid bodies, so "D" holds for ordered triples whose first member is a non-negative real number.

MP10 $\quad\quad\quad\quad\quad Drxy \supset (r \in \text{Real Numbers} \,\&\, r \geq 0).$

We can now define directed distance (DD) as a function from pairs of points to positive and negative quantities in the following way:

D1 $\quad\quad\quad DDxy = r \text{ feet} \equiv_{Df} (Rxy \,\&\, Dryx) \lor (Ryx \,\&\, D\text{-}ryx).$

Part II

The concept of *force* we require for linear statics is a very simple one; it is a direct generalization of the pushes and pulls we feel with our muscles. It leads to the concept of directed force, just as the concept of *having greater length than* leads to the concept of directed length.

Primitive terms: "F", "C", "one-pound-force-standard", "U", "AF", and "Dn".

Interpretation, formation rules, and meaning postulates:

"F" and "C" function here just as "L" and "J" function in Part I. "F" is a relation holding between forces, which is asymmetric, transitive, and whose relational complement is also transitive.

MP11 $\quad\quad\quad\quad\quad\quad\quad Fxy \supset \sim Fyx$

MP12 $\quad\quad\quad\quad\quad\quad\quad (Fxy \,\&\, Fyz) \supset Fxz$

MP13 $\quad\quad\quad\quad\quad\quad\quad (\sim Fxy \,\&\, \sim Fyz) \supset \sim Fxz.$

"F" is also like "L" in being a quasi-ostensive term. Like "L", it is introduced ostensively, but is also subject to certain formal restrictions embodied in MP11–MP13. How do we observe that one force is greater in magnitude than another?

[225]

That is rather more complicated than observing that one body is longer than another, but the principles are the same. One way is to test the forces against our own muscles, just as one way of judging whether one thing is longer than another is to simply form a direct judgment on the matter. It is more accurate, however, to perform an experiment, if one is possible, e.g., by moving the two bodies so that they lie side by side, or by comparing them by means of a third body which can be moved (a measuring rod). In a perfectly analogous way, we can most accurately judge when one force is greater than another by opposing them to each other, or by opposing them to a set of standard forces, e.g., one pound weights. To accomplish this requires that we be able to change the directions of forces, and also to change from here to there the points at which they act; and this is not a part of the theory with which we are concerned. But neither, in Part I, was there anything about the mobility of rigid bodies, which is just as much required by a complete theory of measurement as is the principle that we can change the direction of a force. In point of fact, we can move rigid bodies around, without having much violence done to our intuitions of length, and we can also, by making use of pulleys and levers and things, move forces about. All of this is some distance from simply *observing* in any simple sense; and yet that does not in any way prohibit us from introducing "greater force than" as a quasi-ostensive term in our theory of linear statics. "Greater force than" has a direct, ordinary language, ostensive meaning, and our technical term "F" embodies at most a slight refinement of this meaning.

"C", like "J", represents a physical operation; in particular it represents the codirectional combination of forces. In order to make this combination with arbitrary forces, we will again have to depend on pulleys and levers and things; but this fact is not a part of the theory with which we are concerned. It is part of the meaning of co-directional combination that it is associative and commutative:

MP14 $\sim F(xC(yCz))((xCy)Cz) \,\&\, \sim F((xCy)Cz)(xC(yCz))$
MP15 $\sim F(xCy)(yCx)$.

The formation rule is the obvious one: if t_1 and t_2 are terms, so is "t_1Ct_2".

"One-pound-force-standard" is a term denoting a particular force. One cannot put a force in a glass case, of course, as one can put a platinum foot-rule in a glass case. But the force which a certain lump of matter exerts on our arms when we pick it up seems fairly constant; we may associate weight with downward force. In this theory, we may take a one-pound weight (*that* one) and take the downward force it exerts to be the standard unit of force. In a more general physics, this would not do: the weight of a body is the force with which it is attracted to some other body, and that depends on its circumstances. In a more complete system, although we would retain the same sort of distance standard, we would define our unit force in terms of acceleration and mass. The pound-

[226]

force we are using here would turn out to be 32.2 feet × pounds/second × second, and pounds and seconds would be defined by reference to more universal standards than weight.

Using just the foregoing primitive terms, it is possible to define quantitative predicates of force, "$_rF$". "$_rF(x)$" will hold just in case x is a force whose magnitude is just r times as great as the magnitude of our one-pound-force-standard:

$$_rF(x) =_{Df} (\cdots x \cdots).$$

We need to be able to speak of particular forces acting at particular points on particular bodies. "AF" will denote the relation that holds between x, y, and z, when x is a force, y a body, and z a point on the body y at which the force x is acting. Here we have a relatively ostensive relation. We can often tell by looking when a force x is acting at a point z on a body y, because we know what forces are—forces are pushes and pulls exerted by weights, springs, and so on—and we know what it is for a force to act at a certain point. A force, a shove or a push or a pull, must make contact at some *point* with the *body* on which it acts. In a more complete system, we would not be able to take this as a very ostensive term (though we might still want to take it as primitive), for not all forces act as obvious points on bodies—e.g., central forces, magnetic and electrostatic forces, act invisibly. There are some meaning postulates that the predicate "AF" must satisfy; one of them is that in our present theory, every force is directed upward or directed downward. If "Ux" is interpreted to mean that x is an upward directed force, and "Dnx" is interpreted to mean that x is a downward directed force, we must have:

MP16 $\qquad\qquad (\exists y)(\exists z)(AFxyz) \supset (Ux \vee Dnx).$

On the basis of this terminology, we can define *directed force* for our limited system as follows:

D2 $\quad DFxyz = r \text{ lb} =_{Df} (AFxyz \ \& \ Ux \ \& \ _rF(x)) \vee (AFxyz \ \& \ Dnx \ \& \ _{-r}F(x)).$

Part III

The subject matter of our study is rigid bodies. "RB" is a predicate that is given mainly ostensively; but we must stipulate that the rigid bodies we are concerned with are relatively long and thin, so that, for example, they have no more than two ends; we take as a meaning postulate:

MP17 $\quad (RBz \ \& \ Enxz \ \& \ Enxy \ \& \ x \neq y) \supset (w)(Enwz \supset (w = x \vee w = y)).$

Otherwise than demanded by this postulate, the interpretation of the relation "En" is to be understood ostensively. In a similar vein, the relation between a pair of points and a rigid body on which they both lie, must be such that if they

[227]

are distinct, one lies to the right of the other. Since we need worry only about points at which forces are acting, we can express this requirement as follows:

MP18 $\quad\quad\quad\quad\quad ((\exists x)(AFxyz) \ \& \ (\exists x)(AFxwz)) \supset (Ryw \lor Rwy).$

We also require (for the sake of the definitions D1 and D2) the exclusiveness of the predicates "U" and "Dn", and the irreflexivity of the relation term "R":

MP19 $\quad\quad\quad\quad\quad\quad\quad\quad\quad Rxy \supset \sim Ryx$

MP20 $\quad\quad\quad\quad\quad\quad\quad\quad\quad Ux \supset \sim Dnx.$

We require one more term, "E", for "is in equilibrium". This is taken here to be a purely ostensive term. In a complete theory of dynamics it, too, might be taken as quasi-ostensive. It is part of the meaning of "in equilibrium", understood in the context of a complete physical theory, that if none of the forces acting on a body changes, then that body will remain precisely in its given state. Thus, for example, if we take a bar of asphalt and balance it on the edge of a board, we will find that although it looks in equilibrium, it is not *really* in equilibrium, because after a month or so at ordinary temperatures it will be dripping down the sides of the board. Nevertheless, "E" is a purely ostensive term here: something is in equilibrium if it doesn't look like it's going to move—i.e. if we watch it until we get bored and nothing seems to happen. This ostensive notion of equilibrium wouldn't work in a larger system, for in a larger system there would be long-term consequences we could draw from an assertion of equilibrium (together with appropriate boundary conditions); but here there is nothing of that nature. Indeed, there can't be, since we do not even introduce a time variable into our theory.

The variables of the system are interpreted as ranging over rigid bodies, forces, and points. We should therefore also have meaning postulates which indicate the kinds of things that the predicates of the system may properly be predicated of (e.g., "$Ex \supset RBx$", "$AFxyz \supset RBy$", "$AFxyz \supset (\exists w)(DF(x) = w \text{ lb})$"), but I shall not bother with those details.

The fact that we require so many meaning postulates illustrates more than the impracticality of strictly formalizing science, or carrying on the business of science in completely and strictly formalized systems. It also illustrates what a tremendous amount of meaning is packed into even the most innocent looking technical terms of science. But by the same token, it illustrates the importance, for the philosophy of science, of making some attempt to formalize fragments of the systems of science; for in the attempt to construct such a formalization we find out not only that there is a large amount of meaning packed into the terms of the system, but also much of what that meaning is.

The two axioms that embody the physical content of our theory of linear statics make use of the fact that under the physical operations J and C, the quantitative predicates $_rL$ and $_rF$ are additive. This concept of additivity was discussed at length in Chapter 3, and that discussion will not be repeated here.

[228]

AXIOM I. If $y_1, y_2, \cdots, y_n$ are all the forces acting on a body x, and they are all distinct, then,

$$E(x) \supset \sum_{i=1}^{n} DF(y_i) = 0 \text{ lb.}$$

AXIOM II. If $y_1, \cdots, y_n$ are all the forces acting on a body x, and they are all distinct, then (where they act at points z_i)

$$E(x) \supset (w) \sum_{i=1}^{n} DF(y_i) \times DD(w, z_i) = 0 \text{ ft. lb.}$$

The rules of inference of this system are just the rules of inference of the logic we have supposed to underlie all of our systems.

We could now (having laid out the calculus of the system) go ahead and prove a lot of theorems. They would not generally be of much interest, of course; we do not set up a formal system like this for the sake of proving just any old theorems, but for the sake of proving theorems that are interesting and useful; and ultimately, for the sake of proving theorems of very restricted generality that can be applied directly to experimental situations or to the conduct of engineering life. Or, in the case of the theory of linear statics, to the conduct of a playground.

The theorems that are of the most direct concern to us in this formal system are conditional in form and answer questions that we can pose directly. For example:

If A is a rigid body in equilibrium 8 ft. long and there is an upward force of 10 lb. acting in the middle, and a downward force of 20 lb. acting at the left end and a downward force of 30 lb. acting at the right end, (what sort of a force must be acting where in order for the body to be in equilibrium?) then there must be an upward force of 40 lb. acting 1 ft. to the right of center.

Or, if B is a rigid body in equilibrium 11 ft. long, and there is a downward force of 80 lb. at the right end, and the only upward force on B is 1 ft. from the left end, (what's happening at the left end, and how large is the upward force?) then there is a downward force of 800 lb. at the left end and an upward force of 880 lb. at the point 1 ft. from the left end.

If C is a boat, 400 ft. long, and its bow is wedged between two rocks, 75 ft. apart by a current pushing on the stern of the vessel with a force that amounts to 5000 lb. acting at a point 100 ft. from the stern, (what are the forces at the bow?) then the force at the very bow is 15,000 lb. and the force at the other rock is 20,000 lb.

Or, if M is a piece of a watch that is 0.005 inches long, and it is pinned at one end, and subject to an upward force of 0.0006 lb. at the other end, and a downward force at its midpoint and it is in equilibrium, (what are these forces?) then the downward force has a magnitude of 0.0012 lb., and the end that is pinned is subject to an upward force of 0.0006 lb.

[229]

I have listed this many minor examples of the kinds of theorems that we can derive in this sort of a formal system, not to show its versatility so much as to illustrate the fact that the interpretation of the relatively ostensive terms of the system will vary from circumstance to circumstance. "Point" in the context of the discussion of the freighter wedged in the rocks is a very different kind of animal from "point" used in talking about a watch part.

II

How would we go about establishing that this theory was a good one? It is a little difficult to tell, because we all do have such good reason to believe it, and it is so familiar to us, that it is very difficult indeed to put ourselves into a frame of mind in which we can doubt it seriously. But we can think of some questions that might come to mind if this theory were being proposed for the first time as a general theory. Thus suppose that we were familiar with see-saws, and formulated this theory to account for the see-saw equilibrium. See-saw equilibrium is a matter of two weights on a plank balanced on a fulcrum. The theory that we have presented above holds for any sort of rigid body, subject to any number of vertical forces—springs pushing up and springs pushing down and weights placed at various points, and weights acting through pulleys so that they pull up instead of pushing down, and so on. Furthermore, the theory entails that it is indifferent what point we take the moments about—even if that point doesn't happen to be on the rigid body. This latter consequence is a purely mathematical point: we prove purely mathematically that if the sum of the moments of the forces acting on a body about one point is 0, then that is also the sum of the moments acting on that body taken about any other point. Though merely an analytic consequence of our definition of *moment*, this is important: it means that we are free to calculate the moments about whatever point it is easiest for us to use.

The former consequence, that the theory will work as well for bars and rods subject to any number of pushes and pulls as it works for see-saws and teeter-totters, is not a consequence of any definition simply, but is a consequence of the two general axioms, which contain no limitation in the number of forces that act on a body in equilibrium. This is the first thing that it might occur to us to test. There are various techniques that we can use in putting this part of the theory to test: we can arrange a situation which corresponds to a theorem of the calculus, and we can select various features of that situation as test variables. Thus we can take a rod, apply a number of forces at a number of points; measure all the forces, and the distance of all but one of the points from a given point; compute all the moments; calculate the distance from the given point that the last force must be applied; and then check to see that that is indeed the distance. Or, we can measure all the distance, all but one of the forces, and calculate the magnitude and direction of the final force.

[230]

All confirmations of this theory will be equally simple-minded. (Unless we forget something, like the force with which the fulcrum of our see-saw pushes upward.) The direct confirmation of the theory consists in accumulating instances of bodies in equilibrium in which the forces and instances are such that they satisfy the predictions of the theory. If this *set* of instances is a random member of the set of all equinumerous instances with respect to indicating the proportion of cases in which the theory holds, then we may infer, on the basis of a large number of satisfactory tests, that the probability is very high $(1 - \epsilon, 1)$ that the proportion of those instances in which the theory is tested in which it will emerge triumphant is at least $1 - \delta$—i.e., between $1 - \delta$ and 1. Since we know of no instances (I am supposing) in which the theory fails, this amounts to taking it as acceptable in any rational corpus of level lower than $1 - \epsilon$, that all the predictions of the theory will hold, provided that $\delta < \epsilon$; and that in turn is tantamount to accepting the theory itself in that rational corpus.

Doubts about the randomness of the sample may be taken in two ways. In the first place there is bare abstract doubt: perhaps the color of the arms of the rigid body is relevant? perhaps if the two sides were painted different colors, the theory wouldn't hold? We have no reason to suppose that this will be the case so the mere suggestion that this *might* be the case cannot prevent our sample (even if it concerns only rigid bodies of uniform color) from being random in the appropriate sense.

But we might feel inclined to assuage these doubts, academic though they be; and it would be easy enough to do: we can include some experiments with varicolored bodies among the data on which we base the theory. Although we are supposing that we know nothing more about physical phenomena here than is expressed formally above, it is still perhaps the case that we have enough background knowledge to suggest the overriding hypothesis that if the relative frequency of failures among varicolored bodies differed at all from the relative frequency of failures among uniformly colored bodies, that difference would be a marked one. In any event, no such difference is discernable. If our theory had originally been accepted on the basis of balancing beams with two arms and two weights, it would have been quite proper to wonder if the theory would also hold for more weights and for more forces acting on the body. But again, it does not take a very large number of instances to show that there is no noticeable difference between the relative frequency of successes in the former sorts of cases and among the latter sorts of cases.

If there is a more plausible ring to doubts based on the supposition that the number of forces acting on a body have some relevant effect, than there is to doubts based on the supposition that equilibrium has something to do with the colors of the bodies concerned, it is only a reflection of our general knowledge about the world. After all, we cannot live in the world without learning something; and to learn is already to generalize.

Perhaps this is a good place to discuss the question of what a *successful* experiment comes to. For we cannot (and do not) demand that if we multiply the forces by the distances to get the moments about a point, and form their sum or even that if we add the upward forces to the downward forces, we get 0. Every measurement of distance yields, not a real number, but a quantity of the form: $r \pm k$ feet; every measurement of a force yields, not a real number, but a quantitative assertion of the form: $f \pm n$ pounds force. When we multiply these things to get moments, we must keep track of these errors, according to rather obvious rules. (If F lies between 1 and 2, and D lies between 2 and 4, all we know about M is that it lies between 2 and 8! But if we know that F and D are normally distributed, we can do a little better.) If we add up the moments (thus represented as intervals), we may expect that the resulting interval will include the 0 point. Or if we set up the experiment so that the experimental result is the measurement of a distance or the measurement of a force, we do not predict a precise number that these measurements must conform to in the first place, and we may perfectly well disregard the experiment even if it yields a result somewhat outside the interval that we do predict will include the result. In the earlier case, we may not regard the experiment as refuting the theory, even if it produces a result—an interval—that does not include the zero point.

This is an important matter. A single deviant measurement among a large group which confirms a theory, is not in itself a refutation of the theory. Indeed, the theory of error that was discussed in Chapter 6 already shows that such deviant measurements are not only possible, but, in the long run, to be expected. If a theory predicts that a certain quantity will, with probability high enough to be acceptable, be 3.46 ± 0.03, and the actual result of the experiment is 3.38 ± 0.04, again with probability high enough for acceptance, we must reject the theory or the experiment, at that level of acceptance. But we do know, from the theory of error itself, that such widely discrepant results will occur with a certain small frequency; and in fact the thing that is often done, is to perform the experiment again—i.e., to take the 3.38 ± 0.04 to be merely a result of half an experiment. If, the second time through, the result is the same, we have two instances; for the same probability we have 3.38 ± 0.027, now, instead of ± 0.04, and a contradiction which can no longer be regarded as a merely deviant result; on the other hand, if we get 3.44, we have a mean for the combined experiment of 3.41 ± 0.027, or a result that does overlap the interval originally allowed.

This sounds perfectly straightforward and so simple as to be not worth remarking on. But, simple and natural and straightforward though it is, the principles which seem to lie behind it should still be made explicit; the analysis in terms of acceptance is important as a means of making explicit principles which will be equally operative, and much more significant, in complicated cases.

The second type of doubt about randomness is more important. This is the doubt based on a general and systematic departure from results predicted by the theory in a particular class of cases. Suppose, for example, that we set up a situation in which we have an iron rod, and beneath one end of it is a powerful electromagnet. Now unless we know about electromagnets and their effects, we can't detect any of the pushes and pulls that we are used to (springs, weights, etc.), acting on the iron rod; and so the theory is clearly falsified. One might be tempted to say that the rod behaves *as if* there were a force acting on it at the point where the electromagnet is; but one could explain things just as well by supposing that there were a couple of other forces acting almost anywhere. (Another couple of forces that provide the same net downward force and the same net moment.) And in any event, the interpretation of "*AFxyw*"— there is a force *x* acting at point *y* of *w*—was ostensive; and there is nothing in the situation that we have described that can answer to that interpretation. There is no shove at the place where the (secret) electromagnet is.

The discovery of this sort of situation does provide a clear and definite ground for rejecting the randomness of the earlier sequence of experiments. Knowing that the theory fails for this class of experiments, we know that the earlier sequence, for which it did not fail, was *not* a random sample of experiments with respect to revealing the proportion of experiments that would fail to refute the theory. But we do not simply reject the whole theory of this account; for in place of our original assertion of randomness we have a new one: namely, that the sequence of experiments first considered are a random sample of experiments of that type—i.e., of experiments without electromagnets—with respect to indicating the proportion of such experiments that will bear out the predictions of the theory; and in the same way, precisely, we take the experiments in which there is an electromagnet to be a random sample of that type of experiment, with respect to indicating the proportion that will refute the theory.

Thus even when there are grounds for rejecting the randomness of a set of experiments, the same grounds will generally be grounds for *accepting* the randomness of the experiments applied in two distinct fields. What we do, essentially, is to find the variable that makes the difference between success and failure, and subdivide the field of applications of the theory according to that variable—in this case, according to the presence or absence of electromagnetic machinery. We have (regrettably) lost some of the universality of our general hypothesis; but in the area in which it still applies, it applies just as unexceptionably as it did before. Of course, as soon as we find out about electromagnetic forces we can reinstitute our laws of linear statics in their full generality, by suitably broadening our concept of force.

III

The theory that we have been discussing is quite trivial from a scientific point of view, yet it is rich enough to provide some basis for the discussion of three

[233]

traditional topics of the philosophy of physics, and indeed of the philosophy of science generally: explanation, prediction, and causality.

Explanation and prediction are both, according to Carl Hempel's well-known view, related to deducibility; both involve the deduction of a statement (the prediction or the explanandum) from a body of statements. The concept of a formal system, regarded as it is regarded here, provides both justification for and clarification of this view. Prediction has already been dealt with, essentially, in the discussion of confirmation, but we may easily generalize that discussion. Consider any body of knowledge that is built on the basis of the formal system described here, by the addition of a number of acceptable statements, expressed in the language of the system. We do not demand that they be observation statements, but the epistemological grounds of their acceptability must be sound; and thus in general (in the present instance) they will be statements that can be and are accepted primarily on an ostensive basis. Among these statements are statements describing a situation incompletely, in the sense that there is a fact missing: a distance, a force, a direction. In the formal system, thus supplemented, it is possible to deduce a statement which will complete the description—i.e., which will supply the missing fact. Such a statement, if the situation has not yet occurred, or is incompletely known experimentally, may often be regarded as a prediction. Thus: I predict that if such and such forces are acting at such and such places on a given body, the body will not be in a state of equilibrium. I predict that if such and such forces are acting on such and such a body, which is in a state of equilibrium, a force of such and such magnitude will be found to be acting at such and such another place. Whether a given statement is a prediction or not, depends, of course, not only on whether it can be deduced from a body of knowledge incorporating the formal system in question, but on whether that body of knowledge consists of statements to which we have an epistemological right, on whether that statement is not already itself a part of that body of knowledge on ostensive grounds (thus one would not *predict* that a body is in equilibrium, when one can *see* that it is in equilibrium), and perhaps on other pragmatic considerations as well. But despite the fact that these considerations are involved in determining whether or not a statement in a given context is to be regarded as a prediction, the crucial core remains the deductive relation between that statement and the body of knowledge built around the formal system.

The question of explanation is somewhat more knotty, partly because there are more important pragmatic considerations to be taken into account. Thus one generally has explanation only in answer to some doubt or question. But the general approach remains the same: we have a rational corpus or body of knowledge, which is built on the framework provided by our formal system, and which contains a number of other epistemologically acceptable statements phrased in the same vocabulary. Among these statements is a set that describes a particular

[234]

situation; this time, however, the description is complete: all of the forces, distance, etc., and the state of equilibrium, are specified. But one of these statements is singled out as demanding explanation, Explanation is provided by showing, by deduction, that a rational corpus just like the one in question, but which does not contain the questionable statement, would entail the questionable statement. Thus: How can that little boy with the crowbar cause that five-hundred-pound rock to move? We must first fill in the details, which may even be included in the question: the crowbar is 6 feet long, and the fulcrum is five inches from the end where the rock is, and the boy is pushing down with a force of fifty pounds. Delete "the bar is not in equilibrium" from the rational corpus; and it will be possible to deduce "the bar is not in equilibrium" from the rest of the statements of the rational corpus.

Explanation in this sense is relative; it is relative to the formal system that provides the framework for the question or doubt or curiosity. Any statement in the rational corpus, including quite general ones expressing universal laws, may be doubted; and may be *explained* by being shown to be consequences of the rest of the body of knowledge. This is not so, of course, of the axioms of a particular formalization; the formal system does not provide a framework within which its own axioms can be explained. But this is not unreasonable, or even surprising: it has long been recognized that the *first principles* of explanation of any body of knowledge or belief themselves cannot be explained within the framework of which they are the first principles of explanation.

The heliocentric theory of the solar system provides an explanation of the principal motions of the planets, but no explanation of why the solar system should be heliocentric. Newton's laws explain why the solar system should be heliocentric, but not why the attraction between any two bodies should be proportional to the product of their masses, and inversely proportional to the square of the distance between them. There is nothing profound or mysterious in any sense, theological or otherwise, in the inexplicability of the first principles; it is like the fact that every ladder has one top rung.

We can, of course, proceed to broader frameworks and more powerful formal systems. We can do this in the case of prediction, just as in the case of explanation. We can find an explanation of our axioms of linear statics by proceeding to a general theory of dynamics, and showing that in that general theory, these particular statements (the axioms of linear statics) are simply logical consequences of the axioms of the larger system. In a precisely similar vein, predictions may be statements of great generality: thus a theoretical framework may, together with the rest of the statements that constitute a body of knowledge, entail a universal generalization; this statement, then, is a prediction in just the above sense. (No essential restriction was made concerning the ostensiveness of a prediction.) Like any other prediction, particularly like any quantitative prediction, it may then be confirmed, refuted, or relegated to the limbo of the undecided.

It is interesting to observe that in this theory of linear statics, which is in many ways a kind of paradigm of physical formal systems, we have not yet introduced the concept of causality. We have not needed to. And yet the concept is one that can plausibly and sensibly be applied to situations describable in the framework of this theory: "A light force of 5 lb. applied to the end of this long bar will cause that boulder to move." It seems that the concept of causality is not involved in the theory itself, but is perhaps a metalinguistic concept that can be used to describe the role that certain statements play in the system, or in the rational corpus incorporating it. There is an element of necessity involved: the boulder not merely *will* move, when the pressure is exerted on the lever, but it *must* move. As in the case of explanation, the characteristic in question lies in the relationship between the statement at issue, and the axioms of the formal system that is serving as the framework. We can infer from those axioms, in the context of the rational corpus built around it, the conditional: "If pressure is exerted, the boulder will move." The conditional itself makes no assertion about causality; it embodies no mysterious, invisible, causal relation. But we say that it is necessarily true, relative to the formal system, because it follows logically from the axioms of that system, taken together with other (boundary condition) statements that we may take to be part of our body of knowledge. Although it is necessarily true, relative to this system of knowledge, it is not true with logical necessity (the axioms of the system are not logically true); and therefore (we say) with *causal* necessity. Given the truth (mere factual truth) of the axioms, the truth of the conditional follows. Note that the axioms themselves may be given a similar necessity, in a broader context, by being deduced (within a formal system) from more general principles.

It is questionable to what extent the concept of causality is of scientific interest. It does play an interesting philosophical role, in connection with the concepts of freedom and necessity; and as a universal principle it can perhaps be given an intelligible meaning. But at this point we have left the philosophy of science and entered the realm of metaphysics.

IV

The second partial system of physics we shall deal with, thermodynamics, is a more interesting and more general topic than linear statics, but it is much farther removed from ordinary experience. It is out of the question to present even a fragment which is self-sufficient, as we have done in the case of linear statics. In what follows, no attempt is made at all to trace to their ostensive roots the various concepts that occur.

Temperature, pressure, and *volume,* are basic quantities of thermodynamics, which we have already encountered in one form or another. Temperature and volume have been discussed in connection with measurement as typical quantitative terms; pressure, in units of force divided by units of area (as pounds-force per square inch), is definable in terms with which we are already familiar. "Pressure" is also an ordinary language term, in the phrase "exerts more pressure than"; and the quantitative concept may be built up on the basis of this primitive relation. But the quantitative concept of pressure may also be defined in terms of force per unit area from the outset. Pressure, temperature, and volume are certainly observable in an ordinary sense; but they are equally certainly not purely ostensive terms. They are, in the way outlined earlier, directly related to the highly (but not purely) ostensive relations: "longer than", "has greater force than", and "warmer than".

The basic concepts of thermodynamics are heat, energy, and work. Heat is related to temperature in the following way. Heat content is a quantitative term, like length. Unlike length, there is no quasi-ostensive term which serves to define it; "is longer than" is quasi-ostensive, and can give rise to the length predicates; but "has greater heat content" is not even quasi-ostensive. Yet we do have perfectly good experimental tests for changes in heat content; and we can form the abstract concept of heat. A hot body cools down; what is happening? Its heat content is decreasing; what is it losing? It is losing *heat*. Once we have the quantitative concept of temperature, we can measure these changes, and define a standard of heat content: the heat that it takes to raise the temperature of a pound of water from 60 to 61°F (the BTU), or the heat that it takes to heat one gram of water from 14.5 to 15.5°C (the calorie). In the point of fact, we can establish (how?) that it takes just about the *same amount of heat* to raise a pound of water one degree at 33°F, as at 210°F, and this makes the measurement of changes in heat content quite simple—at least for bodies in the range of temperatures between freezing and boiling water.

Note, however, that we have not defined *heat content* explicitly in terms of temperature; we introduce the term "$HC(x)$" for the heat content of a body x (at a certain time) or under certain circumstances or at a certain temperature as a *primitive term*. One of the things that we establish experimentally, is that in most cases, when a given body is at a certain temperature, it has the same heat content. That this is not a meaning postulate seems clear from the fact that there are definite procedures—e.g., heating up water—for establishing the heat content of a body. It is perfectly possible that a given body at t degrees may give up ten calories in cooling one degree from $t°$ to $(t - 1)°$ on one occasion, and may, on another occasion, give up only eight calories (depending perhaps on how quickly the cooling is done). We would say that the heat capacity of the substance has changed. Indeed it is perfectly possible physically for the heat capacity of a substance to change. The heat capacity of a substance that has a crystalline structure depends on the particular form of crystalline structure it

[237]

has, if it can have more than one form, and the heat capacities of such substances may change according to their histories.

Here is another situation in which it might be hard to find a definitive argument for drawing the line between meaning postulates and highly confirmed physical generalizations in one place rather than another. One might plausibly claim that it is a matter of convention that a given substance in a given state has just one given heat content. Evidence for this might be that if we find two samples of a substance that have the same volume and temperature, and are under the same pressure, but have different heat contents, we take this to be adequate grounds for attributing different internal structures or states to the two samples. But our conclusion will be the same whether we take the relation, one state—one heat content, to be empirical or definitional; and I have chosen to regard it as the former, since in the vast majority of cases it is quite straightforwardly testable.

Work is another fundamental concept of thermodynamics. Mechanical work is easy to define: its units are force-times-distance. Since work is defined directly in terms of force and distance, which in turn are based on relations with quasi-ostensive interpretations, it need not be introduced as a primitive term. But again, as in the case of pressure, there is a corresponding ordinary language concept; the point is that the ordinary language concept does not itself give rise to the quantitative concept of work (as the ordinary language concept of length does give rise to quantitative length)—the quantitative concept comes in the first place from the definition.

The fundamental fact of thermodynamics is the interchangeability of heat and work. The basic observation (historically) was that the work put into a closed system, from which no work is gotten out, is precisely proportional to a general rise in temperature of the system, and thus proportional to the change in the heat content of the system. We can even determine the factor of proportionality: 778 foot-pounds (force) of work is equivalent to 1 BTU, for example.

This suggests a further measure of abstraction: in ordinary talk, energy is clearly required to perform work; if heat and work are related, why not regard them both as forms of (a technical concept) energy? Thus we introduce the quantitative function U as a primitive concept in the system of thermodynamics, representing internal energy. There must be a certain amount of energy in a system, if we are to get work out of it. According to the particular way in which the energy of a system (a horse, a man, a waterfall) is tapped, and according to where we draw the line between the inside of the system and the outside of the system, the energy may be removed from the system as heat or as work or as any combination of heat and work, or put into the system in any of these ways.

These vague thoughts about heat and energy and work, may now be given precise formulation as follows.

We can measure changes in heat content, but not (initially or naturally) absolute heat content. The same is true of this hypothetical abstract quantity,

[238]

energy: let us speak of the changes of the internal energy of a system. We can then express the first great conservation law as follows: The increase of internal energy of a system is equal to the heat input less the work output. This is the principle of the conservation of energy.

In symbols we express it as follows:

ΔU increase in internal energy;

ΔQ heat input to the system;

ΔW work performed by the system.

(1) $\Delta U = \Delta Q - \Delta W.$

This is one of those equations, like "$f = ma$", which has sometimes been regarded as merely providing an explication or analysis of what we mean by certain terms. Here it is easy to look at this equation as providing a definition of internal energy, for both quantity of heat and quantity of work can be initially and independently measured; the basic way we have of determining the change of internal energy of a quantity of matter is to measure heat input or work output or both. Even if this equation were simply an implicit (indeed, explicit!) definition of change in internal energy it would be useful: it would be useful, convenient, neat, to have a single term for that quantity of which both heat and work are varieties. Even as a definition, the equation expresses the interchangeability of heat and work, which is an important physical fact. It expresses this fact, but does not assert it; we could write this equation whether or not we knew of any quantitative connection between calories and joules (units of work), though of course it is meaningless unless we can express heat and work in the same units, and thus add and subtract quantities ΔQ and ΔW.

But this is not the whole story, for the equation does also serve a very definite empirical function, in view of another fact: that the circumstances, the general state and location, of a quantity of matter, determine its internal energy. Thus, in general, if you take a quantity of matter, put it through all sorts of operations and changes and movements and what-have-you, and bring it back to *just where it was before*, its internal energy is the same. This is simply to say that we regard the internal energy of the substance as a quantity which depends on the state of the substance. Is this analytic? A case could be made for an affirmative answer, but we shall regard this fact as empirical, for the following reason: a special case of the general assertion that the internal energy of a system depends only on the state of the system is that (when $\Delta W = 0$, i.e., when there is no external work performed either on or by the system) the heat content depends only on the state of the system. We have already chosen to regard this latter statement as an empirical generalization, and since it is simply a consequence of the former, we may reasonably regard the former as having empirical content too.

Another factor involved in the usefulness of this law is its generality. It applies to all quantities of matter, always. This is to say that we can apply it to any piece of matter we want to apply it to, and that in turn means that we can apply it to any part of a system. Consider, for example, a steam engine raising a weight. Equation (1) applies to the whole system, of course; at the same time it applies to each part, however we slice that part off. Consider the weight: it is simply moving up, away from the surface of the earth, and not changing its temperature at all. Its internal energy is increasing ($\Delta U > 0$), and work is being done on it ($-\Delta W > 0$, or $\Delta W < 0$). Consider the steam engine itself; it changes its state cyclically, but it is in the same state at a given point in one cycle as it is at the same point in any other cycle. Between one cycle and the next, a certain amount of heat has gone in (with the fresh steam from the boiler), a lesser quantity has gone out (as exhaust steam), and a certain quantity of mechanical work has been performed (the difference in energy content). Consider the boiler: a certain amount of heat has gone in (from the firebox), a certain amount of heat has left as the heat content of outgoing steam, but (essentially) no work is being done by the boiler.

The terms that appear in the first law, all, therefore, have connections with observable quantities: ΔQ and ΔW have obvious direct connections with ostensively definable magnitudes. ΔU, in general, is only connected through ΔW and ΔQ to ostensive predicates; but in a special case of very great importance it has its own connection; namely, when $\Delta U = 0$, the substance is in the same state, and conversely, where "same state" refers to the sameness of measurable characteristics: location relative to other bodies, temperature, physical state of components (gas, solid, liquid), proportions in the various states (gas, liquid, one form or another of solid), pressure and volume.

In some cases—for example, in the case of solids which may exist in more than one crystalline phase—the initial evidence for the existence of different states which are superficially the same was the apparent failure of eq. (1). Thus ice at certain temperatures and pressures, may exist in either of two crystalline forms; and the initial evidence for this is that at these special temperatures and pressures, heat may be absorbed which does not change the temperature of the solid ice. Since we are very interested in having this useful and important relation hold, and since, in any event, the heat is recoverable (we can remove heat without changing the temperature of the substance, too), we may simply postulate that there is some unobserved (we surely need not postulate that it is in principle unobservable!) mechanism in the substance for absorbing and storing internal energy. When we have a well articulated theory of atomic structure, we can find an explanation for this fact, namely, that under different pressures and temperatures, different degrees of freedom of vibration are available to the molecules in question, and that in virtue of these differences, different molecular arrangements are possible, or different crystalline structures. And this explanation can receive quite direct empirical verification through X-ray diffraction experiments.

[240]

This is philosophically interesting, as providing an illustration of the principle that we can and do offer explanations which, considered purely formally, are indistinguishable from *ad hoc* explanations. But we do it in order to preserve a large over-riding generalization, equation (1), which has a host of important empirical consequences; we do not do it out of sheer whimsy. Here, as in earlier illustrations, we find that it is only in the context of a fairly full and well developed formal system that we can make distinctions between humbug (e.g., an *ad hoc* explanation of the sleep-inducing property of opium as being due to its dormative power) and good science (e.g., the *ad hoc* explanation of heat absorption of a solid exhibiting no rise in temperature as being due to some internal, unobserved, change of state).

The second law of thermodynamics is one of the most interesting in modern science. Shortly, it will serve as our introduction to a statistical view of nature which has become increasingly pervasive in recent years. The idea of the second law of thermodynamics can be expressed simply enough: it is merely that heat does not flow uphill. But there are consequences of this law that have nothing to do with heat, and in any event, we would like to have a more quantitative and explicit formulation. (After all, heat, like water, can be *made* to flow uphill, as it is in a refrigerator.) For this more precise formulation, we need the concept of entropy. Entropy is not a primitive concept, but one which is explicitly defined. Unfortunately, the definition is not one that can be given except in mathematical terms. Consider any system; we want to define its change of entropy, ΔS, in passing from State I to State II:

$$\Delta S = \int_{I}^{II} \frac{dQ}{T},$$

where the integration is performed along a path consisting of equilibrium states. Thus to calculate the change of entropy that occurs when a compressed air cylinder bursts in a hermetically sealed room, we must suppose that the equalization of the pressures inside and outside the cylinder takes place, not suddenly and violently, but slowly, as if, for example, a small leak had developed.

With the aid of this defined concept, the second law is stated succinctly as

In any isolated system, the entropy cannot decrease; i.e., $\Delta S \geq 0$, for any change of state of an isolated system.

An equivalent definition of entropy makes use of probability. If w is the probability of the arrangement of molecules in a particular state, the entropy of that state may be defined as

$s = k \ln w$, where k is Boltzmann's constant.

Probability here simply reflects a statistical distribution. We cannot show here that this definition of entropy is equivalent to the preceding one, but we can

[241]

given an application of the definition for the case of a change of volume of an ideal gas, and show that in this particular case the two definitions lead to the same result.

Applying the first definition,

$$\Delta S = \int_{V_1}^{V_2} \frac{dQ}{T}.$$

Since $\Delta U = \Delta Q - \Delta W$, and we are considering a series of equilibrium stages of an ideal gas, the differential change in the internal energy of the gas during a change of volume is 0. Since U does not change, $dU = 0 = dQ - dW$, or $dQ = dW$. But also for an ideal gas, $pV = nRT$, and $dQ = pdV =$

$$\frac{nRT}{V} dV$$

(where n is a measure of the quantity of gas).

Thus,

$$\Delta S = nR \ln \frac{V_2}{V_1} = \int_{V_1}^{V_2} \frac{nRT}{VT} dV$$

Applying the second definition, we must consider what is meant by the phrase "the probability of a particular arrangement of molecules". In a detailed treatment of the subject, this part of the theory would have to be laid out in detail; but whatever the general treatment, we would be led to the following principle for an ideal gas: the probability that a particular molecule is in a particular portion of space will be proportional to the volume of that portion of space. Furthermore, the ideality of the gas insures that the presence of a molecule in one element of volume will be statistically independent of the location of the other molecules in the total volume, so that the probability that a given molecule will be in volume element V is cV (c being merely the constant of proportionality). In view of the statistical independence, the probability that two particular molecules will be both in V is simply the product of the probabilities that each of the molecules will be there, i.e., $(cV)^2$, where c is the proportionality constant. And the probability that N given molecules will be in V is $(cV)^N$. Thus, according to the second definition, $S = kN (\ln c + \ln v)$, and

$$\Delta S = kN(\ln c + \ln V_2) - kN(\ln c + \ln V_1)$$
$$= kN \ln (V_2/V_1).$$

Since we have the relation between k, n, N, and R: $kN = nR$, this yields, as above,

$$\Delta S = nR \ln (V_2/V_1).$$

On this definition of entropy the second law of thermodynamics turns out to have a merely probabilistic character: what is asserted is not that entropy always

[242]

increases, but merely that processes proceed in the direction of greater probability. What is the connection between this probabilistic concept and the concept
of entropy previously introduced? To arrive at the statistical mechanical basis
of thermodynamic principles, we define a set of hypothetical states, subject to
certain constraints, and calculate probability distributions of characteristics
among these states. There is nothing novel about this from the point of view of
our discussion of probability; when we discuss the probability of *a* (micro) state
in the abstract, the randomness criteria are naturally met (they are insured by the
use of the indefinite article), and to make the probability assertion is just to
assert the corresponding statistical statement. When what is at issue is the particular state of a given quantity of gas at a given time, say, again the randomness
requirement is met—simply because we don't ever encounter the improbable
cases in practice—and we always have good reason to accept statements describing
the probable cases. So in fact we are directed to accept just the same statements on
the dynamical approach to thermodynamics as we are on the statistical approach.
The advantage of the statistical interpretation is simply that it leads to explanations of phenomena (e.g., Brownian motion) that the dynamical approach
does not explain.

BIBLIOGRAPHICAL NOTES TO CHAPTER 10

The most readable and the best general introduction to the philosophy of
physics is Rudolf Carnap's *Philosophical Foundations of Physics* (New York:
Basic Books, 1966). Its most penetrating predecessor is Norman Campbell's,
Physics: The Elements (Cambridge, England: Cambridge, 1920); reprinted as
Foundations of Science (New York: Dover Publications, 1957). A general book
on the philosophy of science which is oriented strongly toward physics is Philipp
Frank, *Philosophy of Science* (Englewood Cliffs, N.J.: Prentice-Hall, 1956).

The physicist P. W. Bridgeman, has had a deep effect on the philosophy of
science in general through a number of publications. The earliest and most in-
fluential is *The Logic of Modern Physics* (New York: Macmillan, 1928). It is there
that the doctrine of *operationism* is first developed. Some of Bridgeman's other
books are: *The Nature of Thermodynamics* (Cambridge, Mass: Harvard University Press, 1941); *The Nature of Physical Theory* (Princeton, N.J.: Princeton
University Press, 1936); and *The Way Things Are* (Cambridge, Mass.: Harvard
University Press, 1959).

There are two fine small books on the two most significant recent events in
physics, both by Hans Reichenbach. *From Copernicus to Einstein* (New York:
Philosophical Library, 1942), deals with the development of relativity theory;
Philosophic Foundations of Quantum Mechanics (Berkely, California: University
of California Press, 1948) is concerned not so much with the development as
with the present state of the art.

The fascinating problem of the connection between the second law of thermo-dynamics and the direction of time is also pursued by Hans Reichenbach, in *The Direction of Time* (Berkeley, California: University of California Press, 1956). The same topic is discussed by Adolf Grünbaum, *Philosophical Problems of Space and Time* (New York: Alfred Knopf, 1963).

Chapter 11

PSYCHOLOGY

I

Psychology illustrates a number of the problems of the philosophy of science in particularly clear cut form. It is a young science, and it has not yet developed a theoretical terminology which can withstand the introduction of modifications of theory, or new theories, or even divergent points of view. Whatever cognitive novelty each advance of psychological theory provides, it is sure to bring with it terminological novelty. Furthermore, this terminology varies through the whole spectrum of ostensiveness, from relatively pure ostensive terms such as "up" and "rat", to terms far removed from their ostensive roots, like "libido" and "cathexis". (Some terms, indeed, may not even have ostensive roots; or so some critics maintain.) The theories themselves run the whole gamut of abstraction, from theories which are little more than transcriptions of observations (e.g.,

[245]

resistance to extinction as a function of amount of reward), to theories that are so rarified as to have only the most tenuous connection with observation (the relation between the death wish and the pleasure principle). Experimental techniques are correspondingly varied, ranging from observations of effects on particular forms of behavior caused by stimulation by implanted electrodes, to projective testing of individual human subjects, to the general consideration of broad classes of literary and mythopoeic sources as clues to the nature of a collective human unconscious.

We shall deal here with fragments of two formal systems that are in many ways near the ends of these spectra, Learning Theory, and Psychoanalysis. The specimen of learning theory that follows is not a real one; it is considerably simplified and somewhat neater than the kind of theory presented by Hull in his classic *A Behavior System* (Yale University Press, 1952), for example. But it will nevertheless serve our purposes for the theoretical terms that occur in it are reasonably close in meaning to those employed in more sophisticated systems. It is borrowed from Mandler and Kessen, who use it for illustrative purposes in *The Language of Psychology* (New York, 1959).

Let us begin by considering informally the subject matter of the formal theory. We are interested in general in the phenomenon of learning. We are interested in how college students learn French, in how kindergarten children learn to count, how people learn to solve mathematical problems; we are also interested in learning what we can about how animals learn things, how dogs learn to come when they're called, how rats learn to avoid traps. We are interested in these latter things, not only because they are interesting in their own right, but because they may help to throw light on human learning. Furthermore, it is much easier and less expensive to study the learning behavior of animals under laboratory conditions than it is to study the behavior of people under similar conditions.

One of the approaches to the study of learning, then, is to set up a laboratory-ful of white rats, and to examine their behavior in certain well-defined learning situations. The typical learning situation is this: there is a maze, with a reward (e.g., food) at the end of it. A rat is put in the entrance to the maze. The first time he is put there, he must find his way to the end by trial and error. On subsequent occasions, he eliminates some of his errors; eventually, he learns the maze, in the sense that he can proceed directly from the beginning to the end, without running up any blind alleys or making any wrongs turns.

What aspects of this behavior do we want to observe? There are any number of aspects that might interest us; but what we are seeking are those aspects that are related somehow to his learning the maze. One idea we might come up with pretty quickly is that a hungry rat will learn his way through the maze faster than a rat not so hungry. Even this simple idea involves a number of concepts of different degrees of ostensiveness. We generally base our knowledge that a rat is hungry on our knowledge of how recently he has been well fed. The expression

[246]

"...has just been fed" has (despite its modicum of vagueness) a high degree of interpersonal uniformity, as has "...has not been fed for 24 hours". These expressions serve to give interpersonal uniformity to certain applications of expressions like "... is not hungry", and "... is hungry", which are themselves rather more theoretical. Note that we do not want to *define* hunger in terms of food intake; not only does it make perfectly good sense to say, "I haven't eaten for three days, and (oddly), I'm still not hungry," but we want to be able to say things like, "Drug X stimulates the appetite—after an injection of X a rat will be hungry even though he has just had a large meal." Furthermore, we want to make an analogous distinction between the disposition of the rat to learn the maze effectively, which is a relatively theoretical concept, and indicators of that disposition, such as the number of errors he makes in running the maze, or the speed with which he runs it. The former we will call response strength, the latter we will call performance. In general, of course, the greater the response strength, the better the performance, just as in general, the longer it has been since you have eaten, the hungrier you are. But we no more wish to *define* response strength as performance than to define hunger in terms of deprivation.

There are obviously other factors than hunger that bear on the performance a rat turns in on a given trial. One of them is habit: if he is used to the maze, and has had a number of chances to find his way through it before, then he will find it easier to perform well than if the maze is new to him. "Habit" is a somewhat theoretical term, but one indication of it is the number of preceding trials he has made in the same maze. Another factor is represented by the reward he expects to find at the end of the maze.

It is not sufficient, of course, merely to speculate in this manner. Not only do we wish to put our speculations to the test (they might, after all, be wrong), but we might hope to replace these relatively vague concepts by more precise ones, and perhaps even by quantitative concepts, and to develop a theory that will indicate how important these factors are under particular circumstances, and how they are to be combined. All of this is facilitated by adopting a relatively formal approach.

The intuitive meanings offered in the right-hand column of the table on page 248 are intended to be suggestive only; they do not represent the interpretation of the expressions of the formal system, but are only a heuristic aid to the understanding of the meaning postulates and axioms that follow. The official interpretation (or rather interpretations, since there will be two of them) will be postponed until after the entire calculus has been presented.

Meaning Postulates: (In the following meaning postulates, we use "$\overset{e}{\vee}$" to serve as a sentential connective expressing exclusive disjunction.)

MP1 $(x)(y)((T(x)\ \&\ T(y)) \supset (K(x)\ _K{>}\ K(y)\ \overset{e}{\vee}\ K(y)\ _K{>}\ K(x)\ \overset{e}{\vee}$
    $K(x) = K(y)))$
   $(x)(y)(z)((K(x)\ _K{>}\ K(y)\ \&\ K(y)\ _K{>}\ K(z)) \supset K(x)\ _K{>}\ K(z))$

Vocabulary	Formation Rule (by example)	Intuitive Meaning
T	$T(x)$	x is a trial.
A	$A(x)$	part of response strength on trial x due to incentive
B	$B(x)$	part of response strength on trial x due to habit
C	$C(x)$	part of response strength on trial x due to drive
K	$K(x)$	reward on trial x
L	$L(x)$	number of trials preceding trial x
M	$M(x)$	maintenance ration preceding trial x
R	$y \in R$	y is a degree of response strength
$\circ$	$z \circ y$	the combination of the degree x and the degree y of response strength
Z	$Z(x)$	quality of performance on trial x
S	$S(x)$	response strength present on trial x
$_R>$	$x _R> y$	x is a greater degree of response than y
$_K>$	$x _K> y$	x is a greater reward than y
$_L>$	$x _L> y$	x is a greater number of preceding trials than y
$_M>$	$x _M> y$	x is a greater pretrial maintenance ration than y
$_S>$	$x _S> y$	x is a greater response strength than y
$_Z>$	$x _Z> y$	x is a higher quality performance than y.

MP2 $(x)(y)((T(x) \ \& \ T(y)) \supset (L(x) \ _L> L(y) \ \overset{e}{\vee} \ L(y) \ _L> L(x) \ \overset{e}{\vee}$
        $L(x) = L(y)))$
     $(x)(y)(z)((L(x) \ _L> L(y) \ \& \ L(y) \ _L> L(z)) \supset L(x) \ _L> L(z))$

MP3 $(x)(y)((T(x) \ \& \ T(y)) \supset (M(x) \ _M> M(y) \ \overset{e}{\vee} \ M(y) \ _M> M(x) \ \overset{e}{\vee}$
        $M(x) = M(y)))$
     $(x)(y)(z)((M(x) \ _M> M(y) \ \& \ M(y) \ _M> M(z)) \supset M(x) \ _M> M(z))$

MP4 $(x)(T(x) \supset (A(x) \in R \ \& \ B(x) \in R \ \& \ C(x) \in R))$

MP5 $(x)(y)((x \in R \ \& \ y \in R) \supset x \circ y \in R)$

MP6 $(x)(y)((x \in R \ \& \ y \in R) \supset (x _R> y \ \overset{e}{\vee} \ y _R> x \ \overset{e}{\vee} \ x = y))$
     $(x)(y)(z)((x _R> y \ \& \ y _R> z) \supset x _R> z)$

MP7 $(x)(y)((T(x) \ \& \ T(y)) \supset (S(x)_S > S(y) \ \overset{e}{\vee} \ S(y) _S> S(x) \ \overset{e}{\vee}$
        $S(x) = S(y)))$
     $(x)(y)(z)((S(x) \ _S> S(y) \ \& \ S(y) \ _S> S(z)) \supset S(x) \ _S> S(z))$

MP8 $(x)(y)((x \in R \ \& \ y \in R) \supset x \circ y = y \circ x)$

MP 9 $(x)(y)(z)((x \in R \ \& \ y \in R \ \& \ z \in R) \supset x \circ (y \circ z) = (x \circ y) \circ z)$

MP10 $(x)(y)((x \in R \ \& \ y \in R) \supset x \circ y_R > y)$

MP11 $(x)(y)((T(x) \ \& \ T(y)) \supset (Z(x)_z > Z(y) \ \overset{e}{\lor} \ Z(y)_z > Z(x) \ \overset{e}{\lor}$
                 $Z(x) = Z(y)))$
              $(x)(y)(z)((Z(x)_z > Z(y) \ \& \ Z(y)_z > Z(z)) \supset Z(x)_z > Z(z))$

AXIOMS:

I1 $(x)(y)((T(x) \ \& \ T(y)) \supset [(K(x)_K > K(y)) \supset (A(x)_R > A(y))])$

I2 $(x)(y)((T(x) \ \& \ T(y)) \supset [(L(x)_L > L(y)) \supset (B(x)_R > B(y))])$

Definition: D1 $C(x) <_R C(y)$ for $C(x) \neq C(y) \ \& \ \sim(C(x)_R > C(y))$.

I3 $(x)(y)((T(x) \ \& \ T(y)) \supset [(M(x)_M > M(y)) \supset (C(x)_R < C(y))])$

I4a $(x)(y)((T(x) \ \& \ T(y)) \supset [(A(x) \circ B(x)_R > A(y) \circ B(y)) \supset$
           $S(x)_S > S(y)])$

I4b $(x)(y)((T(x) \ \& \ T(y)) \supset [(A(x) \circ C(x)_R > A(y) \circ C(y)) \supset$
           $S(x)_S > S(y)])$

I4c $(x)(y)((T(x) \ \& \ T(y)) \supset [(B(x) \circ C(x)_R > B(y) \circ C(y)) \supset$
           $S(x)_S > S(y)])$

I4d $(x)(y)((T(x) \ \& \ T(y)) \supset [(A(x) \circ B(x)) \circ C(x)_R >$
           $(A(y) \circ B(y)) \circ C(y) \supset S(x)_S > S(y)])$

I5 $(x(y)((T(x) \ \& \ T(y)) \supset [S(x)_S > S(y) \supset Z(x)_z > Z(y)]).$

I shall state only three rather simple theorems. They do have content which is interesting; it will be discussed when we discuss the interpretation of this calculus.

THEOREMS:

T1 $(x)(y)((T(x) \ \& \ T(y)) \supset [\sim(S(x)_S > S(y)) \supset (A(y) \circ B(y)_R >$
           $A(x) \circ B(x) \lor A(y) \circ B(y) = A(x) \circ B(x))])$

T2 $(x)(y)((T(x) \ \& \ T(y)) \supset [S(x) = S(y) \supset B(x) \circ C(x) \circ = B(y) \circ C(y)])$

T3 $(x)(y)((T(x) \ \& \ T(y)) \supset [S(y)_S > S(x) \supset (A(y) \circ B(y)_R > A(x) \circ B(x)$
           $\lor A(y) \circ B(y) = A(x) \circ B(x))]).$

There are two interpretations of this calculus which are consonant with the intuitive meanings of the terms of the primitive vocabulary. Both interpretations are quantitative in the sense that they take the theory to embody assertions of relative magnitude. The first interpretation goes only this far. But the second interpretation goes farther; it supposes that the functions of the theory (A,K, etc.) are fully quantitative in the sense that they can be understood to have values that can be expressed in terms of a pure number multiplying a unit. In the latter interpretation, it will make sense to speak of adding and multiplying these entities, while in the former it will not.

"T"—a predicate characterizing the objects of our inquiry: trials or tests. "$T(x)$" means that x is a trial. "T" is, in this context, a purely ostensive term.

[249]

It delimits the field of inquiry. We are talking about "*this* sort of thing", not "that sort of thing". The boundaries may be a little vague, and may vary from worker to worker in the same field; "*T*" may be explained verbally, or exhibited. But even the verbal explanation will be essentially ostensive, in the sense that it ends with "etc.", or "and similar situations". The function of the verbal explanation is to call certain types of situations to mind, in lieu of exhibiting them to the senses. Our ordinary, largely ostensive, language allows instances of the appropriate types of situations to be presented to the mind.

"*R*"—a term denoting a set of objects representing *amounts* of push or response strength. "*R*" is a purely theoretical term, like the abstract "length". We may think of the elements of R as representing measures of some physiological characteristic, additive in some appropriate sense, which is directly related to actual response strength. The actual response strength on a given trial x is $S(x)$; this in turn must be distinguished from the actual performance on the given trial, $Z(x)$. The elements of R represent states of the organism, and contain no implicit reference to any particular trial. But presumably the state of the organism will be some function of habit and incentive and drive operating at a given time; and also presumably the state of the organism will determine (roughly) the strength of the response in given circumstances.

"*A*"—a function-term; the function maps trials into a set of objects denoted by R. "$A(x)$" stands for the amount of *push* operating in trial x due to incentive.

"*B*"—a function-term; the function maps trials into R. "$B(x)$" stands for the amount of *push* operating in trial x due to *habit*.

"*C*"—a function-term; the function maps trials into R. "$C(x)$" stands for the amount of *push* operating in trial x due to *drive*.

"∘" represents a combining operation on the elements of R. It is stipulated to be symmetrical and associative (MP5, MP8, MP9).

"$_R >$ " is an ordering relation holding for elements of R (MP6). It is related to the combining operation by MP10.

The set of elements, R, the combining operation on these elements, ∘, and the ordering relation $_R >$, constitute a purely theoretical structure. They do not represent any observable qualities, quantities, or phenomena. They are *indirectly* related to more ostensive terms through the whole structure of the system. Actual performance, Z, is taken to be relatively ostensive; it is the ostensive expression of somewhat theoretical property, actual response strength, S. It is S, in turn, that is related to R. It is perfectly possible that in some different formal systems, these terms ("R", "∘", and "$_R >$ ") could be more directly related to observation; thus we might hope to have a formal system, which includes the one under discussion as a part, in which "$_R >$ " is explained directly in terms of relative nerve

[250]

potentials, "∘" represents a simple sum of electrical potentials, and the elements of R are themselves simply measurable nerve potentials. But this possibility has nothing to do with the legitimacy of the concepts in the present system in which nerve potential plays no role at all.

The functions A, B, and C provide a connection between the entities with which we are directly concerned (the trials or tests, the x's such that $T(x)$), and this theoretical structure involving "R", "$_R>$", and "∘". The connection is embodied in MP4 which says that the range of each of these functions is R. They are functions or mappings from individual trials, into the set R. They are still theoretical expressions: we cannot *observe* that A has a certain value on a certain trial. We might be able to know something similar to this in the case of experiments on ourselves; we can tell something, surely, about our own motives, incentives, and habits. We can even tell something about the motives, incentives, and habits of other people. But when it comes to rats in boxes, it is likely to be very difficult for people to achieve good agreement in the use of these terms, whereas it will be much easier for them to agree both on the application of terms of the next degree of ostensiveness, and on the meaning relations that hold between these terms and the terms reflecting motives and incentives and so on.

These meaning relations are embodied in the first three axioms, I1, I2, and I3, which stipulate that certain relations hold between the functions A, B, and C, and the more ostensive functions, K, L, and M. Although these axioms express meaning relations, I have called them "axioms" because they are so classified in the original system.

"K" denotes a function mapping trials into reward; i.e., $K(x)$ is the reward on trial x. "K" is (in this context) purely ostensive.

"$_K>$" is a relation among rewards; it is stipulated (MP1) that rewards are simply ordered by this relation, i.e., that no two rewards are unrelated to each other. "$_K>$" is a somewhat theoretical relation, like "longer than", it is ostensive in that there are situations in which we can simply see that the relation holds: e.g., when it is a question of one food pellet or two food pellets, one pat on the head or two pats on the head. But it is not at all obvious or clear that one pat on the head is more of a reward than two food pellets, or even that they are comparable at all, in any ostensive sense. But we are free to make words mean what we want them to mean, and in the context of this formal system, we *stipulate* that of any two rewards either the first is greater than the second, the second is greater than the first, or they are the same. (Note that for "the same" we can use ordinary identity; but the ordering relation is different from that which holds for the objects of R, for example, and certainly and obviously different from the ordering relation that holds for real numbers.)

"L" represents another function, one that maps trials into the number of preceding trials (i.e., the number of trials that precedes the given trial). The function-term "L" is not purely ostensive, for its values are numbers (natural numbers)

[251]

and people, after all, can miscount. The values of the function, the numbers, must obey the usual arithmetical rules. But in the context of this formal system, we do not need to proceed to any more ostensive or more basic expressions; we are perfectly free, in virtue of the high interpersonal uniformity of usage of number terms, to take this function as satisfactorily ostensive.

" $_L>$ " is the corresponding relation term. Here it is just the numerical, arithmetical, *greater than*. It was given the subscript "L" in the statement of the terms of the system, for it is only in virtue of the interpretation of the function L, as one that has as its values natural numbers, that the arithmetical " $>$ " holds among the values of L. This interpretation of L renders MP2, the meaning postulate that stipulates that " $_L>$ " induces a simple ordering among the values of the function L, a purely arithmetical truth. Given this interpretation of L we do not need to have MP2 as a meaning postulate of our system.

" M " denotes a function mapping trials into the amount of food in the maintenance ration preceding the trial. Again, we have a purely ostensive expression; the amount of food and kinds of food are what they are.

" $_M>$ " expresses a relation among the values of the function M. As in the case of K, these values are not simply and obviously ordered. Two ounces of pellets are more than one ounce of the same kind of pellets; but there is no obvious and ostensive relation of more and less between a pound of grain and ten pounds of hay. As in the case of the relation $_K>$, then, we must stipulate that the relation $_M>$ induces a simple ordering on the values of the function M. Also as in the case of K, we can, in experimental practice, simplify things by using always the same kind of food. In that case, weights provide a measure of the maintenance ration. But the stipulation that maintenance rations are comparable does not restrict us to this particularly simple experimental case; and so we express that stipulation perfectly generally in MP3.

The first three axioms, together with the first four meaning postulates, provide a connection between relatively ostensive expressions (function-terms, operation-terms, class-terms, and predicates) and the more abstract expressions of the theory. The connection is one way: it is embodied in conditionals whose antecedents involve the more ostensive terms, and whose consequents involve the more theoretical terms. So far we have no connection between the abstract theoretical structure involving "R", "$_R>$", and "$\circ$", and any observable consequences.

This connection, the descending connection from the lofty theory to the mundane sphere, is provided by the interpretations of the remaining two expressions.

" S " is a function-term; S is a function mapping trials into response strength. Like A and B and C, it is a theoretical function; i.e., it maps trials into a set of entities which are not taken to be directly observable or ostensive. Again, a case could be made for the introspective ostensiveness of response strength; and to

[252]

some extent for its ostensiveness as applied to other people (how else would we learn to apply it to our own responses?); but we cannot apply the notion of response strength to animals with any respectable degree of interpersonal uniformity, and so we introduce it in this context as a *theoretical* term, related by meaning postulates to more directly observable phenomena.

The elements of the range of S, the entities that the function S takes for its values, are simply ordered by the relation $_S>$, just as those of ranges of the other functions are ordered by their respective relations. This is a matter of stipulation (as it is in the case of the functions A, B, and C), and is expressed in Axiom I5, which, like axioms I1–I3, might better be considered a meaning postulate.

Finally, Z is a function from trials into some indicator of response strength, such as speed running down a maze, or the number of errors made prior to making the correct response. Z is a function whose values can be observed; it is like K, L, and M (depending on the particular form it takes), more or less ostensive. By the same token, depending on the particular nature of the function Z, MP11 either expresses the stipulated simple ordering of the entities into which the trials are mapped by the function Z, or else (e.g., if Z maps trials into periods of time, say, or numbers of errors) expresses a logical or physical fact.

To summarize, we have on the most ostensive level the original predicate characterizing the subject matter with which we are dealing, T; we have the four functions, K, L, M, Z, which take elements of T into elements of some range of "observable" properties; and we have the four corresponding order relations, $_K>$, $_L>$, $_M>$, $_Z>$. These functions may or may not be ostensively defined in any absolute sense. For example, if M represents grams of food per day in the maintenance relation, to observe M requires the performance of an experiment—i.e., weighing out the food. What is then ostensive in the most absolute sense is that a needle (of a weighing balance) is motionless. But we have no need to graft a theory of weights and measuring onto our psychological theory in order to use such a function as M. Similarly, even if the order relations are as directly ostensively definable as can be, we will nevertheless be free to limit this ostensiveness by adopting the meaning postulates that insure that these relations *do* impose an *order* on the elements they relate.

It suffices for our purposes in constructing this formal system to take the relatively ostensive base to be whatever satisfies these criteria: (1) that statements involving these expressions (T, K, L, M, Z, $_K>$, $_L>$, $_M>$, $_Z>$) be statements about which it is very easy to arrive at interpersonally uniform judgements; and (2) that the elementary meaning postulates concerning these terms (MP1, 2, 3, and 11) be satisfied.

On the next level, we have purely theoretical expressions, A, B, C, and S, that are directly related to these highly ostensive expressions; Axioms I1, I2, I3, and I5 provide this connection. The only direct connection that these terms have with our experience is through the mediation of the more ostensive terms just discussed. These functions have as their values the elements of a common range R, according to MP4.

R is on the third and final level; here there is no direct ostensive connection at all, but only an indirect connection, through the mediation of the intermediate terms, A, B, C, and S, down to the ostensive terms K, L, M, and E. The operation $\circ$ and the ordering relation $_R>$ have a certain semantic structure, embodied in the meaning postulates MP5, 6, 8, 9, 10, but otherwise their connection with empirical facts occurs through the agency of the most empirical postulates, 4a—4d. The structure of the purely theoretical set of entities, R, represents the empirical content of the theory.

Before proceeding to examine the next interpretation of the primitive terms of this calculus, let us try to answer a question that may have popped up in the mind of the inquisitive student. He will have observed (or this may be taken as an exercise) that it is easy to construct an alternative form of the calculus in which the primitive terms "A", "B", "C", and "S", and the corresponding relational terms "$_R>$" and "$_S>$", do not appear. Why bother then with these intermediate terms?

There are several answers. One is that the calculus would become simpler in the sense that it does not have as many primitive terms, but it would become more complicated in the sense that the statement of the axioms would be more cumbersome. A part of the content of the system would have to be expressed by an axiom as complicated as,

$$(x)(y)((T(x \ \& \ T(y)) \supset \{[(K(x) \ _K> \ K(y)) \ \& \ (L(x) \ _L> \ L(y))] \supset Z(x) \ _Z> \ Z(y)\}).$$

Furthermore, there would need to be a greater total number of axioms. If there were a number of distinct measures of response strength S, the axioms would become very complicated indeed, as well as very numerous. So from a purely clerical point of view, the introduction of the terms A, B, C, and S yields some benefit, in unification and systematization.

Another answer, and an even better one, is that we introduce these quantities as objects *for* research, as well as results *of* research. Once we have a calculus in which the function A appears, for example, it is natural to want to investigate the range of that function. And if we can find a number of ways of measuring it, or confirming sentences that involve it, then it becomes a theoretical entity in its own right; it is then very difficult to eliminate the terms without a great deal of complication.

Finally, we may have very good reason, in the form of scientific knowledge from some other area (say physiology, in this case) to suppose that some such entities exist. The elements of R, for example, may be taken as quantities measuring a physiological readiness to respond; and we may at some point be able to get at these quantities—to measure them—by paths other than those indicated by the functions A, B, and C. The same is true of response strength, S.

[254]

For the second interpretation, we suppose that all these functions are quantitative. Although I used quantitative illustrations before, there was nothing in the system as it was set up to preclude the use of nonquantitative functions, just so long as the ranges of the functions were simply ordered in some way. Now we suppose that these functions are fully quantitative. We can do this in the simplest way by taking $K(x)$ to be the number of pellets used as reward on trial x, $L(x)$ to be the number of trials that preceded trial x, $M(x)$ to be the number of grams of food in the daily maintenance ration, and $Z(x)$ to be the number of seconds it takes to travel through a specific maze. In a somewhat more complicated way, we can devise scales, applicable to a number of different experimental setups, different mazes, different foods, different rewards, in which case we are taking K, L, M, and Z to be relatively abstract functions.

If we do this, the value of each function can be expressed as a pure number multiplying a unit. Thus

$$K(x) = n \times U_K,$$

where n is a number, an integer, and U_K is the unit of reward.

$$L(x) = r \times U_L,$$

where r is a number and U_L is the unit of number of trials—i.e., one trial.

$$M(x) = s \times U_M,$$

where s is a real number and U_M is the unit of rations—e.g., 1 gram.

$$Z(x) = t \times U_Z,$$

where t is a real number, and U_Z is the unit of response—e.g., 1 sec.

Once we have done this, of course, the relational predicates need no longer be regarded as primitive; we can introduce them by definitions:

$$K(x) \;{}_K{>}\; K(y) \quad \text{if and only if} \quad K(x) = n \times U_K \;\&\; K(y) = m \times U_K \;\&\; m > n.$$

But if we go to the trouble of introducing quantitative functions here, the chances are that we have something more in mind than a calculus of inequalities. We might therefore come to replace the original axioms by stronger ones, so that we can operate with identities rather than with inequalities. In order to do this we need a unit for the abstract quantities R, or degree of physiological readiness to respond, U_R; and for it to be significant, we must also have an independent method of attributing R-quantities to trials. But if we can do all this, we can establish a set of axioms like this:

I 1' $(x)(T(x) \supset A(x) = 100(1 - 10^{-0.04K(x)}))$
I 2' $(x)(T(x) \supset B(x) = 100(1 - 10^{-0.20L(x)}))$
I 3' $(x)(T(x) \supset C(x) = 100 - 100(1 - 10^{-0.35M(x)}))$
I 4' $(x)(T(x) \supset S(x) = A(x) \times B(x) \times C(x))$
I 5' $(x)(T(x) \supset Z(x) = -2 \ln(1 - 0.001S(x))).$

[255]

It will be noted that the units or dimensions embodied in these equations are rather curious; we must suppose that there are implicit in these equations suitable dimensional constants, such as units of R per units of $1 - 10^{-0.04}$ *units of K*. Be that as it may, we now have a theory which is easy to provide quantitative tests for, provided that we can begin with the uniformity of behavior for which we hope. Let us see how we could test the quantitative version of this theory.

To begin with, can we be sure that $Z(x)$ is some function of $L(x)$, $M(x)$, and $K(x)$? It would be nice to hold $L(x)$, $M(x)$, and $K(x)$ constant for a series of trials, and to see if $Z(x)$ remained constant. But since L represents the number of previous trials, we cannot very well hold that constant for a given individual while we perform trials with him. What we must do is to test a number of individuals at the same level of experience, reward, and maintenance. But one immediate problem arises: there will be individual differences. The theory does not purport to provide absolute predications, but only statistical predictions. If we find that a certain group of individuals, at a certain level of maintenance ration, given a certain number of practice runs, and rewarded by a certain amount of food, exhibit response strengths (running times) that are reasonably closely grouped together, then we may suppose the underlying conjecture of the theory is correct. The next step might be to confirm the stability of the learning behavior at other values of L, M, and K. And finally, we might consider whether or to what extent the values of Z and L, M, and K are related as the theory proposes. This is clearly not a simple matter, and must raise many questions. And yet it does not appear to be complicated or inscrutable in principle. Even the fact that the confirmations of the theory, or of the particular forms of the equations that compose part of the theory, must be statistical confirmations, does not in any sense distinguish this sort of theory from Newtonian mechanics: the prediction of a length or a mass or a time can only be confirmed by comparing the statistical distribution of an actual series of measurements with the expected statistical distribution of measurements to which the theory leads. (The theory predicts a length, but the length only predicts a statistical distribution of measurements of length.)

Although this theory is an artificial one, it illustrates something of the nature of the down-to-earth psychological theories, such as learning theory. There is a large literature in psychology that concerns just such formal systems as the one I have presented. Although some terms occur in such systems that do not have direct ostensive interpretations, they often occur only as so-called "intervening variables", like A, B, and C, and S; they represent merely mathematical conveniences, and although the theory would be very much complicated by eschewing them, it might not be regarded as theoretically different. We have here a kind of theory with a minimum of theoretical superstructure. The next theory we shall explore involves a large amount of superstructure together with a relatively inexact and special ostensive base. ("Special" in the sense that the ostensive base

[256]

is accessible only to people with special training and aptitude.) It should be borne in mind, however, that there is no sharp division between the two kinds of theories, and that a search of the literature of psychology would turn up theories of any intermediate degree of abstractness.

III

This time, instead of presenting the formal system more or less cold, as a calculus, we shall begin with a more or less colloquial presentation of the Freudian fragment we are going to consider. We do this for two reasons. First, the Freudian theory, being far removed from ordinary experience and language would be quite totally unintelligible as a calculus; generally the letters used as predicates in a calculus are so suggestive that even though the calculus is presented without its interpretation, it is clear (roughly) what the intended interpretation will be; and this indefinite background knowledge is sufficient to help us in understanding the structure of the calculus. Lacking this kind of familiarity, the Freudian calculus would perhaps be too unintelligible to serve its function.

Second, no formal system develops its calculus first, its interpretation second. We begin with a number of facts; perhaps they are expressed in pretheoretic ordinary language, or perhaps in the language of a current theory; or, possibly even more likely, they are not expressed in language at all, but simply absorbed, understood. Next, some scientific poet creates a vocabulary and a poem about these facts. No more than a conventional poet does he write his vocabulary on a tabula rasa: he uses words that are current, perhaps a few words that are new—but even then, like the poet who writes new words, he bases them on roots that are current in the language as it exists and that carry with them the right connotations. He does not write his theory in strictly novel language; but neither does he write in an ordinary language. The scientist uses metaphor and allegory, just as the poet does; but in science the metaphor and the allegory become crystallized in theory and lose their poetic character: they come to be understood literally, though the new literal meaning is no longer the old literal meaning.

The development of the theory is thus in a way utterly free; it is no more bound by rules and conventions than the development of a poem. Though one can, after the fact, discover certain conventions of style in scientific theorizing as in poem making, these conventions are not binding on either the poet or the scientist; they are useful for the ordinary scientist, but for the innovator, the prophet who sows a new field, they are irrelevant.

There is a condition, however, of applicability in the case of a scientific theory, and of intelligibility in the case of a poem, that must always be satisfied; that is, there must be roots that extend into the region of ordinary experience and ordinary language. Furthermore, in the case of a theory, its acceptability is subject to rules: rules of rationality, or rules of inductive support. These rules are formal and precise; but they are not rules of scientific theorizing; rather, they are rules

[257]

of argument *about* scientific theories, rules of scientific justification. The theory comes before the justification, and for the creation of the theory there are neither recipes nor rules.

In making our systems of knowledge formal, we begin with a body of generalizations and relations, which are more or less informal and vague; our formalization of the not-so-strict formal system with which we begin serves primarily to codify, to make precise, what we already for nonformal, even for noninductive, reasons, have in mind. In the case of Freudian psychoanalytic theory we begin with a world of facts about the mental life and behavior of individuals. There is a broad region of this world in which we know, at least of our selves, how various motives, desires, wishes, intentions, and purposes, function; we can make certain broad regions of our behavior and the behavior of others intelligible in these terms. Jones desires to be respected by his faculty colleagues; this motivates him to sit down and write a learned article. He also desires to make a contribution to his field of knowledge, and this contributes to his motivation. He intends to write a good article; he understands that this requires deep reflection; and so on. When he is asked for an opinion, he offers advice. When he is crossing a street, and he suddenly sees a car bearing down on him at eighty miles an hour, he is afraid. All of these things are understandable, intelligible, in terms of a garden variety psychological theory so common and ingrained that it hardly seems necessary to dignify it with the appellative "theory".

On the other hand, there is a region, smaller, to be sure, but not at all negligible, in which this kind of intelligibility is not to be found. There are slips of the tongue, for example, which are not made "on purpose", but "for no reason", or "accidentally". There are dreams, which do not "make sense". There are rashes and fears and panics that come on "for no reason", or at any rate, no appropriate reason: thus it is unreasonable for a brave soldier to faint with fear at the sight of a hypodermic needle; it is unreasonable for a person to break out into a nervous sweat when riding in an elevator. Observe that it is not that we need regard these things as *uncaused* in order to be interested in them and to find them deserving of explanation; we can suppose (but we need not) that there are perfectly determinate physiological causes for them. And yet as long as we cannot employ our knowledge of these physiological causes to construct explanations and predictions of behavior, the physiological causes, even if they do exist, do not give us the kind of understanding we are seeking. For we might suppose, in the case of normal, nonproblematic behavior, that there are physiological causes underlying that behavior, and yet to understand those causes (supposing that we did) would be quite a different thing from understanding the behavior in the sense in which we actually do understand it. It is understanding of the latter sort that we are seeking to provide for the odd kinds of behavior.

This is the sort of understanding that psychoanalytic theory seeks to provide. With this understanding, it seeks to provide some degree of prediction and

[258]

control. It seeks to provide understanding of the odd and apparently accidental bits of behavior, and it seeks to provide this understanding in terms of the same categories in which we understand ordinary, deliberate behavior. As an example, let us consider the psychoanalytic theory of neurosis.

The central idea of this theory is that a far greater part of the mind is unconscious than we are wont to suppose, and that the categories which we apply to the behavior of the conscious mind also apply, in more or less similar fashion, to the unconscious mind. Psychoanalytic geography divides the mind into three regions: the *id*, the *ego*, and the *superego*. The id is largely unconscious; it is the seat of impulses, desires, instincts, urges, drives, etc. The ego is largely conscious or preconscious. (Something is preconscious when it can be brought up into consciousness.) It is the ego that integrates and organizes and adjudicates the claims of the outside world and the desires of the id. The superego, finally, represents the internalized voice of father. It is the conscience, and also perhaps the source of humor—for this also requires "objectivity", standing back and looking at oneself from a higher standpoint. The metaphor is thus that of three individuals, three psyches: the id, whose role is to say "I want" without regard to the compatibility of the wants with the world, with the rest of the personality, or even with each other; the superego, whose role is to lay down the rules, to say "you must"; and the ego, whose role is to coordinate the demands of the id and the superego, with each other, and with the outside world. As persons, the id, ego, and superego are clearly metaphorical. But as parts of the mind, they represent really separable functions. The oceans feel the influence of the sun and the moon, metaphorically; but the gravitational attraction of those bodies really does cause the tides of the oceans.

Within this framework we can express the psychoanalytic theory of neurosis in four propositions (I follow Waelder, *Basic Theory of Psychoanalysis.*)

1. *Conflict:* "...psychoneuroses are due to an inner conflict between an impulse and the interconnected rest of the personality—the so-called 'ego'";

2. *Repression:* "...in the case of neuroses, the conflict has not been solved in favor of one or the other side, nor by a suitable compromise, but ...the impulse whose claim could not be reconciled with the interests of the rest of the personality has become unconscious through a process called 'repression'";

3. *Return of the repressed:* "...the repression, however, has been unsuccessful; i.e., has succeeded only in expelling the impulse from consciousness but not in rendering it innocuous, and...the repressed impulse has found its way back into conscious manifestations in disguised form";

4. *Genesis:* The impulses which give rise to the conflict are sexual, and the conflict initially occurs in childhood.

This is the abstract theory; it carries with it no means of specifying boundary conditions which will allow us to relate the theory to the everyday world. This is a common form of complaint: we infer the existence of the conflict from the neurosis, and then use that conflict to explain the neurosis. How circular! But the complaint is not well taken; it is easy to imagine situations in the application of our physical theory of see-saws, in which just the same complaint could (implausibly) be made—i.e., a situation in which we used the theory to calculate a force, and then used the theory in the other direction to make a prediction based on (among other things) knowledge of that force. In order to apply the theory, however, we do need to impose connections between the theoretical terms and the terms which express the ostensive base of the theory.

One such term is "neurotic symptom". We can't list all the possible neurotic symptoms, but, as in the case of the terms that are to be regarded as quasi-ostensive in other contexts, we can give some examples, and say "and so on". Thus, for example, a general sense of worry and anxiety, having no plausible basis, may be a neurotic symptom; or the fear of high places, or of closed places, or of open places—we may include the whole range of phobias. Headaches and coughs and paralyses: these too may be regarded as neurotic symptoms in some of their occurrences, though of course they are also often straightforwardly organic in origin. There are many headaches and coughs and fears that would not be classified as neurotic symptoms, so that a given type of overt behavior (which might be regarded as ostensive in a deeper sense) will be taken to reflect a neurotic symptom or not, according as it can be made to fit into another explanatory framework. For the purposes of the psychoanalyst, however, and for our purposes here, the neurotic symptoms can be regarded as ostensive, in the sense that interpersonal uniformity in their use does not depend on psychoanalytic theory; this uniformity may depend on general physiological or medical theory—but that is another matter, and in no way detracts from the relative ostensiveness in psychoanalytic theory of the term "neurotic symptom".

For a particular example, to fix our ideas, let us select as a typical neurotic symptom a tendency to cough that has no organic basis. According to the theory, such a symptom must be tied up with the repression of a sexual impulse in childhood, and this repression in turn must be tied up with punishments or threats of punishment accompanying initial expressions of these impulses. A typical Freudian example is the threat of castration as a punishment for masturbation on the part of little boys. Again, of course, the number of ways in which an impulse can be frustrated in such a way that it becomes repressed, is legion; and again we can demand only that the relative ostensiveness of the particular kinds of frustration depend on other than psychoanalytic theories.

Thus we have two quite different kinds of connection between ordinary experience and psychoanalytic theory at the two sides of the theory. At the temporally earlier side, we have overt suppression and frustration that leads to conflicts and repressions and so on. At the temporally later side, we have the overt expression of neurotic symptoms.

[260]

We also have, within the body of the theory itself, a source of contact with experience. For psychoanalytic theory has as further hypotheses concerning neurosis, the following:

> The contents of the unconscious can be brought into consciousness.
> If the repressed impulses are brought into consciousness, then they can be handled in a new and better way.

With the help of these two further propositions, we have greatly increased the possibilities of confirmation for the theory, or of confrontation between the theory and its empirical subject matter. If unconscious contents that are hypothesized by the theory can be brought into consciousness, they can be testified to by the patient; and if neurosis is the poor handling of demands of impulses and other aspects of the personality, and it is possible to improve the relationships among these parts of the personality, then we should be able to modify or alleviate neurotic symptoms, through psychoanalysis.

That someone is being treated by psychoanalysis is perfectly ostensive; and that his symptoms change or improve is perfectly ostensive; and that he testifies as to what is present in his conscious mind is perfectly ostensive. That he testifies veridically is another matter, and one that requires theoretical support.

IV

The formalization that follows contains an implicit parameter indicating the person concerned; let us call him John. The vocabulary, the formation rules, and the interpretation, intermixed with a few meaning postulates, follow.

$NS(x)$ x is a neurotic symptom of John; relative to the system of psychoanalysis, this is intended to be an ostensive predicate.

$C(y,w)$ the conflict of y and w.

$Imp(y)$ y is an impulse, an instinctive drive.

$E(w)$ w is a part of the contents of John's ego.

$I(x)$ x is a part of the contents of John's id.

$S(x)$ x is a part of the contents of John's superego.

Definitions: (or meaning postulates)

MP1 $Ego(z)$ $z = \hat{w}(E(w))$.
MP2 $Id(z)$ $z = \hat{x}(I(x))$.
MP3 $Sup(z)$ $z = \hat{x}(S(x))$.

$Beh(x)$ x is an element of John's behavior.
Meaning postulate:

MP4 $NS(x) \supset Beh(x)$.

[261]

Res(x,z) x is the result of z, where we have
Meaning postulates:

> MP5   Res(x,z) $\supset$ Beh(x).
>
> MP6   Res(x,z) $\supset$ ($\exists y$)($\exists w$)($z = $ C(y,w)).

Conc(x) x is a conscious mental content.
Prec(x) x is a preconscious mental content.
Unc(x) x is an unconscious mental content.
Meaning postulates connecting mental contents with mental geography:

> MP7   Conc(x) $\supset$ E(x) $\vee$ I(x) $\vee$ S(x).
>
> MP8   Unc(x) $\supset$ E(x) $\vee$ I(x) $\vee$ S(x).
>
> MP9   Prec(x) $\supset$ E(x) $\vee$ I(x) $\vee$ S(x).

Sex(x) x is a sexual impulse.
Meaning postulate:

> MP10   Sex(x) $\supset$ Imp(x) & I(x)

Ov(x,y) x overcomes y.
Comp(x,y)   A compromise is formed between x and y.
Rep(y) y is repressed.
PCPE(x) x is punishment of John for erotic precocity.
DF(y,y') y is a disguised form of y'.

AXIOMS:

A1   NS(x) $\supset$ ($\exists z$)(Res(x,z) & ($\exists y$)($\exists w$)($x = $ C(y,w) & Imp(y) & Ego(w)))
A2   I(y) & E(x) $\supset$ Ov(y,x) $\vee$ Ov(x,y) $\vee$ Comp(x,y) $\vee$ Rep (y)
A3   Rep(y) $\supset$ Unc(y)
A4   Rep(y) $\supset$ ($\exists y'$)($\exists x$)(DF(y',y) & Conc(y') & Res(x,y'))
A5   [Sex(y) & Rep(y) & ($\exists x$)(PCPE(x))] $\supset$ ($\exists y'$)($\exists x$)(DF(y',y) & Res(x,y')NS(x)).

From these axioms it follows that if a is a neurotic symptom, it results from some childhood repression of a sexual impulse; and further that if John is frustrated in childhood, he will develop a neurotic symptom. This isn't much to get from all these symbols; but it does suggest, I hope, that even Freudian theory can be formalized with greater explicitness than it usually is. Whether or not psychoanalysis is ready to profit from this sort of formal formalization may be an open question; the point at issue here is not that every body of science should be presented in the most formal manner possible, but that the categories required for the understanding of more highly formalized disciplines are useful in the understanding of less highly formalized disciplines, too.

[262]

BIBLIOGRAPHICAL NOTES TO CHAPTER 11

The fragment of learning theory is taken from George Mandler and William Kessen, the *Language of Psychology* (New York: John Wiley & Sons, 1959). Their system in turn is presented as an illustration of the style of psychological theorizing embraced by C. L. Hull, the foremost formalizer in psychology. The two most important books by Hull are *Principles of Behavior* (New York: Appleton-Century 1943) and *A Behavior System* (New Haven: Yale University Press, 1952), in which an attempt is made to provide a complete formalization of a rather large fragment of psychology (learning theory).

The fragment of Freudian Theory is adopted from an excellent little book by Robert Waelder, *Basic Theory of Psychoanalysis* (New York: International Universities Press, 1960). Background material that has a clear bearing on the kind of example discussed here will be found in Freud, *A General Introduction to Psycho-Analysis* (New York: Liveright, 1920) and *New Introductory Lectures on Psycho-Analysis* (New York: Norton, 1933).

There are a number of interesting essays in *Minnesota Studies in the Philosophy of Science*, volume I (Feigl and Scriven, Eds., Minneapolis: University of Minnesota Press, 1962), which is largely devoted to issues involved in the philosophy of psychology; they include (to pick extremes) "Critique of Scientific Concepts and Theories" by B. F. Skinner, and "A Study of Radical Behaviorism," by Michael Scriven. Papers by Albert Ellis (a psychologist) "An Operational Reformulation of Some of the Basic Principles of Psychoanalysis," and by Antony Flew (a philosopher) "Motives and the Unconscious" have a bearing on the matters discussed in the last section of this chapter.

A good general essay on psychological theory is Herbert Feigl's "Principles and Problems of Theory Construction in Psychology," *Current Trends in Psychological Theory* (Dennis, Ed., Pittsburgh: University of Pittsburgh Press, 1951). Melvin Marx (Ed.), *Theories in Contemporary Psychology* (New York: Macmillan, 1963) contains an unusually wide spectrum of theoretical materials by psychologists, ranging from learning theory through psychodynamics.

Chapter 12

SOCIOLOGY

I

Sociology is a subject in which mathematization has been charging ahead at a furious rate over the past decade. Although mathematization and formalization are not the same thing, it is often true that they go hand in hand. It should be quite clear by now that formalization, although it involves symbolic or mathematical logic, need not use explicitly mathematical notions, and it should be even more clear that a discipline, such as physics, can use mathematical structures as tools without embedding them in an explicit formal framework.

One of the leading exponents of mathematization and formalization in the social sciences is Herbert Simon; for our formalized sample of sociology we shall take the mathematization he provides in *Models of Man* (New York: John Wiley, 1957) of a part of the theoretical system employed by George Homans in *The*

Human Group (Harper & Row, New York: 1950). Homan's system of concepts is designed to provide a theoretical framework for much of social theory. In *The Human Group*, he applies that theory to five groups of people, ranging from a kinship group in a South Pacific culture to the management of a large modern business concern. The particular applications of the theory, and even the problem of establishing connections between the theoretical terms of the theory and the observation terms in which experimental results must be reported, are matters that do not concern Simon. They will, however, concern us. Simon is concerned primarily with what we have called the *calculus* of the formal sociological system; we shall be at least as much interested in the interpretation of the calculus as in the calculus itself.

I shall begin neither with the calculus nor with the interpretation, but with a very informal and abbreviated description of the five societies that Homans takes as his test cases. I shall pull certain concepts out of these descriptions, and in terms of these concepts, construct a calculus embodying Simon's mathematical structure, and then I shall turn to the serious and interesting problem of interpretation. Finally, I shall look at the problem of confirmation.

1. The first group Homans describes is the *bank wiring group*, a group of factory workers, employed in the manufacture of banks of electrical terminals, who were studied extensively in the 1930's. The group included nine wiremen who connected wires to banks of terminals for telephone equipment, three soldermen, who soldered the connections, and two inspectors, who inspected the work. The behavior of the individuals in the group is analyzed by Homans (using the data of the original study) in terms of *interaction, activity*, and *sentiment*. These three concepts appear interrelated in two systems: the external system, which involves the interaction, activity, and sentiment imposed on the group by the external environment; and the internal system, which involves the same three elements, not, however, as they are required for the survival of the group in its environment, but insofar as they arise spontaneously out of the activities of the group. In Simon's mathematization, the two systems are analyzed together; since interaction and sentiment are primarily interesting insofar as they are ingredients of the internal system, they are treated as single variables. Activity however, takes two quite distinct forms: activity that is undertaken as part of a response to the environment of the group, and activity which arises spontaneously within the group. In the case at hand, the activities of wiring, soldering, inspecting, moving pieces of equipment about, etc., are clearly different in character from such activities as horseplay, eating candy, making bets, playing games, and so on, which were also among the activities performed by the group under study. Among the generalizations proposed by Homans as part of his theoretical structure are

p. 102   If the scheme of [externally imposed] activities is changed, the scheme of interaction will, in general, change also, and vice versa.

p. 104   Whatever changes occur in the scheme of [externally imposed] activities of a group, the scheme of interaction between the leaders of various levels and their followers tends to keep the same general pyramidical [*sic*] form.

p. 111   Persons who interact frequently with one another tend to like one another.

p. 112   If the frequency of interaction between two or more persons increases, the degree of their liking for one another will increase, and vice versa.

p. 112   If the interactions between the members of a group are frequent in the external system, sentiments of liking will grow up between them, and these sentiments will lead in turn to further interactions, over and above the interactions of the external system.

p. 118   Persons who feel sentiments of liking for one another will express those sentiments in activities over and above the activities of the external system, and these activities may further strengthen the sentiments of liking.

p. 120   The more frequently persons interact with one another, the more alike, in some respects both their activities and their sentiments tend to become.

In this first group, it is easy to see how these hypotheses could be evaluated: we would look at the group and see whether, in fact, those individuals who interacted frequently with each other were particularly friendly; if individuals who are particularly friendly indulge in activities above and beyond those required by the environment; and so on.

2. The second human group that Homans analyzes within the same conceptual framework is "the Norton Street Gang", a group of young men from a depressed neighborhood in a large city, who "hang around together", go bowling together, etc.

3. For the third illustration of his theory, Homans chooses family life in Tikopia, a Pacific island which has been thoroughly studied by Raymond Firth. The particular relationships and activities that are of concern here are family and kin relationships, and the simple activities related to survival in the environment.

The fourth and fifth examples are examined from a dynamic point of view, rather than a static one. The other three groups were looked at primarily as they existed at a particular time; there was no attempt to take account of the changes that would occur as the demands of the external environment changed—e.g., as members of the gang found steady jobs or got married, as members of the working group at the electric company were fired or promoted, or the wiring work was discontinued or (as in the case of the Tikopia) the group came into contact with new ideas and techniques.

4. The fourth example is the disintegration of a New England town, which he calls Hilltown, as it changes from a tightly knit, thoroughly organized, self-sufficient unit in the mid nineteenth century, into a bedroom suburb in the mid twentieth century.

[266]

5. The fifth group consisted of the management group of a small electrical company that was undergoing internal changes. It was a case, as Homans characterizes it, of social conflict, in which the prestige and importance of some groups and individuals were increasing, the prestige and importance of other groups and individuals decreasing.

II

The variables introduced by Simon are taken to be functions simply of time; they are:

$I(t)$—the intensity of interaction among members of the group at t.
$F(t)$—the amount of friendliness among members of the group at t.
$A(t)$—the amount of activity carried on by members of the group within the group at t.
$E(t)$—the amount of activity carried on by members of the group which is imposed on the group by the external environment at t.

Since in Simon's system, these variables are taken to be related by differential equations, it is clear that they are intended to be real-valued. More accurately (recalling what was said earlier about quantity), we should say that they represent quantitative predicates, having the structure of the real number system. We already know what is required to introduce such predicates into a formal system. It will be particularly interesting, however, to see how they are introduced in such a system as this, in which there are no obvious and natural ways of introducing them directly.

For the sake of presenting Simon's calculus, we shall simply take the functors "A", "I", "F", and "E" as primitive signs; and shall adopt real-number axioms to govern them. This amounts to positing, in a blatantly Platonistic manner, a whole nondenumerably infinite realm of degrees of friendliness, another of degrees of interaction, another of degrees of internal activity, and still another of external activity. We suppose also that we have appropriate terms and axioms to render time a quantitative concept—i.e., to make the variable "t" that occurs in the functions introduced by Simon a quantitative variable.

The axioms presented by Simon, from which the generalizations offered by Homans follow, are the following three:

$$(1.1) \quad I(t) = a_1 F(t) + a_2 A(t)$$
$$(1.2) \quad dF(t)/dt = b[I(t) - \beta F(t)]$$
$$(1.3) \quad dA(t)/dt = c_1[F(t) - \gamma A(t)] + c_2[E(t) - A(t)],$$

where the constants a_1, a_2, b, c_1, c_2, β, and γ are all positive.

So far as the calculus offered by Simon is concerned, this is the end. He is not particularly concerned with the interpretation of the terms introduced. "In this

[267]

paper we will assume that operational definitions (Homans' or others) have been assigned to the variables, such that the behavior of a group at any moment in time can be measured in terms of the four real numbers [*sic*] *I, F, A,* and *E.*" (p. 100).

It is obvious that matters are not quite this simple. We could provide an operational definition of "*I*" that is quite as definite as we could wish, by identifying *I* with the total number of back-slaps exchanged among members of the group in a specified time interval. But then *I* is an integer, not a real number; and that in turn implies that *F* and *A* only admit a finite number of values, and that makes the differential Eqs. 1.2 and 1.3 false. We can avoid this silliness by taking *I* to stand for a continuously variable *tendency* to interact, and taking the number of backslaps to be an integral measure of this continuous tendency. But then we have two clearly distinct concepts: tendency to interact, *I*, which is continuous and unobservable; and (say) *N*, number of backslaps, which is what we observe. We do not have a *definition*, operational or otherwise, of *I*, but simply a connection—an analytic, logical, connection, perhaps—between *I* and something else, which we take to be on the observational level. At this point we must recognize that *I* is being taken as a primitive term, and as a quantitative one; and that there is no reason for taking any particular form of observation to be critically (or even analytically) relevant to it: it may be indicated by backslaps, or by talk, or by exchanged glances, or by the avoidance of exchanged glances (the secret lovers at the ball interact constantly, though they studiously avoid each others' eyes).

Let us therefore introduce *I* (and the other functors) in the same way we introduced the length functor. We can all, perfectly well, distinguish between instances in which there is much interaction in a group and instances in which there is little interaction. That is, as in the case of length, there is a relation term (longer than, exhibits more interaction than) that we take to be initially well understood. But the analogy with temperature is closer than that with length, for there is no way of adding degrees of interaction which is natural and fruitful. In order to arrive at a good scale of interaction, we must relate interaction to something else, just as, in the case of temperature, in order to arrive at a scale of temperature, we must relate temperature to something else, for example length or pressure. Note that this does not make the law of thermal expansion (in general) analytic; it is a part of a whole body of laws that may be regarded as having an analytic component.

Thus we need some term, some quantitative term, to function in the measurement of interaction in the way in which length functions in the measurement of temperature. One such term suggests itself immediately: the amount of time that is spent in interaction in the group—i.e., the number of seconds during the day that person 1 is talking to or otherwise engaged with person 2, plus the number of seconds that person 1 is talking to or otherwise engaged with person 3, plus..., plus the number of seconds during the day that person number $n - 1$ is talking to or otherwise enaged with person n. There are still problems. We would probably want to count as interaction that of person 1, with person 5, with person 7, and with person 10, if he is telling all three of them a joke at the same time. (Surely there is more interaction here than there would be if he were only telling the joke to one person.) And yet, do we want to count as interaction the relation between person 1 and person 8, who merely happens to be eaves-dropping on the joke? Again, there are kinds of interaction and kinds of inter-action.

What we should take to be a measure of this vague quantitative concept, *amount of interaction*, is a complicated problem. Furthermore, it is clearly not solved by providing an arbitrary precise measure—as seconds of speech, or oc-casions of speech—because the concept of interaction that we are after is one that we already have an intuitive grasp of, and the concept of our formal system must be one that does not do too much violence to that intuitive concept; and furthermore it must be a concept that fits into our formal system. The whole point of having such a concept as *interaction* is that it fits into a formal frame-work that is confirmed by observation. The arbitrary precise measure might happen to be such that the formal system employing "interaction" was refuted by observations. If the system seemed to be all right on a vague intuitive level, and yet was refuted by observation when we took (say) frequency of speech acts to be the measure of interaction, we would have not only motivation, but per-fectly rational grounds for saying that the hypothesis that degree of interaction could be measured by frequency of speech acts was false. There are then, not merely meaning postulates, but auxiliary hypotheses that are required in forging the connection between the abstract theory and the world of observation.

What we shall do, therefore, is to impute a certain structure—the structure of the positive real numbers will do—to the range of the functions I, F, E, and A. As in dealing with lengths, temperatures, and other more familiar quantities, we suppose that it makes perfectly good sense to talk about a set of entities (lengths, temperatures, degrees of interaction, and degrees of friendliness), many of which may never be represented in the real world. We could list postulates concerning each of these sets of entities (degrees of interaction, degrees of friend-liness, etc.) which will insure that they have the appropriate structure. But it will be simpler merely to postulate that there is a one-one order-preserving mapping from these sets of entities to the nonnegative real numbers. We intro-duce $\mathcal{F}$ as a set of entities comprising the *possible* values of the function F; the range of F is included in $\mathcal{F}$: for every t, for the given group, $F(t)$ is an element of $\mathcal{F}$. And then we take as a meaning postulate, that there is a one–one mapping ϕ whose domain is $\mathcal{F}$, whose range is the set of nonnegative real numbers, and which is such that if x,y are elements of $\mathcal{F}$, then $x >_F y$ if and only if $\phi(x) > \phi(y)$, where "$x >_F y$" means that x is a greater degree of friendliness than y. This

[269]

suffices to justify the use of differential equations as our basic theoretical postulates.

The relations $>_F$, $>_I$, etc., are observational at least some of the time. We can look at a group of people and be perfectly sure that there is more interaction going on at one time than at another. We can look at a couple of groups of people and be perfectly sure, and in perfect agreement, that there is more interaction going on in one of them than in the other. There are other cases— perhaps the majority—in which we might find it hard to agree, or even to form a private judgment, concerning whether or not there was more interaction in one group than in the other, or vice versa, or neither. It is partly for this reason that we cannot plausibly construct the continuum of degrees of interaction as we did the continuum of lengths, by beginning with indistinguishability classes. In order to test our theory, we need to have more specific knowledge than this concerning degrees of interaction, and it is this more specific knowledge that requires us to invent some way of measuring the values of the functions F, E, etc. It is these techniques of measurement that are provided by so-called operational definitions, which are really (in view of the fact that we can sometimes judge directly that there is more interaction in a group at one time than another) auxiliary hypotheses.

Homans rests content with the intuitive judgments, which are, after all, good enough for testing the rough verbal statements that he offers. Simon suggests— almost parenthetically, since testing these hypotheses is not his concern so much as mathematizing them—the following auxiliary hypotheses:

Interaction:
> We might let I_{ij} represent the number of interactions that take place between individual i and individual j during the day. The amount of interaction in the group, then could be computed as the average, per member, of the quantity I_{ij}; i.e., $1/n \sum I_{ij} = I_a$. [p. 100]

Observe that although Simon calls this a "definition", it simply won't do as a definition. I_a is a quantity that admits only a finite number of values, and cannot be regarded as entering into differential equations. However, it can serve the function we ask of it: it can give us a more detailed ranking of degrees of interaction than we can obtain from unaided intuitive judgment. That is, we can formally define I_a as suggested, and take as our auxiliary hypothesis the conditional:

$$\text{If} \quad I_a(t) >_{I_a} I_a(t'), \quad \text{then} \quad I(t) >_I I(t').$$

To strengthen this into a biconditional, as Simon suggests, would make hash of the differential equations. Furthermore, it cannot be taken as analytic or conventional, because there are perfectly clear grounds on which we could be led to reject it: namely, if we find a number of groups (one or two we might dismiss as freaks, pending a better indication of I) in which, although $I_a(t) >_{I_a} I_a(t')$, we can easily *see* that not-$(I(t) >_I I(t'))$. The conditional must, therefore, be regarded as a factual auxiliary hypothesis, or, to prune a useless adjective, simply as a factual hypothesis.

The same is true of the natural zero of interaction. I_a will have the value zero interactions, if nobody in the group interacts with anybody else in the group; and we shall then assign the value zero also to the corresponding theoretical variable I. Thus

$$I_a(t) = 0_{I_a} \quad \text{if and only if} \quad I(t) = 0_I.$$

Observe that the units are still not the same, even for this special case. "0_{I_a}" stands for zero units of observable interactions—items of conversation, or seconds of attention—while "0_I" stands for the zero degree of the abstract quantity, interaction or tendency to interact. The biconditional displayed above is factual, as was the earlier conditional. There is even good reason to think that in the final analysis, this biconditional is false: it is difficult to imagine how there could be a *group* in which there was a zero degree of interaction, though it is easy enough to suppose that for every possible observable indicator of interaction, there is some group for which the observed value of that indicator is 0. Nonetheless, the biconditional represents an ideal for our indicator, which may be very closely approached by adopting some combination of observable characteristics as the indicator.

Just as there is a natural zero for our indicator, and thus a natural zero for the theoretical quantity, so there is a natural unit for the indicator and a corresponding unit for the theoretical quantity. One way to express this would be to tie the two quantities together (say) all the integral values of I_a, just as we tied them together by a biconditional at the zero value of I_a. Thus we might propose the hypothesis:

For any integer n,

$$I_a(t) = n_{I_a} \quad \text{if and only if} \quad I(t) = n_I.$$

This, like the preceding hypotheses, would be empirical. We could perfectly well have grounds for accepting the statement that "$I(t)) = I(t') = n_I$" and at the same time, the statement "$I_a(t) \neq I_a(t')$". These grounds would be grounds for looking for a less defective indicator than I_a.

We can simplify things if we take as our empirical hypothesis connecting amount of interaction—the theoretical quantity—with observed interaction, just the statement that observed interaction is *a measure of* real (theoretical) interaction, where by saying that one thing is a measure of another we are accepting the precise statistical statement that the distribution of the first is approximately normal, with a mean equal to the value of the other. (Strictly speaking, the supposition of the normality of the distribution would clearly be false: there are a lot of values of $I_a(t)$ that cannot be observed—e.g., irrational values, or

[271]

values other than the ones that can be expressed as a fraction whose denominator represents the number of people in the group.)

The variance of $I_a(t)$ taken as a measure of $I(t)$ is not specified in the hypothesis. But there are perfectly standard ways of estimating the variance—it is a perfectly conventional and straightforward statistical problem. This is why we need merely specify two things: that the distribution of $I_a(t)$ is normal, and that the mean of that distribution coincides with $I(t)$. Note that even in this weakened form, our hypothesis connecting I_a and I is an empirical hypothesis. Indeed, weakened though the form is, it can be refuted on more than one count. We can easily discover that the observations I_a are not normally distributed; and we can also (somewhat less easily) discover that their mean does not coincide with I.

All of this is equally true of the other variables of the theory. Consider friendliness, F. The friendliness of the group at a given time is represented by $F(t)$. But how do we measure friendliness? We can judge it directly and intuitively. That is, we can make judgments of the form, "There is more friendliness now than there was," or "There is less friendliness now than there was." And whatever we choose as a measure of friendliness, it must not be such as to do violence to these intuitive judgments—at least not in the cases in which the intuitive judgments are clear and universal. This is the point—or one point—behind the feeling that many people have that the social sciences should be conducted on the level of intuition and empathy. But this point—namely, that violence shall not be done to the most clear cut of our intuitions—is illegitimately inflated to the claim that no measuring instruments are allowable, or even the claim that systematization and formalization are *a priori* altogether out of place in the social sciences. But the situation is not essentially any different from the situation in physics. There we uncovered the same point in connection with the measurement of length: namely, that the introduction of the abstract concept, length, had to take place in such a way as to avoid doing violence to the original judgments with which we began—that is, the clear and universal judgments of the form: this body is definitely longer than that body. Those judgments are the base, the ground, from which we begin in formulating the concept of length in physics, just as the clear and universal judgments of the form: "This group is definitely friendlier now than it used to be," form the ground from which we begin in formulating the quantitative concept of friendliness in the theory of groups.

The quantity F must be a *quantity*; that is, it must admit of a one-one mapping into the real numbers. How do we get from the basic judgments of the form, "This group is friendlier than it was," to the attribution of a numerical value to its degree of friendliness? The same way in which we get from judgments about which body is longer to judgments of degree of length. We use an instrument. A psychological test or battery of tests in the first case; a ruler in the second.

The former instrument is far harder to use than the latter; and the underlying concept of friendliness is much less precise than the underlying concept of length. Furthermore, rulers are far better standardized than psychological tests —to choose a psychological test for friendliness is somewhat like plunging your hand into a barrel of rubber rulers of all degrees of flexibility and elasticity. Nevertheless, as I hope the third chapter has shown, the difference between the two instruments is one of degree. Both the ruler and the psychological test yield results with a fairly high degree of interpersonal uniformity; where they differ is primarily in the richness and fruitfulness of the theoretical framework in which the thing measured plays a role. We can quite reasonably ask if *friendliness*, as it appears in the theory, is what the friendliness test really measures, while we would not ask the same question about measurement with a ruler. This may seem like a large difference, until we recall that the ruler is in a sense a product of the very theoretical framework that it is used to confirm. The quantity that appears in the theoretical framework (length, friendliness) and the instrument used to measure it (ruler, test) do not develop independently. The test and the theory together help to determine what it is we are trying to measure, and therefore whether we are managing to do it successfully or not. To argue that there is no point in constructing a quantitative theory until we have accurate measuring devices, or that there is no point in devising accurate measuring devices until we know what they measure, is to misconstrue badly the relation between the theory and the measuring device.

Homans devotes some space to the problem of assessing friendliness, though for the most part he rests content with intuitive judgments. In the case of the bank wiring group, however, various tests were given (as part of the general research program), which allowed more precise judgments to be made. We shall suppose that there was a test or battery of tests which was designed to measure friendliness, i.e., which yielded in every application to a group, a result $F_b(t)$. $F_b(t)$ we take to be distributed normally with mean $F(t)$. As in the measure of interaction, as indeed in the measurement of length, the auxiliary test variable F_b does not supercede the abstract variable F completely: we can make certain intuitive judgments of F (of the form, "$F(t) >_F F(t')$"), and should the test variable F_b fail to conform to such judgments, so much the worse for the test variable. We do not (as has sometimes been suggested) take the test result F_b to be what we *now*, in this formal context, mean by friendliness; it is an empirical hypothesis that the test result F_b reflects friendliness in the sense that it does not conflict with our intuitive judgments.

We therefore take the following four hypotheses to indicate the structure of the quantity F, and its relation to a specific observational quantity F_b:

(1) There is an order preserving function mapping values of F one-to-one onto the nonnegative reals.
(2) $F_b(t)$ is normally distributed (approximately).
(3) The mean of $F_b(t)$ is $F(t)$.

(4) If "$F(t) >_F F(t')$" is acceptable on observational grounds, then so is "$F_b(t) >_{Fb} F_b(t')$."

The functors "A" and "E" admit similar kinds of analysis. All we require formally, is that they represent quantities—i.e., have the structure of the reals and be at least partially ordered by an observational ordering relation. Nevertheless, there are interesting differences between the development of measures for these variables and for the other two.

"A" represents the amount of activity carried on within the group in what Homans calls the internal system. It is distinguished from E, the activity performed in the group as a result of environmental pressures. Thus in the bank wiring group, the talk and horseplay as well as the giving of help represent internal activities; the necessary production of wired banks is accomplished by activities belonging to the external system, or, caused by the pressures of the environment. As the example of one person giving help to another shows, it is sometimes hard to draw the line between the two types of activities. Furthermore, we do not simply want to divide the time that a person spends in a group into two parts: a part devoted to internal activity, and a part devoted to activities that arise in response to environmental stimuli. For there may be periods of time in which the individual is there, but not engaged in any group activity of either sort; and there may be periods of time when he is engaged in activities of both kinds simultaneously.

Regarding the concept of activity within the group, Simon writes:

The concept of "activity within the group" might [sic] require rather sophisticated treatment. For example, time spent by a worker in daydreaming about his family or outside social relations might, ideally, be excluded from his activity with the group. For some purposes, we might wish to regard as "activity within the group" uniformities of behavior among group members—that is, the degree to which activity lies within the group might be measured by similarity of behavior. [p. 100 n]

These complications arise even on the basis of Simon's proposal that "A might be defined as the average amount of time spent per member per day in activity within the group" [p. 100]. But this is surely too gross an oversimplification; the amount of activity in the sense that interests us here must involve some measure of the intensity with which the activity is pursued, as well as the length of time during which it is pursued. Simon suggests that similarity of behavior may be a plausible measure of this intensity, and yet it does not seem to quite do: a group of people sitting around in identical poses, with similar looks of abstraction on their faces, thinking of their wives making similar suppers, would not be an instance of a group exhibiting intense internal activity.

As in the case of the preceding two variables, we do have an intuitive basis to go on in assessing internal activity. We can order groups, often with considerable uniformity of opinion, with respect to the amount of internal activity they exhibit. Indeed, this is just what Simon himself does, and Homans as well,

[274]

when they talk about the formal system under consideration. In effect, Simon takes the bare, intuitive judgments of comparison ("$A(t) >_A A(t')$"), to be judgments of comparison between quantities. Note that with respect to I and F, there are also these immediate judgments. But they are supplemented by sets of postulates giving a method of measurement, and auxiliary predicates for expressing the results of measurement ("I_a" and "F_b"). Simon supposes that we have some such auxiliary predicate in the case of internal activity as well; but in point of fact, it is not necessary. Although the heart of the theory is expressed in differential equations, and we are bound to consider A a *quantity*—we must suppose that there is a one–one order preserving mapping of the range of A into the real numbers—the theory is not in a state in which it makes sense to look for numerical confirmations, e.g., of the prediction that $A(t)$ will turn out to be 1.43 A-units. All we are looking for, according to Simon, are directions of change (e.g., is $A(t)$ larger or smaller than $A(t')$?), and certain conclusions we can draw about the constants of the differential equations from the fact that there exist equilibrium states. Simon says he will "try to make use only of the ordinal properties of the measuring scales" [p. 100]; and for this, of course, intuitive, direct comparative judgments may often suffice to connect the theory to experience and observation, and thus help to establish the required techniques of measurement.

The variable "E", which Simon says "might be defined as the average amount of time that would be spent per member per day in activity within the group if group members were motivated only by external pressures," admits, like the variable "A", of no obvious and simple technique of measurement. The "definition" suggested by Simon even introduces new difficulties through being dispositional. Even if we could devise a measure of the amount of time that *is* spent by a person in activities motivated by external pressure (and this would leave out of account the intensity of that activity), there could be no direct way of measuring the amount of time that *would be* spent by a person in these activities in the absence of any but external pressure, because the person in the group is never (not if the theory is right) motivated only by external pressure. "In most cases we would attempt to measure E indirectly in terms of the magnitude of the force producing E—in somewhat the same manner as the force of the magnetic field is sometimes measured by the strength of the current producing it" [p. 101 *n*]. This is plausible and helpful. But observe that we can measure the intensity of a magnetic field by measuring the current producing it, only in virtue of a rich and complex theory of electricity and magnetism. Analogously, we can only measure the value of E indirectly with the help of a rich and complex theory of motivation. Perhaps things are not quite this bad; we should say rather that we could only measure the value of E *precisely* with the help of such a theory of motivation. But with the help of a vague and general theory of motivation, we can come to some judgments about the value of E;

[275]

and, as in the case of the variable "A", we can make comparative judgments, with some degree of interpersonal uniformity, on the basis of intuition alone.

III

The upshot of all this is that the formal system suggested by Homans, mathematicized by Simon, and filled out to allow for formal connections between abstract theory and observation, will have roughly the following form:

Calculus	Interpretation
A. Vocabulary:	
1. Standard vocabulary for logic and set theory	1. Standard interpretation
2. Standard physical vocabulary to provide for time variables and constants and relations (t, $t' > t$, etc.)	2. Standard interpretation (see Chapter Three)
3. New vocabulary for the theory of groups:	
F	°friendliness functor
I	°interaction functor
A	°internal activity functor
E	°external activity functor
F_b	*friendliness test score
I_a	*interaction rating
$>_F$	°exhibits more friendliness than
$>_I$	°exhibits more interaction than
$>_A$	°exhibits more internal activity than
$>_E$	°exhibits more external activity than
$\mathscr{F}$	set of degrees of friendliness
$\mathscr{I}$	set of degrees of interaction
$\mathscr{A}$	set of degrees of internal activity
$\mathscr{E}$	set of degrees of external activity
$\mathscr{F}_b$	set of possible friendliness test scores
$\mathscr{I}_a$	set of possible interaction ratings
$>_{Fb}$	*has higher friendliness test score than
$>_{Ia}$	*has higher interaction rating than

[276]

*The expressions with starred interpretations are strictly observational; thus, applying this theory to a particular group, we can *assert*, on the basis of direct observation, statements of the forms:

$$F_b(t) = f$$
$$I_a(t) = i$$
$$F_b(t) >_{Fb} F_b(t')$$
$$I_a(t) >_{Ia} I_a(t'),$$

where "t" and "t'" represent particular times, and f and i are particular elements of $\mathcal{F}_b$ and $\mathcal{I}_a$, respectively. Such statements will be asserted or denied with a high degree of interpersonal uniformity, on direct experiential grounds.

°The expressions whose interpretations are marked with "°", are in part observational. Applying this theory to a particular group, we can sometimes, with a fair degree of interpersonal uniformity, assert on the basis of direct observation statements of the forms:

$$F(t) >_F F(t')$$
$$I(t) >_I I(t')$$
$$A(t) >_A A(t')$$
$$E(t) >_E E(t'),$$

where, again, t and t' are definite times. We cannot always make such judgments; often it will happen that we can neither assert "$F(t) >_F F(t')$," nor "$F(t') >_F F(t)$," nor yet "$F(t) = F(t')$." Observe also that what assertions of these forms we can make on a direct experimental base, depends on how high a degree of interpersonal uniformity we require. If we require a very high degree of interpersonal uniformity in the acceptance of such statements as "$F(t) >_F F(t')$", then we will be able to make such a statement only when the difference in friendliness is very clear cut, very apparent. But we will always be able to make some such judgments. We cannot demand perfect uniformity, even for designedly observational sentences like "$F_b(t) >_{F_b} F_b(t')$."

B. Formation Rules:
  1. Standard formation rules for logic and set theory.
  2. Standard formation rules for the fragment of physics needed to provide time constants and variables and relations.
  3. Formation rules for the new vocabulary: These are functors operating on time variables and
     a. "F", "I", "A", "E", "F_b", "I_a" constants. The set of
        may occur only followed by "(", a times is the common do-
        time term, and ")". The result is a main of the correspond-
        term. The set of time terms can be de- ing functions.
        fined with the help of Formation
        Rule 2.

[277]

b. "$\mathcal{F}$", "$\mathcal{I}$", "$\mathcal{A}$", "$\mathcal{E}$", "$\mathcal{F}_b$", "$\mathcal{I}_a$" are terms.

c. "$>_F$", "$>_I$", "$>_A$", "$>_E$", "$>_{F_b}$", "$>_{I_a}$" are relation terms; they occur flanked by individual terms to form sentences.

C. Axioms:

1. Standard set of axioms for logic and mathematics.

2. Standard set of axioms for the physics of dates.

3. $(x)(y)(x >_F y \supset (x \in \mathcal{F} \ \& \ y \in \mathcal{F}))$
   $(x)(y)(x >_I y \supset (x \in \mathcal{I} \ \& \ y \in \mathcal{I}))$
   $(x)(y)(x >_A y \supset (x \in \mathcal{A} \ \& \ y \in \mathcal{A}))$
   $(x)(y)(x >_E y \supset (x \in \mathcal{E} \ \& \ y \in \mathcal{E}))$
   $(x)(y)(x >_{F_b} y \supset (x \in \mathcal{F}_b \ \& \ y \in \mathcal{F}_b))$
   $(x)(y)(x >_{I_a} y \supset (x \in \mathcal{I}_a \ \& \ y \in \mathcal{I}_a))$

Analytic: "$>_F$" represents a relation between elements of $\mathcal{F}$, "$>_I$" a relation between elements of $\mathcal{I}$, etc.

It can plausibly be maintained that it is part of the meaning of the term "$>_F$" that it holds true only between degrees of friendliness; on the other hand one might equally plausibly accomplish the same result through the agency of the formation rules by stipulating that "$x >_F y$" is to be *meaningless* when x and y are not friendliness terms. The latter approach is a little messier.

4. $(t)(F(t) \in \mathcal{F})$
   $(t)(I(t) \in \mathcal{I})$
   $(t)(A(t) \in \mathcal{A})$
   $(t)(E(t) \in \mathcal{E})$
   $(t)(F_b(t) \in \mathcal{F}_b)$
   $(t)(I_a(t) \in \mathcal{I}_a)$

Analytic: The range of the various functions lies in the corresponding set of degrees.

5. $(\exists \phi)(\phi \text{ maps } \mathcal{F} \text{ 1–1 onto } R \ \& \ (x)(y)(x >_F y \equiv \phi(x) > \phi(y)))$
   $(\exists \phi)(\phi \text{ maps } \mathcal{I} \text{ 1–1 onto } R \ \& \ (x)(y)(x >_I y \equiv \phi(x) > \phi(y)))$
   $(\exists \phi)(\phi \text{ maps } \mathcal{A} \text{ 1–1 onto } R \ \& \ (x)(y)(x >_A y \equiv \phi(x) > \phi(y)))$
   $(\exists \phi)(\phi \text{ maps } \mathcal{E} \text{ 1–1 onto } R \ \& \ (x)(y)(x >_E y \equiv \phi(x) > \phi(y)))$

Analytic: R is the set of real numbers, and these axioms merely state that $\mathcal{F}$, $\mathcal{I}$, etc., are to be regarded as *quantities*.

6. $F_b(t)$ is approximately normally distributed with mean $F(t)$; $I_a(t)$ is approximately normally distributed with mean $I(t)$.

? Somewhat analytic; but there is a synthetic element. We can test for normality; but we can only tell that

[278]

7. $(\exists a_1)(\exists a_2)(I(t) = a_1F(t) + a_2A(t))$
$(\exists b)(\exists \beta)(dF(t)/dt = b[I(t) - \beta F(t)])$
$(\exists c_1)(\exists c_2)(\exists \gamma)(dA(t)/dt = c_1[F(t) -$
$\quad\quad \gamma A(t)] + c_2[E(t) - A(t)])$

D. Rules of Inference:
Standard.

the mean of $F_b(t)$ differs from $F(t)$ if there is a really marked discrepancy. Clearly synthetic. These three axioms embody the heart of the Homans–Simon theory.

IV

The system laid out here is based quite directly on Homans' hypotheses. But as Simon points out, there are many consequences of the mathematical formulation of the postulates of the system, which would not be obtainable from the verbal formulation. For one thing, the system of three equations could be solved explicitly to give the state of a group at any given time, starting from a known point and being given the values of the seven constants. This would be highly testable, if we had a way of evaluating the constants and an easy and effective way of measuring the quantities A, F, I, and E.

More down-to-earth and practical are the relatively qualitative conclusions we can draw from these equations that concern groups at or near a state of equilibrium. Simon makes such deductions (they are too complicated to be reproduced here) and shows that they conform to the data cited by Homans. For example, it is possible to show that if there has existed a state of equilibrium, then the rate of change of friendliness, of interaction, and of internal activity, with respect to a change of externally motivated activity, is positive. Symbolically: $dF/dE > 0$, $dI/dE > 0$, and $dA/dE > 0$. Thus if E is increased, so (near equilibrium) will be F, I, and A; and conversely, if E is decreased, so will F, I, and A decrease. Hilltown provides one illustration: since the mid-nineteenth century, activities dictated to the group by the environment have decreased drastically; and the disintegration of the group is the reflection of decreases in friendliness, spontaneous activity, and interaction. Another illustration is provided by the differences between Tikopia family life and urban American family life.

It may be seen that the confirming evidence for this formalized theory is not highly specific. Not only do the confirmations point to no specific values for the constants of the theory, but indeed would equally confirm similar theories whose differential equations were quite different. One might ask—it has been asked— what such a formalized theory as this can contribute that we do not already have in the form of common-sense generalizations, such as "People who work side by side are friendlier than those who come into contact only accidentally," and "Birds of a feather...," and the like. To ask such a question as this is to misconstrue the function of formalized theories. One function of formal theories may be to codify and crystallize a certain body of facts in a brief and convenient and (hopefully) beautiful form. But another function of formal theories—one far more important in regions where our knowledge is misty than merely codifying known facts—is to embody the general outlines of a research program. It is this latter function that the kind of theory presented above is designed to perform. Having formalized the theory, where do we go? The answer is clear: we must develop tests for measuring friendliness, interaction, the various forms of activities; in terms of the numbers yielded by these tests, we can attempt to confirm, in particular groups, the existence of the constants a_1, a_2, etc. Failing to find that these constants are really constant, we may seek improved measuring devices for the variables involved. That is, we will look for measuring devices that (a) conflict minimally with our intuitive comparative judgments, and (b) yield numerical values of the variables that come closer to satisfying the requirements of the theory. At some point we might give the whole theory up as a bad job; the chances are that we would not abandon it until we had a more promising theory in hand.

BIBLIOGRAPHICAL NOTES TO CHAPTER 12

The example discussed in this chapter is taken from Herbert Simon, *Models of Man* (New York: John Wiley, 1957). Simon in turn is discussing an example of nonnumerical theorizing performed by George Homans, *The Human Group* (New York: Harper & Row, 1950). Homans in his turn developed and illustrated his theory with the help of observational material collected by other social scientists, including, for example, Raymond Firth, whose observations were published in *We, the Tikopia* (London: G. Allen & Unwin, 1936) and *Social Change in Tikopia* (New York: Macmillan, 1959).

Other recent works on the philosophy of the social sciences include, Richard Rudner, *Philosophy of Social Science* (Englewood Cliffs, N.J.: Prentice-Hall, 1965), who writes from a point of view similar to that expressed here, and Abraham Kaplan, *The Conduct of Inquiry* (San Francisco: Chandler Publishing Co., 1965), who writes from a slightly different point of view. Ernest Nagel, in *The Structure of Science* (New York: Harcourt, Brace and World, 1961), provides an acute and judicious review of various philosophical standpoints in his Chapters 13 and 14. A collection of articles representing various points of view may be found in David Braybrooke, *Philosophical Problems of the Social Sciences* (New York: Macmillan, 1965). Part III of Carl Hempel's important collection of essays, *Aspects of Scientific Explanation* (New York: The Free Press, 1965), is concerned with problems in the philosophy of science that are of particular importance in the social sciences.

Chapter 13

BIOLOGY

I

It is a common bit of prescientific knowledge that children look something like their parents. Dark parents have dark children, light parents have light children, short parents have children who grow up to be short adults, and so on. It is also well known that this phenomenon is not universal: sometimes two short parents will have a very tall child, or two fair parents a child with dark coloring. The same thing can be observed among plants. If one plants seeds from tall sweet peas, for example, the resulting plants will mostly be tall. In the nineteenth century, the Augustinian Monk, Gregor Mendel, embarked on a lengthy, careful, and ingenious study of the manner in which certain physical characteristics of garden peas were inherited. The principles he uncovered are the basic principles of the modern theory of heredity.

One of the reasons for Mendel's success was that he chose to work with a plant whose varieties differed in clear-cut, distinguishable ways. Some varieties of peas have white flowers, others have red flowers; some are tall, others are dwarf; some have round seeds, others have wrinkled seeds, etc. It was well known, to begin with, that it was possible to develop pure-bred varieties of peas, that is, varieties which would breed true, in the sense that all of the off-spring would resemble the parent plants in the respects under study. Mendel's procedure was to study the various possible crosses of pure-bred varieties, crosses of the resulting hybrids, and crosses between hybrids and pure-bred varieties. The first startling result was that the hybrid generation was uniform with respect to the characteristics in question: cross a red flowering pea with a white flowering pea, and the offspring will all have red flowers; cross a yellow-seeded variety with a green-seeded variety, and the offspring will all have yellow seeds; cross a tall variety with a dwarf variety, and the offspring will all be tall. The second, even more startling, result, was that when the hybrid generation was crossed, the physical characteristics that had disappeared in the first crossing (wrinkled seeds, white flowers, green seeds, dwarf size) would reappear in the offspring of the hybrid generation.

Mendel's explanation for this phenomenon was that there were certain *factors* in the plants which were related to certain physical characteristics, but which would not always manifest themselves. In particular, in the hybrid generation, although all of the plants would have red flowers, a certain proportion of them would contain the factor for producing white flowers. If the offspring of a cross receives one factor from each parent, then every hybrid will carry a factor for red flowers and a factor for white flowers, although only the red-flower factor will manifest itself. When a hybrid is crossed with a hybrid, four possibilities arise: the offspring may arise from the combination of the red factor from the first plant and the red factor from the second; from the combination of the red factor from the first and the white factor from the second; from the combination of the white factor from the first and the red factor from the second; or from the combination of the white factor from both parents. Three of these combinations will lead to a red flowering plant, one will lead to a purebred white flowering plant. These are almost precisely the ratios observed by Mendel.

The *factors* proposed by Mendel have become the *genes* postulated by modern genetic theory, and there is now a rich theoretical background in cell biology for this genetic theory. This theory nevertheless remains one for which the primary evidence is unusually accessible (anyone can count the numbers of red flowers and white flowers), and which is yet a particularly elegant theory, particularly amenable to formal treatment.

For our bit of biology, we shall therefore take a fragment of genetic theory formalized by J. H. Woodger, who has also formalized parts of cell theory. The part of genetic theory we shall be concerned with is the part embodied in Mendel's first law: that there are as many sorts of egg cells, and as many sorts of pollen cells, as there are possible constant combinations of forms. Woodger's interest in this bit of formalization is two-fold: first, to uncover the "considerable wealth and complexity of hidden assumptions" in the conventional formulations of Mendel's first law; and second, "to inquire how far the Mendelian hypotheses may now be having an inhibiting effect by restricting research to those lines which conform to the basic assumptions of Mendel. It may be profitable to inquire into those assumptions in order to consider what may happen if we search for regions in which they do not hold." ("Studies in the Foundations of Genetics," p. 408.)

II

The genetical axiom system (fragment of genetics) that Woodger provides is fully formalized as a calculus: that is, primitive terms (vocabulary) are listed explicitly, postulates are laid out, and standard rules of inference for set theory and logic explicitly employed. From our point of view, however, the formal system is still incomplete, because the interpretation of the system is only indicated, rather than spelled out in detail. Indeed, to spell out the interpretation in detail, in such a way as to enable us to tie our formal system to observational statements, the calculus of the system must be slightly extended. Thus although I shall follow closely the scheme of Woodger's calculus, I shall supplement it here and there.

Vocabulary	Formation rules; Syntactical role	Preliminary interpretation; Meaning postulates
G	set	of gametes
F	operation	of fusion
Z*	set	of zygotes

Meaning Postulate: MP1 $z \in \mathbf{Z}^* \supset (\exists x)(\exists y)(x \in \mathbf{G} \ \& \ y \in \mathbf{G} \ \& \ z = \mathbf{F}(x,y))$

E*	set	of all environments
dlz	relation	zygote x develops in environment y into life z

Meaning Postulate: MP2   **dlz** $(x,y,z) \supset (x \in \mathbf{Z}^* \ \& \ y \in \mathbf{E}^*)$

The opportunity has been resisted here of taking "**dlz**" as a primitive in terms of which both "**E***" (which might be regarded as "$\hat{y}(\exists x)(\exists z)(\mathbf{dlz} \ (x,y,z))$"), and "**Z***" (which might be regarded as "$\hat{x}(\exists x)(\exists y)(\mathbf{dlz} \ (x,y,z))$") could be defined. It has been resisted because we might want to consider environments in which there are no zygotes, and zygotes that never develop into lives. But there are no lives that do not begin as zygotes and develop in some environment, so we can define:

DV1 $\mathbf{L^*} =_{Df} \hat{z}(\exists x)(\exists y)(\mathbf{dlz}(x,y,z)))$

In a similar way we can define a relation between a gamete and a zygote that Woodger takes as primitive: "creates by fusion (with something else)"

DV2 $u\mathbf{F}x \equiv_{Df} (u \in \mathbf{G}\ \&\ (\exists y)(y \in \mathbf{G}\ \&\ \mathbf{F}(u,y) = x))$

Vocabulary	Formation rules; Syntactical role	Preliminary interpretation; Meaning postulates
gam	relation	produced by
Meaning Postulate:	MP3	$u\ \mathbf{gam}\ z \supset (u \in \mathbf{G}\ \&\ z \in \mathbf{L^*})$
♂	set	male gametes
Meaning Postulate:	MP4	$♂ \subset \mathbf{G}$
♀	set	female gametes
Meaning Postulate:	MP5	$♀ \subset \mathbf{G}$
phen	set	phenotypes—a set of sets of lives
Meaning Postulate:	MP6	$x \in \mathbf{phen} \supset (y)(y \in x \supset y \in \mathbf{L^*})$

Rules of Inference:

The standard ones.

Postulates:

P-1

P-1 is provable from postulates P-2, P-3, and P-4; it is presented as Theorem A below.

P-2 $\qquad\qquad\qquad (\exists u)(u\mathbf{F}x\ \&\ u\mathbf{F}w) \supset x = w$

P-3 $\qquad\quad (u\mathbf{F}x\ \&\ v\mathbf{F}x\ \&\ u \neq v) \supset ((u \in ♂\ \&\ v \in ♀) \vee (u \in ♀\ \&\ v \in ♂))$

P-4 $\qquad\qquad\qquad\qquad ♂ \cap ♀ = \Lambda$

THEOREM A (P-1):

$\qquad (u\mathbf{F}x\ \&\ v\mathbf{F}x\ \&\ u \neq v) \supset \sim(\exists w)(w\mathbf{F}x\ \&\ w \neq u\ \&\ w \neq v)$

PROOF (by *reductio ad absurdum*):

1. $(\exists u)(\exists x)(\exists v)(u\mathbf{F}x\ \&\ v\mathbf{F}x\ \&\ u \neq v\ \&\ (\exists w)(w\mathbf{F}x\ \&\ w \neq u\ \&\ w \neq v))$		CP
2. $u\mathbf{F}x\ \&\ v\mathbf{F}x\ \&\ w\mathbf{F}x\ \&\ u \neq v\ \&\ w \neq v\ \&\ w \neq v$		EI
3. $(u \in ♂\ \&\ v \in ♀) \vee (u \in ♀\ \&\ v \in ♂)$		2, P-3
4. $(u \in ♂\ \&\ w \in ♀) \vee (u \in ♀\ \&\ w \in ♂)$		2, P-3
5. $(v \in ♂\ \&\ w \in ♀) \vee (v \in ♀\ \&\ w \in ♂)$		2, P-3

[284]

6. $(u \in \male \ \& \ v \in \female \ \& \ w \in \female \ \& \ v \in \male) \lor (u \in \male \ \& \ v \in \female \ \& \ w \in \female \ \& \ w \in \male) \lor$
$(u \in \male \ \& \ v \in \female \ \& \ w \in \male \ \& \ u \in \female \ \& \ v \in \male \ \& \ w \in \female) \lor (u \in \male \ \& \ v \in \female \ \&$
$w \in \male \ \& \ u \in \female) \lor (v \in \male \ \& \ u \in \female \ \& \ u \in \male \ \& \ w \in \female) \lor (v \in \male \ \& \ u \in \female \ \&$
$u \in \male \ \& \ w \in \female \ \& \ w \in \male) \lor (v \in \male \ \& \ u \in \female \ \& \ w \in \male \ \& \ w \in \female) \lor (v \in \male \ \&$
$u \in \female \ \& \ w \in \male \ \& \ v \in \female)$ 3,4,5

7. $\sim(v \in \male \ \& \ v \in \female) \ \& \ \sim(w \in \female \ \& \ w \in \male) \ \& \ \sim(u \in \male \ \& \ u \in \female) \ \& \sim (u \in \male \ \&$
$u \in \female) \sim (u \in \female \ \& \ u \in \male) \ \& \sim(u \in \female \ \& \ u \in \male) \ \& \sim(w \in \male \ \& \ w \in \female) \ \&$
$\sim(v \in \male \ \& \ v \in \female)$ P-4

8. $v \in \male \ \& \sim v \in \male$ 6,7

9. Theorem A—the denial of line 1.

P-5 $(\mathbf{dlz}(x,y,z) \ \& \ \mathbf{dlz} \ (u,v,z)) \supset (x = u \ \& \ y = v)$

P-6 $[\mathbf{dlz} \ (x,y,z) \ \& \ \mathbf{dlz} \ (x',y',z') \ \& \ (\exists u)(u \ \mathbf{gam} \ z \ \& \ u \ \mathbf{gam} \ z')] \supset x = x'$

Definitions:

(For clarity, Greek letters will be used as variables whose values are classes of gametes, and capital Roman letters will be used as variables whose values are classes of lives or zygotes or environments.)

D-1 $U \ (\alpha,\beta) =_{Df} \hat{x}[(\exists u)(\exists v)(u \in \alpha \ \& \ v \in \beta \ \& \ u \neq v \ \& \ uFx \ \& \ vFx)]$

$U(\alpha,\beta)$ is the class of zygotes formed by the union of a gamete of class α and a gamete of class β.

D-2 $L_E(Z) =_{Df} \hat{z}[(\exists x)(\exists y)(\mathbf{dlz} \ (x,y,z) \ \& \ x \in Z \ \& \ y \in E \ \& \ Z \subset Z^* \ \& \ E \subset E^*)$

$L_E(Z)$ is the class of lives developing from a zygote of class Z in an environment of class E.

D-3 $G_E(X) =_{Df} \hat{u}[(\exists x)(\exists y)(\exists z)(\mathbf{dlz}(x,y,z) \ \& \ y \in E \ \& \ E \subset E^* \ \& \ z \in X \ \&$
                                                         $X \subset L^* \ \& \ u \ \mathbf{gam} \ z)]$

$G_E(X)$ is the class of gametes produced by lives of the class X developing in an environment of the class E.

D-4 $\mathbf{Fil}_{K,M,E} \ (X,Y) =_{Df} \hat{z}[(\exists x)(\exists y)(\exists u)(\exists v)(u \in G_K(X) \ \& \ v \in G_M(Y) \ \&$
                                                    $uFx \ \& \ vFx \ \& \ u \neq v \ \& \ y \in E \ \& \ E \subset E^* \ \& \ \mathbf{dlz}(x,y,z))]$

$\mathbf{Fil}_{K,M,E} \ (X,Y)$ is the class of offspring, developing in an environment of class E, one parent being of class X and developing in an environment of class K; the other parent being of class Y, developing in an environment of class M.

D-5 $D(\alpha,\beta,E) =_{Df} L_E(U(\alpha,\beta))$

$D(\alpha,\beta,E)$ is the set of lives developing from zygotes formed by the union of a gamete from class α and a gamete from class α, developing in an environment of class E.

D-6 $G(\alpha,\beta,E) =_{Df} G_E(L_E(U(\alpha,\beta))$

[285]

$\mathbf{G}(\alpha,\beta,E)$ is the set of gametes produced by lives developing from zygotes formed by the union of a gamete from class α and a gamete from class β, developing in an environment of class E.

D-7 $\qquad \mathbf{F}'_{K,M,E}(\alpha,\beta;\gamma,\delta) =_{Df} \mathbf{Fil}_{K,M,E}(\mathbf{D}(\alpha,\beta,K),\mathbf{D}(\gamma,\delta,M))$

$\mathbf{F}'_{K,M,E}(\alpha,\beta;\gamma,\delta)$ is the set of offspring developing in E, one parent being a life formed from gametes of class α and of class β, developing in K, the other parent being a life formed from gametes of class γ and class δ, developing in M.

D-8 $\qquad F_E(\alpha,\beta;\gamma,\delta) =_{Df} F'_{E,E,E}(\alpha,\beta;\gamma,\delta).$

In Mendelian cases we need be concerned only with a single class of environments.

D-9 $\qquad$ **genunit** $=_{Df} \hat{S}((\exists P)(\exists \alpha)(\exists E)(S = \{P,\alpha,E\}$ & $P \in \textbf{phen}$ & $\mathbf{D}(\alpha,\alpha,E) \neq \Lambda$
$\qquad\qquad$ & $\mathbf{D}(\alpha,\alpha,E) \subseteq P$ & $\mathbf{G}(\alpha,\alpha,E) \neq \Lambda$ & $\mathbf{G}(\alpha,\alpha,E) \subseteq \alpha)).$

A genetical unit is a set of three things: a phenotype, an environment, and class of gametes; it breeds true—i.e., neither the process of development ($\mathbf{D}$) nor the process of gamete formation ($\mathbf{G}$) yields anything that does not belong to the genetical unit.

We require the notion of randomness in two respects: randomness of union of gametes and randomness of development in an environment of a given class of environments. As Woodger points out, randomness in such contexts as these does not require explication by means of a complicated theory of probability— all it involves, in either context, and indeed in genetics generally, is the persistence of certain relative frequencies, or proportions.

Woodger takes these relative frequencies to be simply relative frequencies in large but finite classes. I shall follow him in this, though it should be noted that the "large but finite classes" should be very large, and may often be not classes of actual existing entities, but classes of possible or potentially existing entities. (A more elegant approach might be to speak of propensities, as Popper does, or chance setups, as Hacking does, but this would involve introducing a new term.) Since the classes are finite, we can speak directly of the proportion of a given class that has a given property. Following Woodger, we define

$\Delta 1 \quad py =_{Df} \hat{x}[(\exists z)(\exists v)(v$ is a finite cardinal number & z is a finite cardinal
$\qquad\qquad$ number & $z \neq 0$ & $x \in z$ & $x \cap y \in v$ & $v = pz)].$

py is thus the set of all finite sets, a proportion p of which belong to y.

Another set-theoretical notion we shall need is that of the pair-set of two sets x and y, written "$[x,y]$". It consists of all those sets consisting of one object from the set x and one object from the set y. The definition is

$\Delta 2 \qquad\qquad [x,y] =_{Df} \hat{z}(\exists u)(\exists v)(u \in x$ & $v \in y$ & $z = \{y,v\}).$

[286]

Some set-theoretical theorems (I have retained Woodger's numbering) used in the proofs of the theorems of genetics that follow are

THEOREM VII.

$$(x \text{ is finite } \& x \neq \Lambda \& x \subseteq y) \supset (x \in 1y).$$

THEOREM X.

$$(x \text{ is finite } \& x \neq \Lambda \& x \subseteq y \cup z \& y \cap z = \Lambda) \equiv (\exists p)(x \in py \cap (1 - p)z).$$

The next two definitions, which involve the notion of randomness, bear much of the weight of the formal system we are concerned with. It is therefore important to struggle through their complexity and to arrive at a clear understanding of what they say.

D-10 **rand U** $=_{Df} \hat{S}\{(\exists S_1)(\exists S_2)(S_1 \in \textbf{genunit} \& S_2 \in \textbf{genunit} \& (S = S_1 \cup S_2 \vee (\exists R)(R \in \textbf{phen} \& S = S_1 \cup S_2 \cup \{R\}) \& (\alpha)(\beta)(\gamma)(\delta)(\zeta)(\theta)(E)(P)((\alpha \in S \& \beta \in S \& \gamma \in S \& \delta \in S \& \zeta \in S \& \theta \in S \& E \in S \& [\textbf{G}(\alpha,\beta,E), \textbf{G}(\gamma,\delta,E)] \in p[\zeta,\theta]) \supset \textbf{U}(\textbf{G}(\alpha,\beta,E),\textbf{G}(\gamma,\delta,E)) \in p\textbf{U}(\zeta,\theta)))\}$.

I have, I hope in the interest of clarity, rearranged Woodger's definition. **rand U** is a set of sets, each of which is the union of two purebreeding genetical units $S_1 = \{P_1,\alpha_1,E_1\}$ and $S_2 = \{P_2,\alpha_2,E_2\}$, supplemented, if neither phenotype P_1 nor P_2 is a dominant over the other, by a third phenotype R, the phenotype produced by zygotes resulting from the fusion of a gamete of class α_1 and a gamete of class α_2, in an environment belonging to either the class E_1, or the class E_2. Further, observe that the pure genetic constitution $\alpha_1\alpha_1$ may yield a new phenotype P_1^* under an environment of class E_2, and similarly that lives developing from zygotes produced by the fusion of gametes both of class α_2 may yield a new phenotype P_2^* in an environment of class E_1. In the Mendelian case this does not happen since $E_1 = E_2 = E$, and novel phenotypes P^*_1 and P^*_2 will not be called for. Similarly, though S_1 and S_2 are genetically closed, if their union includes two classes E_1 and E_2 of environments, there may be produced novel gametes. Thus although (by the definition of **genunit**) we have both $\textbf{D}(\alpha_1,\alpha_1,E_1) \subseteq P_1$ and $\textbf{G}(\alpha_1,\alpha_1,E_1) \subseteq \alpha_1$ for S_1 and $\textbf{D}(\alpha_2,\alpha_2 E_2) \subseteq P_2$ and $\textbf{D}(\alpha_2,\alpha_2,E_2) \subseteq \alpha_2$ for S_2, we must in their union take account of $\textbf{D}(\alpha_1,\alpha_1,E_2)$, and $\textbf{D}(\alpha_2\alpha_2E_1)$, which may not be included in P_1 and P_2, respectively, and of $\textbf{G}(\alpha_1,\alpha_1,E_2)$ and $\textbf{G}(\alpha_2,\alpha_2,E_1)$ which may not be included in α_1 and α_2, respectively. In the Mendelian case, as I said, we don't have to worry; but the question of non-Mendelian cases, which could perfectly well arise in actual fact, is one which might not be thought of except for the formalization of the theory.

Given, now, that the set S is either $\{P_1,\alpha_1,E_1,P_2,\alpha_2,E_2\}$ or $\{P_1,\alpha_1,E_1,P_2,\alpha_2,E_2,R\}$ —and usually we will have $E = E_1 = E_2$—D10 further stipulates that *if* the proportion of pair classes of the two classes of gametes $\textbf{G}(\alpha,\beta,E)$ and $\textbf{G}(\gamma,\delta,E)$ that belongs to the pair class $[\zeta,\theta]$ is p, *then* that same proportion of the kinds of gametes will obtain in the zygotes produced by the fusion of gametes from the original two classes $G(\alpha,\beta,E)$ and $G(\gamma,\delta,E)$. The variables $\alpha,\beta,\gamma,\delta,\zeta$, and θ have as their relevant values only α_1, and α_2; E may be E_1 or E_2.

In a similar fashion, we define randomness with respect to development. Again I shall modify Woodger's definition—this time because there is an error in it: "E" occurs as a free variable on the left-hand side of the definitory biconditional, and only bound on the right-hand side. Presumably, some of the occurrences on the right-hand side are to be regarded as free, corresponding to the occurrence in the definiendum. The problem arises from our natural tendency to think of the Mendelian case in which E is simply a constant.

D-11   **rand D** $=_{Df} \hat{S}\{(\exists S_1)(\exists S_2)(S_1 \in$ **genunit** $\& \ S_2 \in$ **genunit** $\&$
$S = S_1 \cup S_2 \lor (\exists R)(R \in$ **phen** $\& \ S = S_1 \cup S_2 \cup \{R\})) \ \&$
$(\alpha)(\beta) \ (\gamma)(\delta)(\zeta)(\theta)(E)(p)((\alpha \in S \ \& \ \beta \in S \ \& \ \gamma \in S \ \& \ \delta \in S \ \&$
$\zeta \in S \ \& \ \theta \in S \ \& \ E \in S \ \& \ U(G(\alpha,\beta,E),G(\gamma,\delta,E)) \in p U(\zeta,\theta)) \supset$
$D(G(\alpha,\beta,E), \ G(\gamma,\delta,E),E) \in p D(\zeta,\theta,E))\}.$

The definition, like the preceding one, stipulates first that the objects belonging to **rand D** are sets of the form $\{P_1,\alpha_1,E_1,P_2,\alpha_2,E_2\}$, or of the form $\{P_1,\alpha_1,E_1,P_2, \alpha_2,E_2,R\}$ in situations in which there is no dominance. $\{P_1,\alpha_1, \ E_1\}$ and $\{P_2,\alpha_2,E_2\}$ are to be genetical units. Should the circumstances be Mendelian, with $E_1 = E_2 = E$, we simply have a redundant mention of E in these descriptions. The definition next stipulates that whatever classes of gametes $\alpha,\beta,\gamma,\delta,\zeta,\theta$ may be (each one must be α_1 or α_2, for those are the only two classes of gametes that belong to S), *if* the proportion of zygotes formed from the union of a gamete from the class $G(\alpha,\beta,E)$ with one from the class $G(\gamma,\delta,E)$ that are also zygotes formed from the union of a gamete from class θ and a gamete from class ζ is p, *then* the same proportion of the class of all lives developing from zygotes formed from the union of gametes of these two classes will be also lives developing from zygotes formed by the union of a gamete of class ζ and a gamete from class θ— all in environment E, of course.

There follow a few of the theorems that Woodger includes in his systematic presentation. The theorems are all self-explanatory. The reference to the right of each theorem indicate the basis of its proof.

THEOREM 1

$U(\alpha,\beta) = U(\beta,\alpha)$ D-1

THEOREM 2

$U(x,x) = U(x \cap \male, x \cap \female)$ D1, P-3

THEOREM 10

$D(x \cap \male, x \cap \female,E) = D(x,x,E)$ D-5, T-2

[288]

THEOREM 12

$[G(\alpha,\alpha,E) \subseteq \alpha] \supset [D(G(\alpha,\alpha,E),G(\alpha,\alpha,E),E) \subseteq D(\alpha,\alpha,E)]$

D-1,D-2,D-5

THEOREM 13

$F_E(\alpha,\beta;\gamma,\delta) = D(G(\alpha,\beta,E),G(\gamma,\delta,E),E)$ D-8,D-7,D-4,D-5,D-6,D-1,D-2

THEOREM 14

$\{P,\alpha,E\} \in$ **genunit** $\supset F_E(\alpha,\alpha;\alpha,\alpha) \subseteq P$ T-13,D-9,T-12

The theorems toward which Woodger is working are those that concern the distribution of phenotypes among offspring of hybrids. These theorems are hypothetical in form, and bear complex antecedents; so, following Woodger, we introduce some abbreviations:

H-1 *for* $\{P,\alpha,E\} \in$ **genunit** & $\{Q,\beta,E\} \in$ **genunit**

H-2 *for* $D(\alpha,\beta,E) \subseteq P$

H-3 *for* $R \in$ **phen** & $D(\alpha,\beta,E) \subseteq R$).

There follow three forms of Mendelian hypothesis:

H-4a *for* $G(\alpha,\beta,E) \cap \male \in \frac{1}{2}\alpha \cap \frac{1}{2}\beta$ & $G(\alpha,\beta,E) \cap \female \in \frac{1}{2}\alpha \cap \frac{1}{2}\beta$.

H-4b *for* $G(\alpha,\beta,E) \cap \male \neq \Lambda$ & $G(\alpha,\beta,E) \cap \male \subseteq \alpha \cup \beta$ & $G(\alpha,\beta,E) \cap \female \neq \Lambda$ &
$\quad G(\alpha,\beta,E) \cap \female \subseteq \alpha \cup \beta$.

H-4c *for* $G(\alpha,\beta,E) \neq \Lambda$ & $G(\alpha,\beta,E) \subseteq \alpha \cup \beta$.

And, finally, two forms of randomness hypothesis.

H-5 *for* $S = \{P,\alpha,E\} \cup \{Q,\beta,E\}$ & $S \in$ **rand D** & $S \in$ **rand U**.

H-5a *for* $S = \{P,\alpha,E,Q,\beta,R\}$ & $S \in$ **rand D** $\cap$ **rand U**.

The main theorems are the following:

THEOREM 15

$$(\text{H-1 \& H-2 \& H-4a \& H-5}) \supset F_E(\alpha,\beta;\alpha,\beta) \in \tfrac{3}{4}P \cap \tfrac{1}{4}Q.$$

This theorem represents the classical form of Mendel's first law. In words, it states that if P and Q are distinct phenotypes that breed true under standard environmental conditions E (H-1), and if the offspring of a cross between the two types P and Q all belong to the type P (H-2), and if the male gametes produced by these hybrids (the P-Q crosses) are half of the type that produces P and half of the type that produces Q, and the same is true of the female gametes (H-4a), and finally, if both the union of gametes and the development of zygotes is

[289]

random in the environment E (H-5), then $\frac{3}{4}$ of the offspring of the hybrids will belong to the dominant phenotype P, and $\frac{1}{4}$ will belong to the recessive phenotype Q. The proof of this theorem is left as an exercise. It will involve the use of the purely set-theoretic theorem:

THEOREM XV

$$(x \cap y = \alpha \cap \beta = \Lambda) \supset ((x \in p\alpha \cap (1 - p)\beta \ \& \ y \in q\alpha \cap (1 - q)\beta) \supset$$
$$[x,y] \in pq[\alpha,\alpha] \cap (p(1 - q) + q(1 - p))[\alpha,\beta] \cap (1 - p)(1 - q)[\beta,\beta]).$$

THEOREM 16

$$(\text{H-1} \ \& \ \text{H-2} \ \& \ \text{H-4c} \ \& \ \text{H-5}) \supset (\exists p)(F_E(\beta,\beta;\alpha,\beta) \in pP \cap (1 - p)Q \ \&$$
$$\mathbf{G}\,(\alpha,\beta,E) \in p\alpha \cap (1 - p)\beta).$$

Theorem 16 asserts that if P and Q are pure-breeding phenotypes, if P is dominant over Q, if there are gametes produced by zygotes formed by the union of a gamete of kind α and a gamete of kind β, and these gametes are also of kind α or β, and finally if both union and development are random in E, then there is some definite proportion p which is both the proportion of offspring of a cross between parents developing from $\beta-\beta$ zygotes and parents developing from $\alpha-\beta$ zygotes, which belong to the phenotype P, and also the proportion of gametes produced by $\alpha-\beta$ zygotes that belong to the kind α. This theorem (whose proof is also left for the student) will help to provide an important link between the abstract theory with its talk of unobservable kinds of gametes, and the real world of white and red sweet peas.

THEOREM 17

$$(\text{H-1} \ \& \ \text{H-2} \ \& \ \text{H-4b} \ \& \ \text{H-5}) \supset (\exists p)(\exists q)(F_E(\alpha,\beta;\alpha,\beta) \in (p - pq + q)P \cap$$
$$(1 - p)(1 - q)Q \ \& \ \mathbf{G}(\alpha,\beta,E) \cap \male \in p\alpha \cap (1 - p)\beta \ \&$$
$$\mathbf{G}(\alpha,\beta,E) \cap \female \in q\alpha \cap (1 - q)\beta)$$

Here we have a theorem which asserts that if we are dealing with a system of two genetic units, with dominance, and zygotes formed from the union of α and β gametes produce in turn both α and β male and α and β female gametes, and unions and developments in E take place randomly, then there will exist numbers p and q such that the offspring of hybrids mated with hybrids will be of phenotype P in a proportion $(p + q - pq)$ of the cases, and p will represent the proportion of male α gametes produced by the hybrids, and q the proportion of female α gametes produced by them.

THEOREM 18

$$(\text{H-1} \ \& \ \text{H-3} \ \& \ \text{H-4b} \ \& \ \text{H-5a}) \supset (\exists p)(\exists q)(F_E(\alpha,\beta;\alpha,\beta) \in pqP \cap$$
$$(p(1 - q) + q(1 - p))R \cap (1 - p)(1 - q)Q \ \&$$
$$\mathbf{G}(\alpha,\beta,E) \cap \male \in p\alpha \cap (1 - p)\beta \ \& \ \mathbf{G}(\alpha,\beta,E) \cap \female \in q\alpha \cap (1 - q)\beta).$$

This theorem says precisely the same thing as the preceding one, without the restriction to cases of dominance, in which the hybrids are of the phenotype *P*. Indeed, Theorem 17 is but a special case of Theorem 18.

III

Like many other formalizers, Woodger does not deal at any length with the problem of providing an interpretation for his calculus, although he provides many informal hints as to how the interpretation should run. We shall trace the connections between the formal signs of the calculus (boldface "**G**", "**♂**", etc.) and terms of ordinary English whose use exhibits relatively high interpersonal uniformity.

"**G**" denotes the set of gametes. We are not, of course, directly acquainted with the set of gametes; but we can sometimes meet individual gametes—spermatozoa, egg cells. Are these kinds of things directly observable? Gametes are not often large enough to be seen with the naked eye, but they can be seen with the aid of a microscope. Although they can't be seen with the naked eye, there seems to be no reason for withholding from them the adjective "observable". That, with a microscope, anybody can see spermatozoa, is simply a fact of the twentieth century. That something which is unobservable at one point in time can become observable at a later point in time, is just a matter of technology. While this may be philosophically disquieting to those who would like to find a profound epistemological distinction between the observable and the unobservable, the alternative of sticking with the unaided senses doesn't really provide the desired sharpness: some people's senses are more acute than others.

But it is still one thing to be able to *see* a gamete, with or without the aid of lenses and microscopes; it is something else again to be able to *see that* such and such an object is a sperm or an egg. Indeed, so great is the wondrous variety of life that it is no simple matter to take a given cell, and be able to tell whether or not it is a reproductive cell, without knowing how that cell functions, or where it comes from, or (yet more theoretical) knowing something of its chromosomal structure.

Thus in the context of a full-blown cell biology, "gamete" is far more a theoretical term than an observation term. On the level of crossing sweet peas, however, it seems to be rather more an observation term than a theoretical term. Perhaps it would be in the interest of precision and clarity to speak of male and female gametophytes, which are more often regarded as observationally identifiable. To come down to cases, on the pea flower we can identify anther and stigma. The anthers are the source of the male gametophytes (pollen), while the stigma is the source of the female gametophytes, the ovules. The male gametophyte contains one cell that is the male gamete; the female gametophyte contains one cell that is the female gamete. These two cells fuse to form the zygote that in turn will lead to a new organism. The zygote goes through a period of development before it becomes a seed, which is again something ostensively identifiable as a certain kind of life. We need two more primitive terms on the observational level: pollen, and ovule.

Vocabulary	Formation Rule	Interpretation
P	predicate	"$P(x)$" means "x is a pollen grain"
0	predicate	"$0(x)$" means "x is an ovule"

We require also the relation "is a (physical) part of" in order to express the connection between our theoretical terms and the observational terms. Carnap, in *Introduction to Logic*, has a full-blown formalization of this concept, designed for biological contexts; but we here need only the property that if x is part of y, then either y is not part of x or $x = y$. And further, we need the fact that "is a part of" is relatively ostensive: there are many instances in which we can see (be shown) two things, and observe that the one is a part of the other. (The tail is part of the dog, the pupil is part of the eye, the cilia are parts of the paramecium.) It is not, however, always ostensive: the gamete is part of the gametophyte, the chromosome is part of the cell, the nucleus is part of the atom. We do suppose that the part-whole relation is the same at these various levels of ostensiveness.

Vocabulary	Formation Rule	Interpretation
Pt	relation	"$Pt(x,y)$" means "x is part of y"

MP-7 $Pt(x,y) \supset (\sim Pt(y,x) \lor x = y)$.

The relationship between these observation terms and the corresponding terms in our theoretical vocabulary is the following: If x is a male gamete, then there is a y such that y is a pollen grain, and x is part of y.

MP-8 $x \in \mathbf{G} \cap \male \supset (\exists y)(P(y) \mathbin{\&} Pt(x,y))$.

And if x is a female gamete, then there is a y such that y is an ovule, and x is part of y.

MP-9 $x \in \mathbf{G} \cap \female \supset (\exists y)(0(y) \mathbin{\&} Pt(x,y))$.

If y is an ovule and x is a pollen grain, then there is no z such that any part of x is part of z and at the same time any part of y is part of z. In other words, a gametophyte is either all male and contains a male gamete, or all female, and contains a female gamete. (In another formalization, this might well be regarded as a substantive postulate.)

MP-10 $(0(y) \mathbin{\&} P(x)) \supset \sim(\exists z)[(\exists w)(Pt(w,x) \mathbin{\&} Pt(w,z)) \mathbin{\&} (\exists v)(Pt(v,y) \mathbin{\&} Pt(v,z))]$.

[292]

The primitive term "F" represents an operation on gametes: the operation of fusion, which gives rise to a zygote. Since neither the entities which fuse, nor the entity which is the result of fusion is ostensive, this operation is clearly not ostensive. Note that it is not the fact that it is an operation that renders it non-ostensive: the operation of poaching, which is performed on raw eggs, and which gives rise (with reasonable luck) to poached eggs, is ostensive. Rather than restricting the scope of the operation F to gametes through the formulation of restrictive formation rules, we shall stipulate that the fusion of x and y always exists, for any terms at all, but is generally the empty set. (We are free, that is, to interpret "F" in any way we want or find convenient, in the cases that are not of serious concern to us.) Furthermore, if one of the entities isn't male and the other female, we still don't get a zygote, and so we shall again suppose that we get the empty set. Our meaning postulates for F, then, are

MP-11	$F(x,y) = F(y,x)$	Fusion is symmetrical
MP-12	$F(x,y) \neq \Lambda \supset [(x \in \male \cap \mathbf{G} \ \& \ y \in \female \cap \mathbf{G})$ $\vee (x \in \female \cap \mathbf{G} \ \& \ y \in \male \cap \mathbf{G})]$	Fusion is restricted to an operation on male and female gametes
MP-13	$F(x,y) \neq \Lambda \supset F(x,y) \in \mathbf{Z}^*.$	The result of a fusion is a zygote

Observe that there is nothing in this theory to say that there aren't gametes that are neither male nor female. There don't happen to be any such things, but we don't need to stipulate it for the bit of genetics we are doing here; it is not part of the *meaning* of the term "gamete".

The term $\mathbf{Z}^*$ stands for the set of all zygotes. Again, as in the case of gametes, we have a set of entities which are not generally ostensive. We might, through a microscope, be shown zygotes, just as we might, through a microscope, be shown gametes. In the twentieth century, against the background of an adequate theory of optics, perception, and general theoretical biology, we can have some ostensive acquaintance with zygotes and with gametes. But again, as in the case of gametes, a part of the significance of the term "zygote" lies in the history of the zygote (it arose by the fusion of a male and female gamete), and a part of its significance lies in the potential future of the zygote: it is generally capable of developing into a life. The historical element, which is more nearly a part of the *meaning* of the term "zygote," is captured by the meaning postulate MP-1.

The class of environments $\mathbf{E}^*$ comes close to being ostensive. Woodger does not intend it to be altogether ostensive, because he wants to be able to consider micro-environments which are clearly inaccessible to observation. And yet there are ways of approaching even this notion of environment ostensively. Mendel's monastery garden, right here, with its weather and sun and ambient temperatures, its varying moisture its soil—this is what I mean by "environment"

[293]

in the first place. This is part of it, and this and this, and that. And things like them. The environment of the developing zygote is (at first) the interior of the ovule—again something that is perfectly ostensive: this is the ovule, and this is its inside. By a natural and continuous extension, we can then speak of the environment that impinges directly on the cell walls of the zygote: the enzymes and nutrients in which it exists and divides.

The same sort of thing is true of the set of lives, L^*. Woodger construes a life to be a segment of time in the life of an entity—so that this plant from 10:00 A.M. to 10:00 P.M. today would be a life; this man from his sixth birthday to his fiftieth birthday would be a life; this turtle from 10:51 A.M. to 10:52 P.M. would be a life. We have already dealt with time variables—for the purposes of our biological system, we can simply take dates for granted. Thus a life is to be understood as a living being (something which is almost purely ostensive in this context) paired with a couple of dates.

Here is a phenomenon that has perhaps not been sufficiently emphasized in discussions of the reduction of one kind of thing, such as living bodies, to another such as chemical organizations. In the formal system we define the ordinary in terms of the extraordinary. In this particular case, we define lives in terms of zygotes and environments. And yet semantically, the lives are prior to the zygotes and also prior to the gametes in terms of which we have defined the zygotes. The definitions function, one might say, opposite to the usual direction: they serve to clarify the definiens rather than the definiendum. We define the set of lives in terms (ultimately) of gametes and fusion and environments. Since we are ostensively acquainted with many lives and environments, this definition serves to establish connections between these things that we are familiar with, and things, such as gametes and fusions, that we are not familiar with. We turn Aristotle on his head, and define the familiar in terms of the unfamiliar. The same thing can be seen over and over again in science. What we are familiar with are bits of stuff; atomic physics defines them in terms of unfamiliar atoms and bonds. We are familiar with table salt and sand; chemistry defines them in terms of such utterly unfamiliar substances as chlorine and sodium and silicon. The procedure sounds pointless— and would be, except in the context of a theory, or a formal system, that exhibits deep interconnections. In that context, what counts is merely that we have some connection, somewhere, between things with which we are familiar, and the things, postulated by the theory, which are strange to us. The theoretical concepts, not the familiar ones, embody our knowledge of the world.

"**dlz**" is again a primitive relation whose use has ostensive roots, and yet whose meaning extends well beyond what can plausibly be called observational. We are perfectly familiar with the way in which things develop into other things under appropriate circumstances: for example, we are perfectly familiar with the way seedlings or young plants develop into mature pea plants (both seedlings and mature pea plants being the kinds of things that Woodger has called lives—organisms and pairs of dates). We can extend this notion of development backwards, and apply it to the development of the seed from a small seed. Indeed, though we can't *see* the seed undergoing this development—it lies inside its pod—we can watch the bumps in the pod grow day by day. And once having the theoretical concept of a gamete, and of a zygote as a single diploid cell that results from the fusion of two haploid gametes, we may in a perfectly straightforward manner consider **dlz** (x,y,z)—the development of the life z in the environment y (these concepts being the same as those in the garden variety sort of development), of, not a seed, not even a tiny seed, but a zygote, x. Furthermore, with microscopes, we can see zygotes, and even watch them begin to develop. Of course, in order to be sure that the zygote was a zygote and not simply a wandering single cell, we should have also to see the zygote formed by the fusion of two gametes. Matters, even with microscopes being accepted at face value, are not completely straightforward and "observational." There is a reasonable amount of theoretical content in the relation **dlz**. But the source of this term, the relatively ostensive notion of development, points the way to the connections between this ostensive notion and its theoretical extension. These are embodied in meaning postulate MP-2.

Let us write "$[\textbf{dlz}](x,y,z)$" for the original *ostensive* notion of the relation of development of an organism (a life) x, in an environment y, into the life z. The connection between **dlz** and [**dlz**] may be expressed:

MP-14 $(\textbf{dlz}(x,y,z) \,\&\, \textbf{dlz}(x,y,z')) \supset ([\textbf{dlz}](z,y,z') \lor [\textbf{dlz}](z',y,z))$

MP-15 $[\textbf{dlz}](z,y,z') \supset (\exists x)(\textbf{dlz}(x,y,z) \,\&\, \textbf{dlz}(x,y,z'))$

The postulate P-5 also seems best construed as a meaning postulate: a given life comes from only one zygote, and develops from it in only one environment.

Postulate P-6 might be regarded as either a meaning postulate or as a material postulate of the system: if a given gamete is produced by one life (organism 0 between 10:00 A.M. and noon), and also by another life (organism 0′ between 9:00 A.M. and noon), and these lives develop from zygotes x and x', then x and x' are in fact the same zygote. That is, a gamete is related, through a developing organism (which may be any number of lives), to a unique zygote.

The relation **gam** is again a mixed one. u **gam** z is interpreted to mean that u is a gamete produced by life z. But although lives are observable and ostensive, gametes, and their production, are at least largely theoretical. Nevertheless the connection between the relation **gam** and matters of observation is fairly close. In the discussion of the theoretical term **G**, it was pointed out that gametophytes are observable, and that many gametes occur in gametophytes as parts. Furthermore, the production of gametophytes is ostensive: you can tell that a plant produces pollen by watching the development of the pollen over a period of time; you can tell that a stigma contains ovules (produced ovules) by taking it

[295]

apart and examining it. Let us write [**gam**] for gametophyte production. Then we have:

MP-16 $x[$**gam**$]z \supset (\exists y)(y \in \mathbf{G}$ & y **gam** z & $Pt(x,y))$.

Part of the (observational) meaning of [**gam**] is given by

MP-17 $x[$**gam**$] z \supset (P(x) \lor 0(x))$.

MP-18 $x[$**gam**$] z \supset z \in L^*$.

And similarly, part of the corresponding theoretical meaning of "**gam**" is given by meaning postulate MP-3.

The only remaining primitive term is "**phen**", which is used to denote the set of phenotypes. Here is something that appears to be completely observational: to decide whether something is of a given phenotype or not, one merely has to look at it; sometimes, perhaps, to perform some kind of simple test. Looking is adequate for the phenotypes with which we are concerned here: Here is a tall plant, and here is a short one; this one has red flowers and that has white flowers; look at these two seeds: see how one is wrinkled and one is smooth? While particular phenotypes offer less problems than any other class, in this system, they do not give us a completely adequate handle for the generic term "**phen**". Our acquaintance with the particular phenotypes appropriate to breeding experiments with peas might enable us to conjecture that location of plant does not represent a phenotype, nor the surname of the gardener who weeds it, but how about the size of the leaves? How about the particular shade of green that the leaves have? How about the number of flowers? Such questions as these show that while the notion of a particular phenotype (wrinkled seeds, smooth seeds, pink flowers, white flowers...) is unusually unproblematic, the general notion of the set of phenotypes is unusually difficult. The set of all phenotypes is very clearly not ostensive in the sense that we can, on the basis of an acquaintance with a few members of that set, make pretty good guesses as to whether or not other candidates for membership in that set actually are or aren't members of it. The members of the set **phen** are thus highly ostensive, but the set itself is highly theoretical; in order to know whether a particular physical characteristic represents a phenotype, we must know that that characteristic is an hereditary characteristic of the species in question. And this, as is well known, is often highly problematic.

For the purposes of this particular bit of biology, we shall take **phen** to be a set composed of individual characteristics which are given ostensively; it is a class whose membership is given by a list; and each entry on the list is ostensively given, or could be given ostensively.

In this biological system, the most direct connection between the theoretical terms of the system, and its relatively ostensive terms, is made on the level of terms that, as the system happens to be set up, are defined terms. We have already noticed this in connection with *develops*, *lives*, and *zygotes*. It will thus perhaps be profitable to run over the defined terms of the system, with a view to their interpretation, though of course that interpretation is determined by the interpretation of the primitive terms.

$U(x,y)$: The class of zygotes formed by the union of a gamete from class x with a gamete from class y.

$L_E(Z)$: The set of lives developing from a zygote of class Z in an environment of Class E.

The ostensive roots of these expressions are most apparent when they are combined in expressions of the form "$L_E(U(x,y))$". We then have the following as a theorem deducible from our meaning postulates, which theorem provides a connection among: a set of living things; a set of ovules; and a set of pollen grains:

THEOREM 19

$$[Ow' \text{ \& } Pu' \text{ \& } (\exists w)(\exists u)(w \in x \text{ \& } Pt(w,w') \text{ \& } u \in y \text{ \& } Pt(u,u') \text{ \& } x \subseteq G \text{ \& } y \subseteq G \text{ \& }$$
$$\text{dlz}(F(u,w),E,z))] \supset z \in L_E(U(x,y)).$$

The theorem states simply that if we have an ovule containing a gamete of class x and a pollen containing a gamete of class y, and these gametes fuze to form a zygote that develops into a life, that life will be one of those denoted by "$L_E(U(x,y))$".

$G_E(X)$: The set of gametes produced by lives of class X in an environment of class E.

THEOREM 20

$$x \in G_E(X) \supset (\exists w)(\exists y)(y[\text{gam}] \, w \text{ \& } w \in X \text{ \& } Pt(x,y)).$$

This is to say merely that if something is a gamete produced by a life of class X, then it is a part of an (observable) gametophyte produced by a life of class X.

$\text{Fil}_{K,M,E}(X,Y)$: The class of offspring developing in environment of class E, one of whose parents is a life belonging to class X, developing in K, and one of whose parents is a life of class Y, developing in M.

THEOREM 21

$$x \in \text{Fil}_{K,M,E}(X,Y) \supset (\exists w)(\exists y)(\exists w')(\exists y')(\exists z)(\exists z')(w \in X \text{ \& } w' \in Y \text{ \& } X \subseteq L^* \text{ \& }$$
$$Y \subseteq L^* \text{ \& } y[\text{gam}]w \text{ \& } y' \, [\text{gam}] \, w' \text{ \& } Pt(z,y) \text{ \& } (Ptz',y') \text{ \& } \text{dlz}(F(z,z'),E,x)).$$

$D(\alpha,\beta,E)$: The set of lives developing from zygotes formed by the union of a gamete from class α and a gamete from class β, developing in E.

THEOREM 22

$$x \in D(\alpha,\beta,E) \supset (\exists w)(\exists y)(\exists w')(\exists y')(\exists z)(\exists z')(w \in \alpha \text{ \& } w' \in \beta \text{ \& } z \in L^* \text{ \& }$$
$$z' \in L^* \text{ \& } y \, [\text{gam}] \, z \text{ \& } y' \, [\text{gam}] \, z' \text{ \& } Pt(w,y) \text{ \& } Pt(w'y') \text{ \& } \text{dlz}(F(w,w'),E,x)).$$

[297]

$G(\alpha,\beta,E)$: The set of gametes produced by lives developing from zygotes formed by the union of a gamete from class α and a gamete from class β, developing in E.

This set of gametes is so far removed from any ostensive basis that it had best be looked on as almost entirely theoretical in character.

$F'_{K,M,E}(\alpha,\beta;\gamma,\delta)$: The set of offspring, developing in E, one parent being a life developing from a zygote formed by the union of a gamete of class α and a gamete of class β, developing in K, the other parent being a life developing from a zygote formed by the fusion of a gamete of class γ with a gamete of class δ, developing in M.

Again we have a set whose membership is determined largely on theoretical grounds. Yet it is precisely the distribution of observable characteristics (pink flowers, wrinkled seeds) in such sets as these that provides—through the theorems—both the strongest connection between theoretical and ostensive concepts, and (what is indeed the same thing) the strongest inductive support for the theory.

genunit: A genetical unit is a set of three things: a phenotype, an environment, and a class of gametes, which breeds true, both phenotypically (it is not a hybrid) and genetically (mutations are disallowed).

In all of these definitions, we are involved in theoretical notions—particularly the theoretical notion of a gamete. We are closest to the observational level, perhaps, in the term "**genunit**", for we can, by conducting breeding experiments over a period of some generations, establish that a given kind (a given phenotype, having a given history) of plant breeds true in the phenotypical sense; and from this fact, together with the rest of the theory, we can infer that it breeds true genetically as well.

Woodger's definitions 10 and 11, of randomness in the union of gametes of two genetical units, and of randomness in the development of zygotes formed by the crossing of two genetical units, are perfectly straightforward and clear; they make stipulations about the preservation of certain relative frequencies. In the first case the stipulation is that the proportion of unions of a certain sort is determined by (and is the same as) the proportion of available gametes that enter into unions of that sort. Similarly, random development stipulates essentially that if a certain proportion of unions are of gametes of a certain type, then that same proportion will be maintained among developing lives, in the standard environment.

It should be noted here, as Woodger notes explicitly, that "random" is not being used in a sense that involves any reference to probability or irregularity or chance. "In genetical statements the notion of randomness frequently occurs. It will be required in two places in the present context. In both of these it means persistence of certain relative frequencies during a process. It means the absence of selection or favouritism." (p. 420) "It will be noticed that no use has been

[298]

made here of the words 'probability', 'chance', or 'independent', although these words are frequently used in genetical books with very inadequate explanation. Here the term 'random' has been used but its two senses have been explained in detail." (p. 427).

IV

There are a number of elements involved in the testing of this theory which, while they involve nothing new in principle, appear in this context in a particularly clear form. The fact that the conclusions of the theory are statistical does not involve anything new over classical statics: the theoretical prediction that such and such a quantity will have such and such a magnitude has as its observational cash value only the claim that the mean of a potentially infinite population of measurements will have such and such a value. For the same reason, even the fact that the boundary conditions involved in the prediction can only be stated statistically is not novel in principle. What is somewhat new and different is the fact that the theory itself is statistical from start to finish, and although this fact does not lead to any novelties in the techniques of confirmation, it does entail that a "prediction", from beginning to end, from observational boundary conditions to observational outcome, is statistical. There is no element of ordinary causal determination or determinism at any point in the theory, except in the connection, which is assumed to be invariable in a given environment, between genotype and phenotype; and even this connection may be weakened.

Let us examine in detail just what is involved in the testing of this theory in a particular case. Let us look at dwarf and standard sweet pea plants. The theorems which we have derived in our theory all carry as hypotheses H-1, H-2 (or H-3; but in our case, H-3 is irrelevant as no new phenotype appears), and one or another version of H-4, and H-5. We begin with the observation that tall and dwarf sweet peas are phenotypes. To say that they are phenotypes implies, in particular, that there is not simply a continuum of sizes between "very short" and "very tall". It also implies that the variation in height is not simply due to differences in fertility of the soil, sunlight, water, or some other external factor, and of course to be able to exclude such etiologies as these requires a firm background of botanical knowledge. Yet despite the fact that there is a theoretical background which can be called upon to *justify* the claim that "tall" and "dwarf" are phenotypes, the terms themselves are ostensive in our system. "The plants in this field represent the dwarf sweet peas." Note the word that is used: *represent*. What we *mean* by "tall" are the plants in these fields, and those like them; what we mean by "dwarf" are the plants in this other field, and those like them. The mean height is close to the mean height in the field; the variance is close to the variance in the field. Thus: representative.

The environment of our tests is standard: it involves adequate light, suitable temperatures, levels of radioactivity, nutrients in the soil, and so on. Here again we have a purely ostensive term, "standard" representing a certain class of environments. As before, however, the structure of the class is to some extent determined by our general knowledge of biology: although we say simply "like this", we mean "like this in the relevant respects". But we do not have to specify the "relevant respects"; that specification is not part of our *genetical* system, but part of another general biological system. If (per absurdum) we had no biological background knowledge, environment "like this" would be purely ostensive: or at the very most broken down into "soil like this, weather like this". And that would be perfectly appropriate, in the absence of biological knowledge.

The genetic factors that enter into the theory are obviously theoretical rather than ostensive; let us denote the gene for tall by "T", which we shall also use to denote the corresponding class of gametes; and we shall use "t" similarly ambiguously to denote both the gene for the dwarf character and the class of gametes carrying that gene.

Our first hypothesis then, H-1, becomes
H-1*

$$\{\text{Tall}, T, \text{standard}\} \in \textbf{genunit} \ \& \ \{\text{Dwarf}, t, \text{standard}\} \in \textbf{genunit}$$

The second hypothesis states that tallness is dominant:
H-2*

$$\textbf{D}(T,t,\text{standard}) \subseteq \text{Tall}$$

Similarly,
H-4a*

$$\textbf{G}(T,t,\text{standard}) \cap \male \in \tfrac{1}{2}T \cap \tfrac{1}{2}t \ \& \ \textbf{G}(T,t,\text{standard}) \cap \female \in \tfrac{1}{2}T \cap \tfrac{1}{2} t$$

In other words, of the set of female gametes produced by lives developing from a zygote formed by the union of a gamete from class T and a gamete from class t—i.e., from a $TTtt$ cross—half will carry the dominant T gene, and half will carry the recessive t gene; and similarly for the set of male gametes produced by the same type of union.
H-4b*

$$\textbf{G}(T,t,\text{standard}) \cap \male \neq \Lambda \ \& \ \textbf{G}(T,t,\text{standard}) \cap \male \subseteq T \cup t.$$
$$\textbf{G}(T,t,\text{standard}) \cap \female \neq \Lambda \ \& \ \textbf{G}(T,t,\text{standard}) \cap \female \subseteq T \cup t.$$

This, a much weaker hypothesis than the preceding, says only that lives developing from zygotes that are formed from the union of a gamete from class T and a gamete from class t, will produce both male and female gametes, and that they will produce only gametes belonging to the two classes T and t.
H-4c*

$$\textbf{G}(T,t,\text{standard}) \neq \Lambda \ \& \ \textbf{G}(T,t,\text{standard}) \subseteq T \cup t$$

[300]

a weaker hypothesis yet, this states merely that lives developing from zygotes formed from a gamete of class T and a gamete of class t, will produce gametes, and that those gametes will belong to the union of T and t.

The fifth hypothesis embodies the randomness conditions.

H-5*

$$\{\text{Tall},T,\text{standard}\} \cup \{\text{Dwarf},t,\text{standard}\} \in \textbf{rand D} \ \& \ \{\text{Tall},T,\text{standard}\} \cup$$
$$\{\text{Dwarf},t,\text{standard}\} \in \textbf{rand U}$$

We can only *test* the theory by finding cases in which the hypotheses of theorems are true—or, better put, cases in which we have grounds for believing that the hypotheses of the theorems are true. If the hypotheses of the theorems never hold, the theory will never be falsified by experience or experiment—but neither, then, will the theory ever be of any use or interest to us, or provide us with information. Our first job, then, is to see that these hypotheses, as stated for the particular kinds of plants we actually have, are satisfied.

The first hypothesis says that we have two genetical units. Referring back to D-9, we see that this requires: that there be some lives developing from zygotes formed by the union of a gamete of class T and a gamete of class T, and that these lives also be of the phenotype Tall; and that there be gametes produced by these lives; and that these gametes be of the class T. Similar requirements must be met by Dwarf, t, and standard. How can we know that these conditions are met? That Tall and Dwarf are phenotypes, we take to be a relatively ostensive matter. The rest of the conditions, however, involve relatively theoretical matters. And yet they are not inaccessible: if we have a group of tall sweet peas, producing numbers of generations under our standard environmental conditions, we have excellent evidence that the zygotes from which they all develop (remember that there are numbers of generations) are all similar in genetic constitution, i.e., formed from the same kinds of gametes. We have before our eyes, then, evidence that all lives developing from a union of two gametes of class T belong to the same phenotype (Tall), and evidence—slightly more indirect—that all the gametes produced by such lives are of the class T. The argument would be that if other kinds of gametes were produced, then, over the generations, they would make their presence known.

The second hypothesis states that one phenotype dominates the other. This is relatively easy to answer, though the answer is still a statistical conjecture. We cross members of the purebred populations, and see if any new phenotypes occur. If the two purebred populations are in fact purebred, so that the gametes which they provide are all of the same class (all of the class T in the case of one population, all of the class t in the case of the other population) then we generally have a clearcut outcome to the test. That is, it will then generally be the case (when there is dominance) that the population resulting from the cross will conform to one or the other of the parent populations. But notice

[301]

that many of the characteristics that we have in mind when we say that one population is like another are quantitative—height, weight, etc.—and that quantitative characteristics often vary considerably from one individual to another. To say of one population that it is (in a given environment) like another in height, is not to say that the members of both populations are all the same height, but that the members of the two populations have roughly the same statistical distribution—e.g., the height in each population is roughly normally distributed with mean about 5 and standard deviation about $\frac{1}{2}$. Like any other statistical conjecture, this one can be rendered no more than probable by the evidence.

Hypothesis 4 occurs in the theorems we have written down in three forms. Hypothesis 4-a* states that half of the female gametes belong to class T (i.e., carry the factor for tallness) and half belong to the class t (i.e., carry the factor for dwarfishness), and that the same is true of the male gametes produced by the hybrid generation.

From these hypotheses, together with the randomness condition, H-5*, the consequent of Theorem 15 follows:

$$\mathbf{F}_E(T,t;T,t) \in \tfrac{3}{4} \text{ Tall } \cap \tfrac{1}{4} \text{ Dwarf.}$$

One way of testing the theory is now clear: We establish that the tall sweet peas are a genetical unit (i.e., that they breed true, and thus that all the gametes, both male and female, are of the same type T) and that the dwarf sweet peas are a genetical unit (i.e., that they breed true and thus that all the gametes, both male and female, are of the same type t). There is a theoretical element in this hypothesis—in the reference to gametes—which makes it seem perhaps as though we must already have accepted the general framework of the theory before we can apply its theorems. But that reference is very general and vague, and need not in itself imply any more than that there is some termination to the quasi-ostensive approach to gametes (through visible gemetophytes) outlined in the discussion of the ostensive roots of the terminology. It is easy to see that H-2* is satisfied —at most that presents a straightforward statistical problem: does the hybrid generation have essentially the same distribution of heights as the Tall parent generation?

The next two hypotheses—H-4a* and H-5*—present more serious problems. We cannot, obviously, simply "see that they are satisfied" and then test our whole genetic theory by "seeing whether or not the consequent of the theorem is also satisfied". Indeed to satisfy ourselves that H-4a* is satisfied, requires performing a test, which is already a partial test of the theory in question. Given that H-1* and H-2* are satisfied, we know that the cross between the genetical units {Tall, T, standard} and {Dwarf, t, standard} will produce lives belonging to the class $\mathbf{D}(T,t,\text{standard})$. We now want to find out if the gametes produced by this class have the character assigned to them by hypothesis 4-a*. We can do this by a back-cross: we take male gametophytes of the hybrid generation, and allow the contained gametes to fuse with the gametes contained in the female gameto-phytes of the genetical unit {Dwarf,t,standard}. Since we know (H-2*) that the lives developing from zygotes resulting from the fusion of a gamete of class T and a gamete of class t will belong to the phenotype Tall, and that the lives developing from zygotes resulting from a fusion of two gametes from class t will belong to the phenotype Dwarf, the proportion of Tall in the generation re-sulting from this back-cross will indicate directly the proportion of male gametes of the first hybrid generation and male gametophytes of the Dwarf, t, standard genetical unit will reveal the proportion of female gametes of class T.

Confirmation of Hypothesis 5*, like the confirmation of Hypothesis 4*, will offer some independent confirmation of the general theory. Hypothesis 5 stipul-ates random union and random development. Random union (see D-10) re-quires essentially that the proportion of zygotes resulting from a union of gametes derived from given classes of parents, that have a certain genetic consti-tution (TT,Tt,tt), be the same as the proportion among all the pairs of gametes that can be formed from the given classes of parents, of pairs that have the cor-responding characters: T paired with T, T paired with t, t paired with t. Put more intuitively, but less precisely, the requirement is that there be no selection, no bias, in the fusion of gametes from the parental classes to form zygotes. Simil-arly, random development (see D-11) stipulates that if the gametes of two parental types form unions in a certain proportion of which the zygote has a certain genetic constitution (TT,Tt,tt), then that same proportion will hold for the lives developing from those zygotes. Again, this amounts mainly to the sti-pulation that there be no selective processes at work.

How can we be sure that the fifth hypothesis is satisfied? Only, it seems, by confirming certain statements about the relative proportions of genetic consti-tutions among the generation in question. Indeed, the problem is more com-plicated than that, for the failure to find these relative proportions could be due to either a lack of randomness in the formation of unions, or a lack of random-ness in the development of lives formed from zygotes. In any event, it is quite clear that we cannot take Theorem 15 as providing a test of the theory in the traditional sense that we can first ascertain that H-1*, H-2*, H-4a*, and H-5* hold, and then cross the hybrids, and examine the hybrid progeny to see if the predicted proportion of Tall Dwarf peas is produced. But there is another way in which we can regard hypothesis H-5*. How would we come to *reject* H-5*? By discovering a selective bias among the progeny of various sorts of parents. Hypothesis H-5* seems to occupy a place midway between the fundamental postulates of the theory (P-2—P-6), and the particular hypotheses of the test theorems. If we set up a particular test of the theory according to Theorem 15, and if the test result did *not* conform to the prediction of the theorem, one

[303]

possibility (which would admit of further testing) is that there is a lack of randomness either in the union of gametes or in the development of zygotes.

To sum up the test of the theory by Theorem 15: We can have quite direct evidence which will allow us to accept H-1* and H-2*. H-4a* also allows of fairly direct test, within the framework of the theory; in point of historical fact this sort of antecedent hypothesis was confirmed by Mendel. Hypothesis H-5*, on the other hand is confirmable only in a more complicated manner than T-15 itself; it remains as a hypothetical antecedent. We perform the experiment: that is, we cross hybrid sweet peas. We find (statistical inference again!) that $\frac{3}{4}$ of the progeny belong to the phenotype Tall, and $\frac{1}{4}$ of them belong to the phenotype Dwarf. The consequent of the conditional theorem is confirmed; and this confirms *both* H-5*, which, if something had gone wrong would have been the first to be rejected, *and* the basic postulates of the theory.

The antecedent hypothesis H-4a* is quite strong, and the two succeeding theorems make use of weaker versions of it, H-4c* and H-4b*. H-4c* is particularly weak; it says merely that $G(T,t,\text{standard})$ is not empty—i.e., that the hybrids produce gametes—and that $G(T,t,\text{standard})$ is included in the union of T and t—i.e., that the hybrids don't start producing new kinds of gametes. The consequent of the Theorem 16 is slightly more complicated than the consequent of Theorem 15, however:

$$(\exists p)(\mathbf{F}_E(t,t;T,t) \in p\text{Tall} \cap (1-p) \text{ Dwarf } \& \mathbf{G}(T,t,\text{standard}) \in pT \cap (1-p)t).$$

This theorem is quite startling, and admits of a definite observational test. It states that the proportion of Tall phenotypes in a back-cross is fixed at some definite value p. However you perform the back-cross, it predicts, you will get the same proportion. It further stipulates that the proportion of T gametes produced by the hybrid generation is p. This part of the consequent of the theorem does not admit of a direct test, but under the preceding hypotheses is equivalent to the preceding statement about phenotypes.

Theorems 17 and 18 introduce no essentially novel considerations. It will nevertheless be instructive for the student to work out for himself tests of the genetical theory that involve these two theorems.

V

One thing that becomes clear from the preceding discussion is that the picture of science as a process of forming hypotheses, subjecting them to definitive tests, and rejecting them when the tests turn out negative, is a highly oversimplified picture. Every observable connection in this biological theory is a statistical one; even the rejection of a statistical consequence of the theory need not lead to the rejection of the theory as a whole, but may only lead to the rejection of some quite special assumption (such as random union, or random development) which is not even, properly speaking, part of the theory. What makes the theory important and acceptable is partly the fact that these special assumptions often

[304]

seem to be satisfied; that when they are not satisfied, we can often account for the fact that they are not satisfied; and that in many simple cases, very simple relations—such as that expressed in Theorem 15—are simply *observed* to hold.

The formalization we have gone through exhibits two other facts beyond those pertaining to the confirmation of scientific theories. One concerns the role of particular concepts in the theory; without formalization, it is possible not to realize how important a role a given concept plays. Apparently this has been the case with respect to randomness in genetic theory. Woodger writes: "The above analysis has shown the central role which is played by the hypotheses of random union of the gametes and of random development in obtaining the Mendelian ratios... These do not receive the attention they deserve in genetical books. Sometimes they are not even mentioned. This is particularly true of the hypothesis of random development..." (p. 427). The other thing revealed by this formalization is precisely what hypotheses are required for the derivation of what results. In laying out these hypotheses explicitly, we are also putting ourselves in a position to doubt these hypotheses, or to consider simpler or more elegant replacements for them. On this, Woodger writes: "Any departure from these [hypotheses and postulates] could affect the result. This provides plenty of scope for reflection. But perhaps the most striking feature of the Mendelian systems is the fact that only one class of environments is involved and is usually not even mentioned. Some interesting discoveries may await the investigation of multi-environmental systems..." (p. 427).

BIBLIOGRAPICAL NOTES TO CHAPTER 13

The material here comes mainly from J. H. Woodger, "Studies in the Foundations of Genetics," which appears in *The Axiomatic Method* (Henkin, Suppes, and Tarski, Eds.) (Amsterdam: North-Holland, 1959). Other parts of biology have been formalized by Woodger in *The Axiomatic Method in Biology* (Cambridge, England: Cambridge University Press, 1935); *The Technique of Theory Construction* (Chicago: University of Chicago Press, 1939), and, more recently, in *Biology and Language* (Cambridge, England: Cambridge University Press, 1952). Rudolf Carnap, in his *Introduction to Symbolic Logic and its Applications* (New York: Dover, 1958) also develops an axiom system for part of biology as one of his illustrations.

The propensity interpretation of probability is to be found in Karl R. Popper, "The Propensity Interpretation of the Calculus of Probability and The Quantum Theory," *The Colston Papers*, Ed. Körner (London: Butterworth's Scientific Publications, 1957); the chance setup interpretation is to be found in the *Logic of Statistical Inference* (Cambridge, England: Cambridge University Press, 1965), by Ian Hacking. Both of these interpretations are empirical (according to the classification offered in Chapter Six), but both are far better suited to the genetical theory discussed here than ordinary empirical interpretations.

Chapter 14

PROBLEMS AND ISSUES

I

There is a cluster of problems in the philosophy of science which, from the point of view adopted here, involve in one way or another the choice of a vocabulary for a scientific formal system. Among these problems are the paradoxes of confirmation, the problem of distinguishing projectible predicates from non-projectible predicates, the question of lawlikeness, and the problem of counter-factual conditionals. These problems are all related to one another. They have received considerable attention in recent years, and while the treatment below does not claim to represent a consensus, I think it is not at variance with a general outlook that has become quite common.

Let us begin with the paradoxes of confirmation, since they were the earliest problems along these lines to be uncovered. Consider the statement, "All ravens are black," conventionally symbolized,

[306]

(1) $$(x)(Rx \supset Bx)$$

Common sense, philosophical consensus, and scientific convention all agree in regarding the observation of a black raven as relevant, confirming, evidence for this statement, and in regarding the observation of a white handkerchief or a black cat as irrelevant. They also agree, however, that if two statements are logically equivalent, they should be confirmed or disconfirmed by precisely the same things. Statement (1) is logically equivalent to:

(2) $$(x)(\sim Bx \supset \sim Rx),$$

and so on precisely the same ground that an observation of a raven that is black confirms (1), the observation of a nonblack thing (a white object) that is not a raven (that is a handkerchief), will confirm (2). Since logically equivalent statements should be confirmed by the same things, (1) is therefore confirmed by the observation of a black crow and by the observation of a white handkerchief. Finally, both (1) and (2) are equivalent to:

(3) $$(x)(\sim Rx \vee Bx).$$

Although this does not quite have the same syntactical form as (1) and (2), it seems natural enough to suppose that it will be confirmed by anything which is either not a raven or which is black—for it simply expresses the fact that everything whatever will fall into one of these two categories. Thus (3) will be confirmed by the observation of a black cat, and therefore so will (1) and (2) be confirmed by the observation of a black cat. We therefore find ourselves having to say that the observation of a white handkerchief, a black cat, and a black crow, each confirms the generalization that all crows are black; or else we have to give up one of the links in the chain of argument that brought us to this conclusion.

One approach—the Bayesian approach—to this situation which has been relatively popular, is to agree that all three of the described instances confirm the hypothesis that all ravens are black, but to remove the sting from the paradox by pointing out that if we quantify confirmation in any of the usual ways, the *amount* of confirmation of (1)—or, equally, of (2) or (3)—provided by a white handkerchief is infinitesimal, compared to the amount of confirmation provided by a black raven, and that almost the same is true of the observation of a black cat. There are, however, considerable difficulties in the quantification of confirmation.

The other major approach to the situation is to reject, in one way or another, the equivalence condition that requires us to treat logically equivalent statements in just the same way, or at least to restrict the scope of its application. This approach is pursued clearly and elegantly by von Wright, in "The Paradoxes of Confirmation," who introduces the concept of the *range of relevance* of

[307]

a generalization. The range of relevance of a generalization is the set of things that the generalization is *about*; there is no certain way to be sure what this is simply by looking at the form of the generalization. (1) may be about birds, or about ravens, or about living things, or about all things whatever. It may even be about nonblack things. In each of these cases the line between confirming instances and irrelevant instances will be drawn differently. What von Wright calls the *natural* range of relevance of (1) is the set of ravens; given this range of relevance, the only instances that are relevant to (1) are ravens; black ones are confirming instances, and of course, nonblack ones are refuting instances. Another possibility is that the range of relevance of (1) is birds; then we may regard (1) as having a suppressed antecedent, and rewrite it this way:

(4) $$(x)(Ox \supset (Rx \supset Bx)).$$

This is equivalent to:

(5) $$(x)(Ox \supset (\sim Bx \supset \sim Rx)).$$

Here nonblack *birds* ("Ox" means "x is a bird") which are not ravens are regarded as confirming instances of the generalization, just as black ravens are. Similarly, black birds of any sort are regarded as confirming instances:

(6) $$(x)(Ox \supset (Bx \vee \sim Rx))$$

It is possible (but perhaps not likely) that (1) may be regarded as being about all things whatever. If that is so, then the equivalence condition for (1) under this interpretation holds unrestrictedly, and the cat, the white handkerchief, and the black raven are all confirming instances.

The natural range of relevance of (2) is the set of nonblack things. If (2) is interpreted as having its natural range of relevance, then of all the things mentioned, only the white handkerchief qualifies as a confirming instance—neither the black cat nor the black raven counts as a confirming instance. Thus if we suppose (as von Wright suggests) that when the range of relevance of a generalization is not specified, it be regarded as having its *natural* range of relevance, then although (1) and (2) are logically equivalent, they are utterly distinct and different generalizations, and in fact nothing which is a confirming instance of one will also be a confirming instance of the other.

The approach to the paradoxes of confirmation which follows from the discussion of induction in Chapter Seven has much in common with von Wright's approach, though it is in some ways even more restrictive. The fundamental form of hypothesis considered there is the statistical hypothesis, and universal generalizations are there regarded merely as an especially interesting form of statistical hypothesis. Two things should be observed immediately: that while

[308]

"All ravens are black" and "All nonblack things are nonravens" are logically equivalent, there is no logical connection between p and q in "The proportion of ravens that are black is p" and "The proportion of nonblack things that are nonravens is q." In particular, if it is true that practically all ravens are black, it *may* also be true that practically all nonblack things are nonravens, but it *may* also be true that practically all nonblack things are ravens! Although looking around among the nonblack things of the universe may give us information about whether or not there are any nonblack ravens, it won't give us any information about the proportion of ravens that are black. And that proportion is what I have taken to be the fundamental thing with which we have to work.

It is not the case that all simple generalizations of the form "All A's are B's" are confirmed directly by looking around the world for A's and seeing whether or not they are B's. But some such generalizations are confirmed this way, and those that are, are those which von Wright would regard as having their natural range of relevance, and which I regard as being essentially statistical hypothesis of the form "Practically all A's are B's." It is true, of course, that "Practically all A's are B's" may be true when "All A's are B's" is false; but when we have very good reason to believe "Practically all A's are B's" and no good reason at all to suppose that there are any A's that are not B's, then I take it we have good reason to believe that all A's are B's. In the case of the generalizations that we say are directly supported, or supported by enumeration, what is really *directly* supported are the corresponding statistical hypotheses; and among these hypotheses the range of relevance is precisely the natural range mentioned by von Wright.

This doesn't settle everything, however, for von Wright suggests that there might be circumstances under which the set of nonblack things is to be taken as the range of relevance of (1)—indeed, it is the natural range of relevance of (2). This seems queer. It is really possible that one might go about sampling nonblack things in order to discover the proportion of nonravens among them? Is it reasonable to be willing to accept any set whatever as a possible range of relevance? I think the answer is "no". In the case of probability statements, what corresponds to the range of relevance is the *reference class*. It is the statistical hypothesis that provides the most important part of the ground for the probability judgement concerning the color of the next raven—in this case, practical certainty that it will be black. In confirming "Practically all ravens are black", we take the range of relevance to be ravens; in using this statistical hypothesis as a ground for a prediction concerning the color of an as yet unencountered raven, we take this same set of ravens to be the reference class.

Consider the set P consisting of all seagulls, together with the next raven to be encountered. Practically all the members of this set, we have good reason to believe, are white or grey. If, relative to our body of knowledge a certain individual is a random member of this set with respect to exhibiting a certain color,

[309]

then it is practically certain that that individual is white or grey. The question is, then, whether the next raven we see is (now) a random member of this set. We don't want it to be, of course. The obvious thing to say is that the next raven (call him *r*) is not a random member of this peculiar set because we know that it belongs to the class *R* of ravens, and that the proportion of black birds among *R* is much higher than it is among *P*. But precisely the same argument would keep *r* from being a random member of *R*, relative to what we know, with respect to being black; for we know that *r* belongs to *P*, and that the proportion of black birds among *P* is much less than the proportion among *R*. It is very hard to find grounds for rejecting it as a random member of our odd set of birds that are not also grounds for rejecting it as a random member of the set of ravens. (All with respect to exhibiting a certain color.) In just the same way, there is no point in confirming that practically all members of *P* are grey or white; *P* is not a useful range of relevance.

There are of course a number of things we could do about this. We could accept *P* as a perfectly adequate range of relevance and a perfectly adequate reference class, and we could concentrate on framing our formal definition of randomness in such a way as to insure that *r* turns out to be a random member of *R* with respect to being black, relative to what we know, and not a random member of *P*, with respect to being black, relative to what we know. But for reasons which will be apparent shortly, we are not going to be able to treat all classes on a par anyway, and so it seems more useful and simpler to impose limitations on the classes that are to be allowed to function as ranges of relevance or reference classes. And these limitations will rule out just such ranges of relevance as the set of nonblack things.

II

Nelson Goodman, in "A Query on Confirmation", has raised a problem quite parallel to the foregoing. It concerns the consequents of conditionals in the same way as problems concerning ranges of relevance concern antecedents of conditionals. Consider, Goodman says, the word "grue", defined to apply to just those things which are green before the year 2000 and blue after the year 2000. Whatever evidence we have that all emeralds are green is equally evidence that all emeralds are grue—that is, a large number of emeralds (the set of emeralds is taken here to be the range of relevance) have been examined, and have been discovered to be green. Therefore practically all emeralds are green. Therefore the first emerald to be examined in the year 2056 will practically certainly be green. But also: A large number of emeralds have been examined and have been discovered to be grue. Therefore practically all emeralds are grue. Therefore the first emerald to be examined in the year 2056 will practically certainly be blue. But we can't be practically certain that the same emerald is both green and blue. So something has gone wrong.

[310]

It is tempting to look for a syntatical clue as to what has gone wrong. In the case in point, "grue" was defined by reference to two color terms and a date. "Green", on the other hand, is just a simple color term. But consider the word "bleen", defined to apply to blue things before the year 2000 and green things thereafter. We can define "green" by reference to grue and bleen and a date, just as we defined "grue" by reference to blue and green and a date. There appears to be perfect syntactical symmetry.

There are differences between the terms: "green" is an expression of ordinary English, "grue" is not; "green" can be given a relatively ostensive interpretation, "grue" cannot. But the former characteristic seems to be accidental, and in any case will not help us with the extraordinary terms of scientific English, and the latter characteristic won't help us directly when it comes to terms which are only remotely connected with relatively ostensive terms anyway, like "dextrorotatory" and "levorotatory" as applied to sugars. (Dextrorotatory sugars in solution cause the plane of polarization of polarized light to rotate to the right, levorotatory sugars cause it to rotate to the left.) Relative ostensiveness is not going to enable us to distinguish between "Lexorotatory", meaning a sugar which rotates light to the left before the year 2000, and to the right thereafter, and "levorotatory" as just defined.

Goodman calls the good predicates like "green" and "levorotatory" "projectible", signifying that they are the kinds of predicates that can be *projected* from past instances to future ones. He takes projectibility to be an empirical property of the predicates, however, so that we can only have *evidence* that a predicate is projectible: we take "green" to be projectible, because we have projected it successfully in the past, and that provides evidence that it is generally projectible. But we might be wrong, though rational.

In conformity with the more formalistic approach adopted here, I shall take the projectible predicates (and relation-terms) to be a proper subset of the set of all predicates and relation-terms definable in a formal system, and I shall take that set of terms to be characterized syntactically. For example, the primitive terms of the formal system will all be regarded as projectible; if P and Q are projectible predicates, then $Px \ \& \ Qx$ will be projectible (but not, in general, $Px \lor Qx$, and not, in general $\sim Px$). It turns out that some statistical predicates are projectible and some are not. The problem of deciding which statistical predicates should be regarded as projectible is somewhat more complicated, but I shall still regard it as a logical problem rather than an empirical one. (It is a largely unsolved problem.) The result of this approach is that projectibility of a predicate is relative to a formal system having a particular primitive vocabulary and formation rules and a particular interpretation. Given a formal system, we can decide on formal grounds which properties expressible in terms of that formal system to take seriously—i.e., to take as determining plausible ranges of relevance or plausible reference classes, to project into the future, and so on.

[311]

We shall refer to both these properties and the terms that correspond to them as *projectible*.

III

One of the classical problems of the philosophy of science is to formulate a distinction between statements which are lawlike, and those which are merely accidental generalizations. Another is the problem of counterfactual conditionals.

The two problems are closely related: "All sugar dissolves in water," is regarded as a lawlike statement, and "If that lump of sugar, which I just ate, had been put into water, it would have dissolved," is a typical instance of a true counterfactual conditional. The lawlikeness of the first statement, it has been said, stems from its ability to support counterfactual conditionals like the second statement. The truth of the second statement, it has also been said, stems from the fact that it is an instance of an acceptable (or true) lawlike statement, namely, the first statement.

As another pair of examples, consider the unlawlike statement, "all the coins in my pocket are copper," and the corresponding, false, counterfactual: "If this dime were in my pocket, it would be copper." Or consider, "All the people in this room are men," and "If Mary Jane were in this room, she would be a man." How are examples like this to be formally differentiated from examples like the sugar example?

To some extent, the considerations of the preceding section may help us. For we may plausibly demand that any statement that lays claim to lawlikeness or lawfulness will involve only predicates of the special class we have singled out before, as corresponding to suitable ranges of relevance and suitable reference classes. At the very least, this demand will rule out a vast number of silly but true statistical laws that could be claimed to support probabilistic counterfactuals that we would all want to say are false. Let T be the set of losses of this coin that land heads and let N be the next toss of the coin, which will never actually be made, because the coin has been thrown into the ocean. "Practically all of $T \cup \{N\}$ are tosses that yield heads," is not lawlike; and "If N had been performed, it would very probably have yielded heads" is false.

A necessary condition that a statement be a *lawlike* universal generalization (all A's are B's) or a *lawlike* statistical hypothesis (the proportion of A's that are B's is about p) is thus that the terms involved ("A" and "B") belong to the special set of projectible terms.

Is this a sufficient condition? Not for lawfulness, of course, but for law*like*ness? I rather incline to think so. But a definitive answer awaits a much more extensive investigation of the special class of projectible terms than is either appropriate or possible here.

It must be observed immediately that there is a derivative sense of lawlikeness which may be attributed to statements that do not have the form proposed

[312]

above, but which are equivalent to statements in that form. Thus if "*A*" and "*B*" are projectible predicates, and "*C*" a nonprojectible one, "$(x)(((Ax \ \& \ Cx) \lor (Ax \ \& \sim Cx)) \supset Bx)$" is not a law-like statement according to the criterion suggested, but it is equivalent to one, namely: "$(x)(Ax \supset Bx)$".

It must also be observed that this solution to the problem of lawlikeness, even if it does turn out to be satisfactory for particular formal systems, depends upon the initial vocabulary of the formal system and upon its interpretation. The solution is formal, given a formal system; but it is a restricted solution, in the sense that it leads to no universal characterization of lawlikeness. Pathological formal systems can easily be constructed in which just the wrong statements would turn out to be lawlike, just as pathological formal systems can easily be constructed in which "grue" is a part of the primitive vocabulary, and "green" is not. What will be claimed here in due course, however, is that the relatively formal systems of science are not pathological in this sense, and do not become pathological when their formalization is completed; and furthermore that there are fairly natural criteria which apply to a formal system as a whole which will serve to help keep us clear of the pathological examples.

IV

Given this sort of solution to the problem of lawlikeness, however, we have still a long way to go to uncover a solution to the problem of counterfactual conditionals. As some writers have already pointed out, the problem of counterfactuals is not the sort of problem that admits of a simple or easy solution in all cases, because it is not true in all cases that we even have a clear idea of which counterfactuals we want to regard as true:

(1) If this crow were a seagull, it would be white.
(2) If this crow were a seagull, some seagulls would be black.

Which of these counterfactuals is true? Or is there some way in which they can both be true?

Let us begin with simpler and less ambiguous cases: If this pat of butter had been heated to 200°F yesterday, it would have melted. If the sugar that was in this bowl had been put into water rather than being thrown in the fire, it would have dissolved. If the solution had contained chloride ions, it would have become cloudy on the addition of silver nitrite. If both parents were hybrid, at least some of the many offspring would have exhibited the recessive characteristic. If p were the largest prime, then $p! \ + \ 1$ would not be prime.

The analysis of all these counterfactuals is roughly the same; if the latter are somewhat more plausible sounding than the former, it is because the form of words, "If X were A, then X would be (would have been) B" is encountered most often in real life as part of a *reductio ad absurdum* argument whose conclusion is "X is not A". Implicit in the use of any such counterfactual statement is a

[313]

formal system, for physics, chemistry, biology, or whatever. The counterfactual asserts that if a statement corresponding to the antecedent (note that the antecedent, "X were A" is not a statement at all) is added to the formal system, the statement corresponding to the consequent becomes either deducible or highly probable. This is of interest primarily when the formal system is an acceptable one—that is, one which forms part of our rational corpus, or our body of reasonable beliefs.

Let us consider the simple counterfactuals we have just listed. "If this pat of butter had been heated to 200°F yesterday, it would have melted." In the fragment of culinary chemistry that we all possess as part of our body of beliefs, the generalization "for all x, if x is a bit of butter and x is heated under ordinary circumstances to 200°F, then x melts" is a theorem. There is nothing in the statement of the counterfactual to indicate that the circumstances are anything but ordinary; in the formal system then, we will be able to deduce from "This pat of butter is heated to 200°F," "This pat of butter melts." Note that there is nothing counterfactual about the interpretation offered for the counterfactual: it reads, "If the statement corresponding to the antecedent of the counterfactual is added, (not "were added"), then such and such a statement will be (not "would be") deducible." The analysis of the sugar example is perfectly analogous.

It is more interesting to analyze counterfactuals which are like those actually encountered in the pursuit of science and happiness. "If the solution had contained chloride ions, it would have become cloudy on the addition of silver nitrate." The formal system in question here is that of chemistry—a rather more formal formal system than that of culinary chemistry—and the statement is true, precisely because if a statement corresponding to the antecedent of the conditional is added to that formal system, a statement corresponding to the consequent of the conditional is deducible. It is useful because we often have in our rational corpus, a statement corresponding to the denial of the consequent, and the counterfactual thus represents a *reductio ad absurdum* argument to the conclusion "no chloride ions are present".

"If both parents were hybrid, at least some of the many offspring would have exhibited the recessive characteristic." Here the implicit formal system is the system of genetics. But here if we add a statement corresponding to the antecedent of the conditional, we find that we cannot *deduce* a statement corresponding to the consequent. What we *can* deduce is that the proportion of sets of 100 offspring of two hybrid parents that exhibit some instances of the recessive characteristic is overwhelmingly high. The counterfactual is (generally) true, because (generally) this statistical statement which can be deduced, in the formal system, from a statement corresponding to the antecedent of the counterfactual, will in turn support a probability statement: the probability is overwhelming that their particular 100 offspring will contain some recessives. To arrive at that probability statement on the basis of the statistical statement requires, however,

[314]

that the 100 offspring of the parents in question be a *random* member of the set of all sets of 100 potential offspring of those parents with respect to exhibiting some recessives, and relative to a certain body of knowledge. In the deductive cases considered above, we needed to consider only part of the body of knowledge in question—the part corresponding to the formal system. But here we must consider a whole body of knowledge. The point is clearly this: if someone knew just what we know about the parents in question, except that he did not know anything about their offspring—and in particular did not know that they exhibited no recessives—and that person added the statement, "Both parents are hybrids" to his rational corpus, then, relative to his rational corpus the probability of the statement "At least some of the 100 offspring of these parents would be recessives", would be very high.

At this point we may seem to have made no progress: we have merely succeeded in interpreting a biological counterfactual ("If these parents were hybrids...") by an epistemological counterfactual ("If someone knew what we know except..."). But the epistemological counterfactual is only expressed counterfactually—it can be equally well expressed in the indicative mood: relative to a rational corpus (body of statements) of such and such a character, so and so will be highly probable, or such and such another statement will also be included in that rational corpus. The question that remains is how to describe the new rational corpus. It is clear that the statement "None of the offspring exhibit the recessive characteristic", which is presumably part of our rational corpus, must be excluded from the hypothetical one. But there are also a great many other statements in our rational corpus which must also be excluded from the new one—e.g., "If two and two are four, then none of the offspring exhibit the recessive characteristic." The most straightforward directive would be to delete everything in the rational corpus that is inconsistent with the statement corresponding to the antecedent of the conditional. But this is not unambiguous. Let A be the statement corresponding to the antecedent of the conditional; our rational corpus may contain B and $B \supset \sim A$. We could eliminate either one of these and achieve consistency; but the directive doesn't tell us which one. Or consider $B_1 \supset (B_2 \supset (B_3 \supset (B_4 \supset \sim A)))$; we can delete this statement itself, or we can delete any one of the statements $B_1, \cdots, B_4$. We therefore need a supplementary principle. What comes to mind is that it is the statements closest to observation that are most dispensable—that is, that can be gotten rid of with the least trauma to our rational corpus. Indeed, in the first examples we discussed, we followed this principle so strongly that we considered only the formal system itself, with A, the statement corresponding to the antecedent of the conditional conjoined to it. In general, however, we do need to consider a whole rational corpus—there is in general a context to be taken account of—and the most direct way to arrive at this rational corpus seems to be to delete everything inconsistent with A, subject to the condition that where there is a choice,

[315]

the eliminated statement be the one closest to the observational periphery of our body of knowledge. The technical details of this procedure remain to be worked out, but there seems to be no reason to suppose that they should be insuperable.

The general approach suggested for handling ordinary counterfactual conditionals may also serve to explicate counterfactual conditionals that involve nomological antecedents: thus "If the gravitational attraction between two bodies varied inversely as the cube of their distance, the orbits of the planets would be more eccentric than they are." Here we must make the appropriate modifications in the formal system of physics, again on the principle that the statements closest to experience are most dispensible; in place of the inverse square law, we put the inverse cube law; and we delete from the formal system everything inconsistent with the inverse cube law, again following the principle that the statements closest to experience are most dispensible. If the quoted statement is true, we will be able in this modified formal system of physics to deduce that the eccentricity of the paths of the planets is greater than it in fact is, i.e., greater than it is predicted to be in the system that embodies the inverse square law.

In some scientific formal systems, there are statements that are counterfactual to begin with. For example, in Newtonian physics we find the statement: "A body not acted upon by external forces will continue in its state of rest or rectilinear motion." In view of the fact that in the same system, we find the statement, "Every body is acted upon by external forces," the former statement would seem to be trivially and emptily true, and in no different way than "A body not acted upon by external forces will perform ever-decreasing spiral gyrations until it disappears", would be true. The two statements are completely different, however, in virtue of the fact that forces and accelerations are construed as vectors, and these vectors can be added. The rest of the theory provides the means for predicting quantitatively the deviations of bodies from their natural paths of indolence, and it is quite irrelevant that no body is ever found pursuing that path.

One could, of course, choose a different natural state than rest or uniform rectilinear motion; and then explain, by means of the rest of the theory, deviations from that natural state. It would still (probably) be the case that the natural state would not occur, just as the Newtonian natural state of freedom from external forces does not occur. It is interesting to note that under Einstein's general theory of relativity, the situation is suddenly altered: a new "natural" state is introduced—uniform rectilinear motion in a non-Euclidean space of four dimensions—which is not only true of some bodies, but which is true of all bodies without exception! No bodies are acted upon by forces.

There are counterfactuals that are problematical in the sense that confronted with the bare counterfactual, we do not know whether to call it true or false. An example is this: Confronted with a black crow, I say: "If this crow were a seagull, then some crows would be nonblack." Or I say, "If this crow were a seagull, then some seagulls would be black." The reason it is hard to tell whether to count these statements as true or false, is that it is hard to know what is being *held constant* in the rational corpus. It is a question of plumbing the intent of the speaker. In particular, it is a question of discovering what it is that the speaker wishes us to delete from our rational corpus as inconsistent with the statement corresponding to the consequent of the conditional. To make the first quoted statement true, we need to delete from our rational corpus all our knowledge of the appearance of this crow—e.g., that it is black. A more explicit way of stating the counterfactual would be: "If this crow looked like (had the coloring of) a seagull, then some crows would be nonblack." To make the second statement true, we need to delete from our rational corpus, our knowledge that the object in question is a crow, (and of course statements from which that would follow); a more explicit way of making the same statement then would be: "If this black object (which happens to be a crow) were really a seagull, then some seagulls would be black." Put more simply yet; the first amounts to: "If this crow were white..." and the second to, "If this black bird were a seagull...".

The proposal made above for the interpretation of counterfactual conditionals thus provides a technique not only for handling counterfactuals whose intent is clear, but also a framework for interpreting counterfactuals whose intent is unclear: if the intent of a counterfactual is not clear, it is because we are not quite sure what we are supposed to delete from our rational corpus and what we are supposed to retain in our rational corpus.

V

There are a number of problems related to what might be called the metaphysical aspects of science. These problems can be divided into two sorts; questions like, "What must we suppose about the universe in order for scientific activity to be possible?" and questions like, "What can we infer about the nature of the universe, given the body of scientific knowledge that we in fact have?" Questions of the former sort we might call *philosophically prior* to science; questions of the latter sort we might call *scientifically prior* to philosophy. I shall not attempt here any sort of exhaustive study (or even an exhaustive listing) of problems of either of these sorts, but some mention should certainly be made of some of them, if only to place the foregoing chapters of this book in a general philosophical perspective.

What must we suppose about the universe in order for scientific activity to be possible? Are there any metaphysical presuppositions of science? Could the scientific enterprise be futile? It is implicit in what has gone before, I think, that there are no metaphysical presuppositions in science. Our scientific activity of constructing formal systems and testing them by observation and experiment is dependent in no sense on the good will or cooperativeness of the universe. It is true that if there were no rational beings there would be no science; but only in the sense that on a planet devoid of life there would be no poetry written.

One particular characteristic of the universe claimed to be essential to science —to be *presupposed* by science—is that causation be universal, that every event have a cause. The view that all events are links in causal chains is often called a clockwork view of the universe—each movement of a gear in a clock is determined by the movements of earlier gears and in turn helps to determine the movements of gears later on in the sequence. One should not push this analogy too far; certain theologians have insisted on asking who winds up the clock, and others have asked what the ultimate function of the clock universe is, as the function of the clock is to tell time. Neither of these question need be asked, or, if asked, be answered, by holders of the clockwork view. The alternative view, that at least some events occur purely by chance is called *tychistic*. This view does not deny that there are causal chains, but only that each link in each chain is in turn caused. The two views may be contrasted this way: Given an observer who known the precise state of the universe at a given moment, and who knows all the physical laws that govern the universe, on the clockwork view he will be able to predict the precise state of the universe at any future time, while on the tychistic view he will at best be able to predict a range of states which the universe might be in at a given future time.

The approach to induction adopted in the foregoing pages makes it clear that universal causation is no presupposition of the view of science adopted here. What is fundamental, on this view, is statistical generalization; and this does not in any way conflict with a view of the universe as tychistic. Nor, of course, is it in conflict with a clockwork view of the universe. But it is certainly clear that scientific inference and generalization do not depend on a principle of universal causation. Furthermore, quantum theory as it currently stands states explicitly that on the subatomic level causality does *not* obtain; and although as one deals with larger and larger numbers of a type of chance event, one approaches closer and closer to certainty, in accordance with the law of large numbers of statistics, one never actually achieves certainty. Practical certainty, yes; but strict universality, no. Thus if quantum theory as formulated is correct, strict causal universality holds nowhere in the universe, and thus can hardly be said to be required to hold everywhere in order for science to be possible.

Less sweeping presuppositions are suggested both by C. D. Broad and by Bertrand Russell. Both of these authors take statistical generalization to be fundamental, but they both feel (as do others who have written on statistical inference) that a "fair sampling" principle is presupposed by the application of statistical methods. We must presuppose, they say, that every possible sample of the size that we have in fact drawn from the universe, has an equal chance of being drawn. It should be clear from the discussion of probability given earlier that this is not in fact at all the case. What we require is not that the particular sample

[318]

of the universe we happen to have taken be chosen by a method which would choose each possible sample equally often, but rather that the particular sample we happen to have be random with respect to the property of representing the character of the universe as a whole. Bias, on this view, is not something merely conjectural, but a matter of fact we discover by taking a larger sample or a different kind of sample. Given that we do not have empirical knowledge of the bias of the particular sample we have drawn, it is, relative to what we know, a random member of the set of all such samples with respect to the property of being representative of the rest of the universe in the respect under consideration; and from here on pure logic takes over: it is simply a logical (set-theoretical) fact that most samples are representative.

Since this is a point that has often been missed, a specific example may help to make matters clearer. Suppose we are sampling balls from an urn. We remove a large number of balls, one by one, replacing each ball after we have observed its color. Our sample is a sample of the potentially infinite set of possible selections from the urn. We are concerned with the proportion, say, of red balls in that potentially infinite population. Suppose that a quarter of the balls we draw are red; we infer that about a quarter of the balls in the parent population—the potentially infinite sequence of draws from the urn—are red. Does this inference *presuppose* that our sampling was "fair"? Not at all. In order for the inference to be inductively valid, there are some things we must *not* know; or put the other way about, the inference could be rendered invalid, or, better, *irrelevant*, by an increase in our body of knowledge. Thus if we discover that the proportion of red balls drawn depends on who does the drawing, or on the day of the week, or on the technique of drawing (e.g., whether the contents of the urn is mixed up or not), then we could make a new and better inference. But *given* the total body of knowledge relative to which the sample that we in fact drew is a random member of the set of all equinumerous samples, with respect to reflecting the proportion of red balls, and *given* the set theoretical fact that the proportion in a large sample is, with very high frequency among the set of all such samples, close to that in the original population, it simply *follows* that the probability is high that the proportion in question is close to a quarter. No presuppositions about fairness or representativeness are involved. For the validity of the inference, it is *not* necessary that the sample drawn be one drawn by a method that would draw every ball equally often in the long run.

Furthermore, it is interesting to observe that this condition is not *sufficient* either. Consider the following method of drawing a sample of n balls: Draw a ball from the urn: if it is red, let the sample consist of the next $n - 1$ red balls drawn from the urn; if it is not red, let the sample consist of the next $n - 1$ non-red balls. Under the usual assumptions, each ball will appear in a sample with the same long-run frequency. But only in two special cases will the samples be representative. The condition of *fairness* is thus neither sufficient nor necessary.

[319]

Although I take the answer to the question, "Are there any metaphysical pre-suppositions to Science?" to be a flat "No," there is a related question which I find interesting and worth answering. It is this related question that many philosophers (Russell for example, in *Human Knowledge*, and Broad, in *Scientific Thought*) are actually answering when they may appear to be answering the metaphysical question. This is the empirical question of the relation between the universe and beings in the universe, which enables those beings to attain knowledge of that universe. This question concerns the psychology of the individuals, as well as the physical characteristics of the universe. Although it is an empirical question, it is one that might quite properly fall within the province of philosophy. It is not, however, quite so germane to the philosophy of science as to the philosophy of perception, or to epistemology.

Causality, mechanism, and determinism are also key concepts in the philosophical questions that one hopes science will help to answer. Is it true, for example, that science reveals that the universe is run along causal lines? It might perfectly well be the case that causality is not a presupposition of science, but rather a consequence of science. It is certainly true that we speak freely about causation (despite the fact that if quantum mechanics expresses the ultimate facts of nature, that causation cannot be altogether strict), and take much of our scientific knowledge to be causal in nature. We know that the bubonic plague is caused by a microorganism carried by rats, that lack of water causes the growth of plants to be stunted, that slips of the tongue are sometimes caused by unconscious desires, etc. But although much of our scientific knowledge is causal in character, some of it is merely statistical. We are a very long way from a universal causal system, in which every event that comes within our purview fits into its causal chain. And, as already mentioned, the evidence of quantum mechanics suggests that that universal causal system does not exist.

Mechanism and determinism are in large part of interest to us in virtue of their bearing on our freedom as human agents. The relation between scientific knowledge (and prediction and explanation) and human freedom is complicated. On the one hand, the more we know of the psychology of motivation and of habit formation, and of basic human drives, the more predictable people become. On the other hand the greater our knowledge of the forces of nature, the less their power over us, and the freer we are from them. This is true even of the psychological forces of our own human natures. Science as it stands does not imply that human freedom is an illusion. Indeed the practice of science has so far operated in ways to (potentially) increase human freedom: the more determination we have discovered *in* nature, the freer we have become from determination *by* nature.

There are many relations between science and other questions of philosophical interest—between science and metaphysics, (How is the universe put together?), between science and ontology (What really exists?), between science and ethics

(What aspects of their behavior may people properly be held responsible for?), between science and political philosophy (What should be the altitude of the state toward scientific knowledge?), and even between science and the philosophy of religion (What are we to make of contradictions between scientific statements and religious statements?). In each case, however, I think the discussion belongs more properly within the relevant field of philosophy. In each case, *science* is the same—it uses the same kinds of terms, the same kinds of statements, the same concept of justification, the same kind of theoretical structure. It is my feeling that scientific knowledge plays a role in connection with most philosophical issues. In view of this pervasiveness, to deal with the connections between the philosophy of science and other branches of philosophy would involve no less than writing in detail on each of those other branches. Even if I were competent to do it, it would be inappropriate to our present concerns, which are to acquire some familiarity with the fundamental nature of scientific laws and concepts. My effort here has been directed at providing tools which can be used to clarify the role which scientific knowledge plays in connection with any philosophical issue. If I have succeeded, the student who knows psychology and ethics will find it easier to explore their relations than before, the student whose concerns are with metaphysics and physics will be better able to put them together; the student of political philosophy will find it easier to see how the limitations imposed by economic or psychological fact can best be handled within a philosophical structure. Science has been viewed here simply as justified empirical knowledge; in that sense science bears on every philosophical discipline; and the philosophy of science is, like logic, just a tool for doing philosophy.

BIBLIOGRAPHICAL NOTES TO CHAPTER 14

For the best recent discussion of the paradoxes of confirmation, see Max Black, "Notes on the 'Paradoxes of Confirmation'," Patrick Suppes, "A Bayesian Approach to the Paradoxes of Confirmation," and G. H. von Wright, "The Paradoxes of Confirmation," all in *Aspects of Inductive Logic* (Hintikka and Suppes, Eds.) (Amsterdam: North-Holland, 1966).

Nelson Goodman's new riddle of induction is discussed in his book, *Fact, Fiction and Forecast* (Cambridge: Harvard University Press, 1955), as well as in "A Query on Confirmation," *Journal of Philosophy 43*, 1946. Solutions to Goodman's new riddle have been proposed by Stephen Barker and Peter Achinstein in their paper "On the New Riddle of Induction," *Philosophical Review* **69** (1960), by Wesley Salmon in "On Vindicating Induction," *Induction: Some Current Issues* (Kyburg and Nagel, Eds.) (Middletown: Wesleyan University Press, 1963), and by Howard Smokler in "Goodman's Paradox and the Problem of Rules of Acceptance," *American Philosophical Quarterly* **3** (1966). Goodman does not yet regard the problem solved.

It was also Goodman, in "The Problem of Counterfactual Conditionals," *Journal of Philosophy* **44** (1947) (this paper is reprinted as part of *Fact, Fiction and Forecast*), who began to make much of the notion of counterfactual conditionals as the touchstone of lawlikeness.

The kinds of problems briefly mentioned in the last section of this chapter are discussed extensively by Bertrand Russell, in *Human Knowledge: Its Scope and Limits* (New York: Simon and Schuster, 1948), by Hans Reichenbach, *The Rise of Scientific Philosophy* (Berkeley and Los Angeles: University of California Press, 1951), and by Alfred North Whitehead, *Science and the Modern World* (New York: Mentor Books, 1949), to mention three authors of unquestioned competence and very enjoyable style.

Russell's discomforts about induction are expressed in *Human Knowledge*, Broad's in "The Principles of Problematic Induction," *Proceedings of the Aristotelian Society* **28** (1928). Similar worries about fair (or unfair) sampling are discussed in Stephen Barker, *Induction and Hypothesis* (Ithaca: Cornell University Press, 1957). C. D. Broad's concern with presuppositions in *Scientific Thought* (New York: Humanities Press, 1952) lies not in the problems of induction, but in problems of sensation and perception: how is it that if what we sense are patches of color, we can infer the existence not only of tables and chairs, but of electromagnetic radiations—e.g., of light? Russell, too, concerns himself with these problems in *Human Knowledge*.

Many of the issues touched on in this chapter have been enlighteningly discussed by the first-rate nineteenth-century American philosopher of science, Charles S. Peirce. For a stimulating collection of Peirce's essays, see his essays in *The Philosophy of Science* (Indianapolis and New York: Bobbs-Merrill, 1957).

INDEX

abstract objects, 51
abstract quantities, 76
abstract terms, 51
Achinstein, Peter, 321
Ackermann, Robert, 172
Ackermann, Wilhelm, 18
acceleration, 84
acceptance of theories, 154-55, 164-66
  see also confirimation, tests
activity, 265, 267-75
addition,
  for natural numbers, 187
  for rational numbers, 190
  for real numbers, 181-82, 191, 193
ambiguity, idiosyncratic, 91
  systematic, 91-93
area, 58, 73-76

conditions for combining,
    see coplanarity, juxtaposition
  triangular, 75-76
arithmetic, Chapter 8
  interpretation of Calculus II,
    see Calculus II
asymmetry, 61-64
  basis for quantitative concepts
    length, 61-67
    time, 81-84
"atom," 106-107
axioms, 12, 46-49, 124-29, Chapter 5
  for formal systems of this book, 30
  material, 117-19, 124-27
  see also Chapters 8-13 for sample for-
    mal systems with axioms, forma-
    tion rules, rules of inference, and

[325]